BOOKS BY CLIFTON FADIMAN

Essays and Criticism

THE LIFETIME READING PLAN
PARTY OF ONE
ANY NUMBER CAN PLAY
ENTER, CONVERSING

Anthologies

DIONYSUS
THE AMERICAN TREASURY
    (with Charles Van Doren)
READING I'VE LIKED
CLIFTON FADIMAN'S FIRESIDE READER
FANTASIA MATHEMATICA
THE MATHEMATICAL MAGPIE
THE SHORT STORIES OF HENRY JAMES

A Case of Vintage Tales about Wine

McGraw-Hill Book Company, Inc.
New York   Toronto   London

DIONYSUS

COLLECTED
& EDITED
WITH AN
INTRODUCTION
BY

CLIFTON FADIMAN

820.8
F

For Alfred A. Knopf

Contents of the Cellar

Introduction

"O N turnpikes of wonder wine leads the mind forth." So wrote the Persian poet Hafiz. A few such turnpikes are explored in these pages. The wayfarers form a varied company. The convergence between these covers of Edgar Allan Poe and Art Buchwald, A. A. Milne and George Meredith stems only from the common circumstance of their having written about wine.

On my shelves are ranged perhaps a hundred books dealing with this agreeable subject. This might appear to be an adequate number for one who makes no claim to authority. However, looking over my small collection a few years ago, I noticed a lacuna. All these books were designedly, or at least basically, instructive. They were ready to teach me more about wine than in truth I needed to know. What was missing was a volume which would be cheerfully non-instructive, made up of fictional or imaginative productions in which wine played some part and which would also display the charms exerted by any well-written story.

Investigation revealed the existence of no such book, so I decided, being by nature a snapper-up of unconsidered trifles, to contrive one myself. *Dionysus* is the outcome of my Autolycan endeavors; and it is up to the wine-loving reader to judge their value as entertainment.

Here at any rate is a mixed case: yarns depending on the complication of plot, a *novella*, humor, science-fiction, poetry, fantasy, mystery, an excerpt from a novel, and a couple of touches of horror, old style and new style. As with any wine-list there are distinguished names—Belloc, Meredith, Robert Graves, Poe, Daudet; and others whose claims to immortality are more modest.

I have included three items not strictly concerned with wine: C. E. Montague's distillation in colored prose of the soul of Irish whiskey; Daudet's delightful gesture of cordiality; and

1

Margery Allingham's ingenious plotting of the point at which cognac and Campion intersect. Also, into a book of prose I have dropped Belloc's "Heroic Poem," the finest English work of imagination generated by the theme of wine. These slight relaxations of anthological rigor I trust will be forgiven.

As I have intimated, this collection of diversions contains no scholarship, and its readers will learn nothing about wine that in all probability they do not already know.

As a matter of fact they will doubtless recognize here and there some small examples of dubious winesmanship. Though all our authors know something about wine, they are not all first-chop experts.

We may rely on the wine-lore decanted into Mr. Scott's touching story, threaded on the memories of a "man of Médoc," for it was vetted by the great Bordeaux proprietor Christian Cruse. I think we may similarly take for granted the authority of the now, alas, ex-connoisseurs E. C. Bentley and Hilaire Belloc.

On the other hand there are a few minor slips that we might note for the record. In Dorothy Sayers' amusing "Bibulous Business" the Count informs us that it is a matter of "common notoriety that Lord Peter Wimsey has a palate for wine almost unequalled in Europe." This is no more than we should expect of that paragon. Yet would he be quite so fulsome in his praise of "Napoleon brandy"? Indeed, would the knowledgeable Count offer it? For it is a matter of common notoriety that "Napoleon brandy" is a mere trade name, a trap for the gullible, and indeed a meaningless label, any cask of 1815 brandy having been in the course of the years continually replenished by newer spirits. (One regrets that Margery Allingham, in her equally ingenious tale, seems to have fallen into the same trap.) Also, unless I misread the text, there is an implication in Miss Sayers' narrative that the adjective "sweet" can be applied to Montrachet. One must demur.

I intend no faulting of the story in saying that one must go beyond mere agreement with the Count in his characterization of his wine menu as a "hazardous mixture." Only in the interests of high-class detection would one care to face a dinner escorted by such a dazzling pleiad as Chablis Moutonne, Chevalier-Montrachet, Schloss Johannisberger, Château Lafite, Clos-Vougeôt, Genuine Imperial Tokay, and, alas, that "Napoleon brandy." Rome was built on seven hills but a good dinner should be built on a less extravagant, a more balanced series of eminences.

(Miss Sayers' mention of the Lafite reminds one of the story, carefully nurtured by the owners of this incomparable growth, about the Duc de Richelieu, grandnephew of the great Cardinal. At 84 he admitted to his bosom his fourth wife, a charming young widow. At 92 he died, in the full bloom of sexual vigor, crediting his powers to the habitual consumption of Château Lafite).

To get back to the Count's flabbergasting wine list: I once, on my birthday a decade ago, offered to a few friends a suite of wines that I think would have been approved even by the exigent Sir Peter. I cite it out of a combination of wistfulness and that forgivable fatuity which is the characteristic weakness of wine-lovers. The apéritif was a Dom Pérignon 1924, a single bottle for the six of us. With the fish appeared a Piesporter Goldtröpfchen, feinste Auslese (my wine-book further qualifies it as Fuder Nr. 9110, Flasche Nr. 174, Original-Abfüllung Reichsgraf von Kesselstatt, Bundes Siegerpreis, 1949). The meat was graced by a magnum of Bonnes Mares 1923. (There was some Romanée Conti 1933 handy to back it up, but it developed no fault). With the dessert we each drank a scant two ounces of Tokayer Ausbruch, 1876. One of the guests, finishing his Bonnes Mares with appreciation, wickedly repeated the complaint of Disraeli's Mr. Mountchesney in *Sybil:* "I rather like bad wine, one gets so bored with good wine."

Whatever we may think of the Count's wine menu, we can but admire the one arranged by Paul Vernier in Mr. Blochman's neatly plotted yarn: Montrachet 1904, Chambertin 1911, Champagne Irroy 1919. Simple and perfect, though one can only hope that a great Burgundy could really be served at its optimum in the latitude of the Dutch East Indies. (But, of course, the point of the story is that the Chambertin—well, read it yourself). Apropos the famous '11: in his agreeable *In Praise of Wine* Alec Waugh recalls a Saintsbury Club dinner which featured that same beautiful vintage. Hilaire Belloc, in eloquent apostrophe, ended his speech thus: "And when I depart from the earth to appear before my belovèd Lord to account for my sins, which have been scarlet, I shall say to Him: 'I cannot remember the name of the village; I do not even recollect the name of the girl, but the wine, my God! was Chambertin!' "

I have only one trifling suggestion to make to Mr. Blochman. If one is going to serve lobster with anything as magisterial (and delicate, too) as the Montrachet '04, it might be judicious, never mind the recipe, to prepare it without "essence of tomatoes." The flavor of tomato, however etherealized, is bound to retain more than a memory of sugar, and never did a fine dry wine much good.

Named like a character in *Pilgrim's Progress*, Mr. Portway in Michael Gilbert's "Income Tax Mystery" radiates all the authority of a classical claret man. Yet it is at least arguable that in claret "the best of the war years" was not 1943, but 1945. But we must be fair: Mr. Portway remarks that he did not really start buying until 1945. As for his beloved Pontet Canet, it can be a very fine claret and doubtless deserves elevation from its fifth-growth position. Yet to call it "almost the best Château" of 1943 seems a shade excessive.

My readers will encounter a few other references that will at least be useful in starting the hare of decanter-discussion. In Mr. Amis' *Brave New World*-ish fantasy, Croft 1919 is cited, with high approbation. In his *Port* (London, 1934) André Simon describes the quality of that year as "irregular." He mentions six shippers, however, who thought it good enough to qualify as a vintage year. Croft is not among them.

G. B. Stern is a true connoisseuse. It is a fine thing to read her story dedicated to the *manes* of a great Hermitage. The superb Rhônes have not really been properly praised since the days of Saintsbury. To a Rhône-lover therefore "The 1865" offers full-bodied satisfaction, whatever one may think of its deceptive finish. One quibble, however: Who is this Saint Dionysius by whom Guy Barracott swears? If he is a typo for the wine-god (quite properly sanctified) who lends his name to this book, well and good. Otherwise I am baffled. A little hagiological research turns up two Saints Dionysius. One was Pope from 259 to 268. The other (*c.* 190–265) was a bishop of Alexandria. Neither of these devout eminences would seem appropriate for a wine-lover to swear by.

Alfred Noyes' story about "The Wine Beyond the World" is a mere thistledown fable, not to be taken too seriously. One can, however, make out a perfectly logical case for its denouement. If the Emperor drank only one glass a year (later on this is further qualified as "less than a thimbleful") each bottle would have to be opened and re-corked at least eight times before exhaustion. Reflect on the consequences. Consider also that "the oldest wine in the world" would under any circumstances be no more than a ghost.

I need not dilate on the limitations of Poe's knowledge of wine.* They have never prevented "The Cask of Amontillado" from winning anthological immortality. Mr. Poe is neatly dissected by the great H. Warner Allen in the paragraphs I have appended to his story.

The distinguished authority William Massee, who was kind enough to examine this book in manuscript, of course spotted Poe's dubious winesmanship. He also raised a polite objection to Roald Dahl's shuddery little masterpiece "Taste" on the grounds that a real expert *could* (or rather would) have identified the fairly obscure claret on which the plot turns. If this is true, the story would lose much of its point. Mr. Massee has forgotten more about wine than I shall ever know. Yet I must in all humility record my opinion that expertise of such a high order would be phenomenal indeed. Perhaps it does inhere in a Lichine or a Simon—or a Massee. But, until I can witness its actual display, Mr. Dahl's fiendish tale will continue to convince me.

It is, to my mind, the best wine story in the book, and one of the best of its peculiar kind ever written. The others, however, have their own attractions for me, and I hope they will bring a similar pleasure to my wine-loving readers. There may be better tales in existence, but these are the most diverting I have

---

* I once wrote a clerihew which I immodestly believe explains Poe's appalling ignorance of wine as contrasted with his familiarity with spirits. It is called

Poe-tatory

Poe's curse
Was mixing stimulants and verse.
No sooner was Poe
Done with his old raven than he started on his Old Crow.

been able to unearth. If any of my readers know of other and perhaps superior tales of wine I hope they will let me know about them. I would esteem it a gracious gesture of oenophilian fraternity.

And so I leave you to open this mixed case and test its contents, some dry, some sweet, some sparkling.

Clifton Fadiman

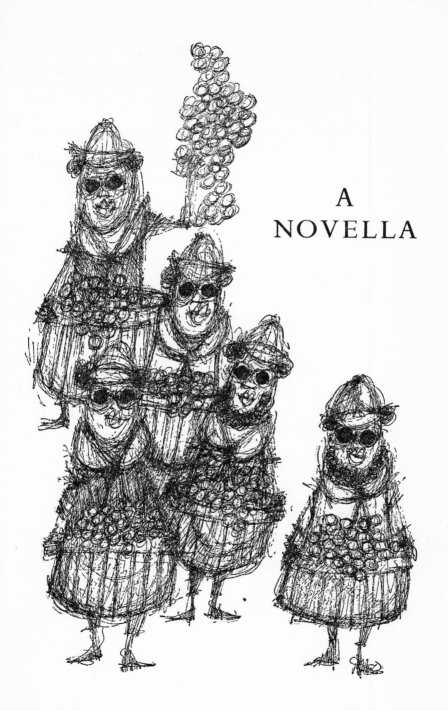

A
NOVELLA

The Man Who Made Wine

J. M. SCOTT

James Maurice Scott was born in Egypt and educated at Fettes College, Edinburgh and Clare College, Cambridge (1925–1928). He has done a great deal of professional exploring in Labrador and Greenland, and was secretary of the 1933 Mount Everest Expedition. At the end of World War II he was Commandant of the British-American Mountain Warfare School in Italy. Since 1948 he has devoted the major part of his time to writing, having turned out (besides this novella) six novels, several being suspense stories of the sea and the mountains. Mr. Scott is married to the sister of the famous explorer Gino Watkins, and they have two children. He writes: "I prefer doing anything myself, however badly— from skiing to mountaineering to ball games—to watching it done, however well."

THE composite trestle-table—it must have been twenty paces long—was in the night shadow of the big cedar tree. Behind, the white-washed outbuildings had a ghostly brightness. In front and to both sides were vineyards stretching down the gentle slope to the fringe of poplars which marked the *palus* ground and the river Gironde. In the full moonlight the line upon line of vine plants with their shiny leaves gave the effect of a gently rippled sea. The silvery countryside was quiet except for the rhythmical whistle of the grasshoppers.

At one end of the table a single candle was burning. It illuminated a row of bottles, wine-glasses and some empty plates. Fifty or sixty people had dined here. But the meal was over and the guests dispersed. From the outbuildings behind there came a sudden burst of concertina music as a door opened; and now

9

and then in the shadows there was the sound of whispering or a girl's gay laugh.

The candle flame, although it rose tall and steady in the still night air, did little more than give each bottle a grotesquely elongated shadow which joined it to the next bottle and the next, but less and less distinctly as the distance from the light increased. At the far end of the table it was so dark that you would scarcely have noticed the old man who sat there. His chin was on his fists, and he was staring out across the sea of vines, motionless as the night.

He was Michel Rachelet, *Maître de Chai* of the Château La Tour-St.-Vincent for the last twenty-three years, *vigneron* of the estate for more than half a century, and retiring from all work today. It was in his honour that the dinner had been given on the eve of this year's vintage. Half an hour ago he, Gros Michel, had been the subject of a flowery recitation entitled, "The Man who made Wine," of several speeches and a toast.

The Marquis, who spoke last, had said: "On this September evening we are not only at the close of a vineyard year but at the end of an epoch. The past belongs to the family Rachelet—to Michel here and to his father, who takes us back beyond the turn of the century. Before asking you to drink to our guest of honour, what shall I say of him?

"There are a hundred stories that I could tell of this individualist—ah, I see some of you smiling. But I shall tell no Rachelet story tonight, for although we are proud that he with his good wife beside him could make us laugh as well as work, that could only light one facet of his character. I could speak of his knowledge, his genius with vines and wine. But they are known and appreciated not only here but wherever the wine of this château is drunk. I—I am only the *patron*. I have nothing to do with it. But seriously, when I first came into my inheritance I trembled before every interview with my *maître de chai*—until he took me under his wing and taught me how to be the proprietor of a great estate.

"What then can I say of him tonight? Nothing. No words of mine could do him justice. Instead I shall ask you to drink his health, slowly and in silence, and while you are doing so to look around you at the vineyard and to appreciate the wine.

"This vineyard is as good as any in France because of the

loving and patient work of Michel Rachelet. And it was he who assisted at the birth of every wine of this château which is drunk today. . . . What makes one wine better than another? Surely in a word it is character. And is not this wine of ours great because it has in it, perhaps, something of the character of the *maître de chai*—the strength of his arms, the warmth and generosity of his heart, the kindly philosophy of his mind?"

Then everybody had drunk Rachelet's health, standing quite silently, glass in hand, some of them smiling affectionately, some thoughtful, some with tears in their eyes. It had been most moving, their silence and the different expressions of young and old.

But the *patron*, having paid his tribute to his faithful Rachelet, shaken him by the hand and kissed him on both cheeks, had gone back to his château. And then, gradually, as the summer darkness fell, the whole party of estate people had dispersed. Dance music had drawn the young ones and the old ones had gone to bed. They should all have gone to bed, Rachelet thought. Let them sing and caper all night when the vintage was in. But the fortnight of hard work would begin at dawn next day. He himself would never have permitted such behaviour, had he still been in charge. But he was no longer responsible. He had nothing more to do. "Oh well," he sighed, "there's time to think a little."

Rachelet sat looking at the vines which shone like silver in the moonlight. He did not admire them now. He preferred the true daylight colours. They were useful: they told you something. That afternoon he had gone into the vineyards to test the grapes. He had been pleased with the colours then. The leaves were healthy and of a shade which proved that the vines had been nourished on the right proportion of lime, potash and nitrates. The leaves had finished their job now, so they could turn golden and fall when they liked. They had taken the raw sap from the roots and in the sun heat changed it into the compound substances which the grapes needed. Now, like old machinery, they were rusting. But the grapes were glowing and bulging like buxom girls. When you bit these grapes—Rachelet threw back his head and shut his eyes—they went pop in the mouth, and how sweet they were! They would make a strong wine which should have a long life before it. But what more could one say—at least until the juice fermented? Rachelet shrugged his shoulders and turned up his palms. (Although alone, he still gestured.) There could, for example, be too much tannin which would make the wine hard and bitter, and might not soften completely before the other elements had begun to deteriorate. With the best palate in the world you could not tell that sort of thing before the vintage, any better than you could judge the character of a child to be born of a certain woman. Up in Champagne they had a story of a blind monk named Dom Perignon who could chew up a handful of the grapes and say exactly what the wine was going to be like. That was the sort of story you expected from Champagne.

If those knobbly old vine stocks with the delicate roots which reached so far down—if they could talk they could say something worth listening to. Vines were so much more sensitive than men. For instance, take a man and woman of Médoc and transplant them to Algeria. Their children would not be black: they would be the same as if they had been born in Médoc. Human organisms were not delicate enough to be affected by differences in water, air and soil. But a Médoc vine in Algeria would produce Algerian wine because vines always repaid exactly what they had been given. Planted in the Côte d'Or, a vine of Château La Tour-St.-Vincent would, of course, remain a *cabernet-sauvignon* among the local *pinots*, but it would produce burgundy, or perish. More than that, plant one of these vines only a stone's throw outside the château boundary—it would no longer produce La Tour-St.-Vincent. It would give artisan wine, peasant wine, *vin ordinaire*. It would at once know the difference in its environment, although the cleverest human chemist would say that the soil, water and air were exactly the same.

Vines could not be cheated. They were the masters and men the servants. Men could understand only when the fruit had been translated into wine—and then it often took years to appreciate the subtleties.

The subtlety and the true greatness of vines had been made clear to him by the way they had reacted to the phylloxera. After all, it was they, not men with their chemicals, who in the end had offered the only road to salvation.

Rachelet remembered his father talking about the phylloxera.

His father's working life had been spent in the shadow of that terrible plague, and he himself had been born—he remembered often being told this—when the evil thing was at its most virulent, when two and a half million acres of French vineyards had already been ravaged by it, and eastwards all the way to Australia the same story was being told. There was no cure. The only way of destroying the tiny, louse-like invader was by burning the vines.

Then somebody suggested a method of immunizing the small remaining garrison of French vines. Michel remembered his father exclaiming against this plan. Rachelet *père* had been a big man, as big as his son had grown, but more red-faced, more passionate.

"What brought the disease?" he had shouted at his wife and startled children. "Imported American vines! So what do they propose to do?—Import more American vines! What sort of wine do they produce?—*bourgeois* at best. Yet it is said that if we graft our vines on to those stocks we shall still get French wine from them. I ask of you, is that reasonable? What gives our French wine its *finesse* if not the soil, and what draws from the soil except the roots?—and the roots will be American. My poor children, you have no future except American wine."

Yet the gamble was tried because nothing else offered any hope at all. Such *vignerons* as could still raise money on credit bought American stocks and grafted on to them the precious French shoots. It was like giving one's children to a foreigner to bring up.

It is three years before a young plant bears grapes from which wine can be made and another year at least before the wine can be good. The *vignerons* had to wait a long time to learn whether they were saved or utterly ruined. You cannot hurry vines. But in the end the plants produced French wine. They knew they were on French soil even though the sap came to them through American roots. So Rachelet *père*, still grumbling, had spent his days grafting and replanting the ravaged vineyards. But to the day of his death he had remained pessimistic about the ultimate result.

"Listen well, Michel," he said often. "This is good for young wine. It is round, it is supple, it has *sève*. But, mark my words,

it will not live as long as the wine we made before the phylloxera.
Therefore it cannot mature to the same perfection. The great
days of wine are past."

Michel did not agree. But although he had been a child at the
time and now was an old man, it was still too early to say with
certainty whether that gloomy prophecy had been correct.

Nailed above the door of the *chai* was an ancient vine stock.
It was without bark, white as the skeleton of some twisted
monster. It was said to have lived for one hundred and thirty
years. It would be the next century before a post-phylloxera vine
could be as old as that, if indeed it were capable of such long life.

Michel Rachelet, sitting at the table, raised his tired grey
head and looked thoughtfully at the vineyard sleeping in the
moonlight. Vines were mysterious. He had given his life to
them, and having learned enough to be modest he would not
have dared to say that he knew all about them—although he
certainly would not have admitted that any man knew more.
Here on the gently sloping ground which faced south-eastward
they had the ideal exposure and soil—a soil in which no other
crop would have grown well, for it was thick with pebbles as
large as a child's fist. That was another aspect of the mystery of
vines. But besides a particular soil they needed also good weather
and proper care. God attended to the weather, and he, Rachelet,
to the care. God had done them well this year—enough rain,
then ample sunshine. And Rachelet, although the strain of daily
work and constant responsibility had grown almost unbearable,
had seen to it that nothing was lacking on his side.

As soon as last year's grapes had been picked and their leaves
had fallen, the ground had been ploughed up, weeded and
manured. Rachelet did not trust the new composite fertilizers
which it was claimed did everything for the minimum of effort.
Chemicals were to be used as a doctor uses medicine, but the
staple diet was farmyard manure, well dug in. It was a saying of
his that land needed a top dressing of human sweat.... In his
mind's eye, the old man could see the scene in front of him as
it had been in the brisk autumn weather eleven months ago—the
well-trained horses with the special ploughs designed to work
along the metre-wide corridors between the rows of vines, the

men and women with their hoes and spades piling the soil up in waves to protect the roots from frost. The smell of newly turned earth and of rubbish fires was in the air. The distant poplar trees were like a row of brooms and a sparkling mist hung over Gironde.

Then had come the first pruning, *la taille sèche*. His team of horticulturists had worked slowly down the rows, cutting away the unproductive wood. They worked bent almost double so that from the distance they looked like some strange species of animal —except when now and then one rose to his full height to ease his aching back. It was a long pilgrimage, the pruning—many kilometres for each man to travel at a snail's pace. And the fences themselves had often to be renewed. There was enough work for everybody in the winter-time.

As spring approached, Rachelet's problem had been the timing of the first green pruning. If the canes were cut early no sap would be lost, but the quickly growing shoots would be liable to damage by frost. If the pruning were done late the vines would bleed. By a combination of experience and instinct Rachelet had learned to pick his time, and this year had got it exactly right.

The extent of pruning called for imagination. Rachelet had trained his men to look at the almost bare canes and picture the plant as it would be when it was fully grown. Then the quantity of leaves and branches must match the root area, yet this must be adjusted by pruning before an eye had turned into a bud.

The *bourgeonnement* had always fascinated him. It was not only the joy of seeing every morning from one's cottage door-way that the vineyard was painted a stronger shade of green: it was the detail of the change. When one looked closely at a particular cane one noticed that the sprouting eyes were larger than when one had seen them last. Soon after this the brown scales fell from the eyes and the woolly buds became visible. Then came the stage which used to excite him so much as a child—and still did. The tiny leaves became separated on their little stalk, even the cluster of minute flower buds was distinguishable. It was a vine branch in miniature.

It would be a real branch soon enough, and meanwhile there was plenty to be done. Each shoot was examined and every one which was imperfect was cut away. And later, when the remaining shoots had grown a little, the ends of some of them were snipped to make them bunch well.

Then the flowering started. This too was a lovely thing to watch in detail. The green hats which the buds wore fell off and the delicate members of the flowers were seen. It was like a conjuring trick. But it was an anxious time for the *vigneron* looking for symptoms of *la coulure*, the disease of barrenness.

The fertilization had gone well this year. When the tiny grapes were forming, the clusters were examined and the least promising removed. And finally, just before the vintage, the old leaves which had done their work were cut away to give more light to the ripening grapes—yet not so much that they would be sunburned.

That covered the plant's development and discipline by pruning. But there had been, besides the active watch for fungoid and insect pests, the passive watch for late frosts and devastating hail. That had been the outdoors round which Rachelet had known for fifty-four years as a qualified *vigneron* and for much of twenty more as a child and apprentice, excluding his years of military service.

But most of his work recently had been in the *chai*. He felt a sudden longing to visit the *chai* before he slept—to walk among the hogsheads of young wine, to go down to the cellar beneath and browse among the thousands upon thousands of bottles which were for him so full of interest and experience.

He thought of all those wines as friends whom he had known since birth. It was his fancy that wine passed through childhood and adolescence in the fermenting vat. That period, which with men lasts fifteen to twenty years, was completed by wine within as many days. But thereafter they lived at much the same rate. The few years which a young fellow spends in settling down to his responsibilities were spent by wine in barrels. It got rid of its wild oats then. When it had cleared its head of clouds and figments it was bottled. But life never stands still: wine, like men, was for ever changing, either for better or for worse. Its numerous and complex elements—alcohol, glucose, glycerol, tartrates, acids, salts—were continually readjusting themselves, altering, blending or falling apart, the waste products being excreted as sediment. How well, at what rate, and for how long a wine continued to mature depended principally on what it was born with. For instance, if it were not strong enough it would become bitter with age instead of richer and better balanced. But on the whole it improved. Each bottle became a more valuable member of the cellar—until it reached the peak of what it was capable of some time in middle age. Then the ever-continuing changes began to be for the worse. One element after another faded—colour, *bouquet*, vinosity. Gracefully or suddenly the wine grew old until you could scarcely recognize in it the youth that you had known. At last it died. It went back to water and the things of earth from which in the sunlight its grapes had been made. That was the fascination of a cellar— a whole series of lives in different stages of development.

Rachelet wanted to visit his cellar, but he remembered that it would be dark there, and that he had recently discovered that the steps were steep and slippery. He sighed, and prepared to resign himself—then noticed the candle. He would take that with him. He would manage very well with a candle.

He rose slowly, pressing down with his arms, then moved along beside the table, touching it with one hand, until he reached the candle. Gros Michel was a tall man but a good deal stooped (so much of his work had been done stooping, both in the fields and among the barrels). His limbs and features were large. At the ends of his drooping arms he had big, horny hands. It was a tradition of the Château La Tour-St.-Vincent that he had never been unable to carry between his fingers enough glasses for a wine tasting by however many visitors. It was also a tradition that Rachelet's hands could pull out a super-annuated vine stock as another man might draw a cork, could cooper a barrel or make a graft which was certain to flourish. Equally it was said that he had the best palate in Bordeaux, which naturally meant of the whole of France, and therefore of the world. He was not only a character, he was a tradition in his lifetime. But he himself was philosopher enough to realize that to be a tradition is to be as good as dead. They were dancing over there, and making love among the shadows. With no strangers to boast to, they had forgotten him. He had grown outside their real world.

His face, now lit by the candle, was wise and sad. The skin was not rough, yet as full of lines as a sawn tree-stump. His deep-sunk eyes were penetrating. They had disconcerted with

their steady stare many amateur visitors who had been brought
into the *chai* to taste the young vintages. They had swished the
wine round their glasses, nosed and sipped it, watching the other
tasters out of the corners of their eyes and trying hard to look
like connoisseurs in front of the famous *maître de chai*. But—
had they known it—Rachelet was not watching them critically.
Their knowledge of wine, or the lack of it, mattered little or
nothing. He himself knew without question what was excellent,
good, or not so good in the barrels and bottles under his care. But
he was waiting, like the tutor of some great family, for an appre-
ciative remark on his young geniuses. Compliments warmed from
whomever they came. It was only on the rare occasions when
criticisms were made that he enquired, politely but firmly, into
the authority of the speaker.

As *maître de chai* he had been a man of importance, for La
Tour-St.-Vincent was almost a self-contained village with its fine
château as a centrepiece. Forty families lived and worked on the
estate. Besides the two hundred acres of vineyard there was as
much again of farm land. The *patron's* horses were famous, so was
the herd of pedigree cattle which produced the necessary manure.
(Hundreds of tons of this were needed every year.) There were
flocks of geese and ducks and chickens; and the fine walled garden grew all the vegetables which were eaten the year round. The
chai itself was a noble structure eighty paces long, its roof supported by two rows of stone pillars. . . .

Next to the *patron*, Rachelet had been the most important man
for the past twenty-three years. But now he was of no consequence and alone. Never mind. For old time's sake he would go
to his *chai*. There he would still feel somebody, for he had
stocked it with most of the wine that it contained. . . . He reached
out for the candle which should guide him there. But in doing so
his foot caught against something and he sat down, luckily on a
chair.

The shock of this little accident made him realize how tired
he was. It had been a long, busy, emotional day. When he had returned to his cottage in the afternoon he had found that his efficient niece had got a barber out from Pauillac to shave him, cut
his hair and iron his moustaches. That had been bad enough, but
afterwards she and her husband had insisted on getting him into
his Sunday best, with a new stiff collar which was so high that it

almost cut his throat. And after that—well, there had been all this
to-do of chatter and speeches and back-slapping and quantities to
eat and drink. It had started in daylight and now it was dark and
he was alone. He was not drunk—far from it. For him wine was
not a light thing of recreation. It was his work, and this evening
with so much to distract him he had scarcely touched anything.
Perhaps it would have been better if he had got drunk. Instead he
felt flat and lonely. He wanted to visit his *chai*, and he felt too
tired and old to get there.

He looked slowly and doubtfully to right and left. He noticed
the bottles. Close to the light he could see them individually and
clearly. He remembered what they were. They were not what
had been provided for drinking. That had been in demijohns
which had been carried away by the dancers. These bottles were
what the Marquis had caused to be brought up from the *bibliothèque* or museum of the cellar, an example of every vintage of
the past fifty-four years. They had been nosed, sipped and ap-
plauded at appropriate moments during the speeches, when reference had been made to some particular year. But everybody
realized that they had been provided as a gesture and a compliment to the retiring *maître de chai* and had controlled himself
from swallowing more than a mouthful even of the greatest
wines.

Rachelet nodded his head at the bottles, greeting them like old
friends. His good *chai* had come to him. He knew now why he
had wanted so much to visit it this night before he slept. The line
of bottles stretched down the table from where the candle stood
to the dark end where he had been sitting a few minutes ago.
They looked something like telegraph poles along a road, linked
by shadows instead of wires. He wanted to travel back along that
road.

It was too dark for his old eyes to read the labels, even with the
candle—he had left his spectacles somewhere. No matter. He half
filled a glass from the nearest bottle. He held it to the light and
then under his nose. His face became suddenly alert.

Rachelet's eyes were too weak to read labels by candlelight,
but they could distinguish and interpret shades of colour; and his
well-trained nose was in its way every bit as sensitive as a dog's.
That vivid purple with more scarlet than blue in it told him the

youth of the wine, and the faint smell, as of flowers in bud, confirmed it. But what told him the year was something thin and hard, an individual sort of unripe fruitiness, in the perfume.

Rachelet threw the wine into the night. He had no wish to taste the 1951 again. He had been sadly disappointed by that vintage which even at the time he had feared might be the last for which he was responsible. He had done all he could for it—but nothing can make up for lack of sunshine. Human geniuses may make their mark in youth; but not wines. And without original sweetness, no wine can live. What there was of it—some 300 hogsheads —would be drunk indifferently, almost apologetically, as a light table wine. No one would lay it down for his children or offer it with pride to his friends on great occasions.

This year—it promised so much better! The hot sun had stuffed these grapes with sugar, potential alcohol. Rachelet wished that he might have remained in charge of the vintage instead of retiring on the eve of it. But the *patron* had been right: he was not up to that fortnight of gruelling work. Wine in its first, fierce fermentation waits for no man. It has all the selfish impatience of youth. He might have made a mess of things.

He shrugged his shoulders. No matter—he was no longer concerned with the present or the future, only with the past.

Rachelet browsed along the next half-dozen bottles without pausing long over any one of them. They had evidently been set out in sequence, but in any case he would have had little difficulty in recognizing the vintages—in fact, where in one instance two bottles had been transposed he noticed it at once. For him there was nothing at all remarkable in this. Wines, like human beings, have a certain range of qualities. Those on the table were all of the same family, but brothers and sisters have individual characteristics which make each unmistakable to a friend. And was not Rachelet the family tutor who had studied them from birth? The '50 and '49 were the most nearly alike. One might think of them as twins. But they were not identical: one could recognize the older.

The '48, a comparatively poor wine, was none the less individual. Like a plain woman who has a charming smile, it had a lovely *bouquet*. In the mouth, the first thing you noticed was the tannin. The '48 would live a long time whether anybody wanted it to or not. The '47—there was a text-book wine, perfectly bal-

anced, almost too well balanced for its age. The '46—well, one
knew it at once because it was so untalented.

Rachelet, in his private analysis, did not employ any of the
conventional connoisseur terms to the wines. In the past when he
had been responsible for selling them he had given a detailed and
most colourful report of each. But he was no longer interested in
their marketable qualities. Their scents and flavours only mattered
to him now for the memories which they evoked. He hurried
through these years because there was nothing worthy to be remembered on this great occasion, either of joy or sorrow. All the
vintages belonged to the period when he was merely holding on,
with great effort lasting out his promised period of service, looking forward to nothing except rest.

The first wine he paused over was the 1945. For a long time he
held its softening purple between him and the candle. He swung
the glass in quick circles, then cupped his hands about it and put
his long nose down so that it almost touched the wine. He
breathed deeply, like a sigh, until his nostrils, his mouth, and all
the delicate surfaces which smell and taste and prod the memory
were flooded with the subtle vapour which rose from the suddenly warmed and agitated wine.

He held the glass away from him, swinging it slowly in the
candlelight. A great wine, the '45—fat and round and full of
promise. But he did not want to drink it again. The wine of
Château La Tour-St.-Vincent had the reputation of maturing
more slowly than any other of the Médoc, and this vintage of '45
was a veritable *corpsé*, the slowest in development of any he had
known. Although already seven years old, it might be three times
that period before it was ready to be drunk. But that was not the
reason why he was unwilling to drink it now.

Once more he breathed the wine, then put the glass down on
the table. The memories of that year were too vivid, too cruelly
contrasting. How well it had promised, in every way! Peace came
with the flowering of the vines. The *patron* returned from the
army. Together they made a tour of the vineyards and the *chai*
while Rachelet reported on the events of the past five years. At
last they came to a halt in the shade of this same cedar tree, and
the *patron* praised Rachelet for his stewardship.

"You have done wonders," he said. "Ever since as a boy you
began to work for my father you have done well—better and

better. And to maintain the vineyard and *chai* throughout the war so that it all looks as smart as the *École Nationale de Viticulture*—it is nearly miraculous! But I realize the strain it must have been. What is your age, Michel—sixty-eight? A ripe age, but you are not yet on the way out. No, no, you have many useful years in front of you. That is why, being conscious of my debt to you, I have something particular to offer."

The Marquis, although he held himself erect as a soldier, was no taller than the stooping Rachelet. Their heads were level, and Rachelet's eyes searched those of the *patron*, wondering what he meant, feeling pride and joy but fear as well.

"My friend," the Marquis said, "most people of your way of life work on for their masters until they are finished. When they retire they can only sit by their firesides and wait for death. But you deserve something better. Besides hands you have a brain. My father often said that if you had had education you would have been a philosopher as great as Voltaire."

"I am what I am," Rachelet murmured. He wished the *patron* was not so fond of making speeches.

"Listen," the *patron* said. "I have a château also in Anjou. The vineyard is small, but it might, I think, be good if it were well cared for—which it has not been for many years. There is a little house of whitewashed stone for the *vigneron*. It has its own vegetable garden and a well of sweet water. To the left one can see the town of Angers, and to the right over the vineyards is the Loire."

"Yes?" Rachelet said.

"You have only to say the word, and that house and the produce of the vineyard are yours for as long as you shall live and thereafter will belong to any heir you name. You are fortunate in your good wife. Together you could make something of the place, I am sure. Of course, you can remain in your cottage here, if you prefer. But it is smaller, with no vineyard of its own. I will not hurry you for a decision. Think it over and tell me when you have made up your mind."

"I have already made up my mind," Rachelet began.

"Ah, you do not waste time! I only hope you will not leave us too soon." The Marquis sounded a little hurt.

"My father taught me that a man can work usefully until he is seventy-five years old." Rachelet went on slowly. "That means I can assist at the birth of seven more wines. My place is here, *patron*."

The Marquis stared. "But the house and the vineyard in Anjou—"

"*Patron*, I am a man of Médoc."

"So you decline land of your own to work for me?"

"I do not only work for you, *patron*," Rachelet answered in the same slow voice. "I have seen every one of those vines planted. I feel responsible for them and for their wine. Pierre Simon, the husband of my niece, who I suppose will succeed me, does not yet know enough."

At that the Marquis grasped his hand. He, a colonel with the *Croix de Guerre*, had tears in his eyes. But Rachelet remained stiff and unresponsive. He was dissatisfied with himself because he had not been entirely honest. For a little while he could not express it, and he frowned. Then the words came.

"*Patron*, I must tell you that if you had offered this two years ago, or a little more than two years ago, I would have answered differently. I suppose every man for whom the future matters longs for his own house and land. But now I have no choice."

"I understand you," the Marquis answered in a soft voice. "But will your wife agree?"

Madeleine had agreed completely. In fact, that decision had brought some happiness and self-contentment to two old lovers who held hands and stared into the empty grate.

It kept them quietly happy until the vintage time. This, naturally, is the most busy period of all the busy year—and the most critical. The September weather was exceptionally hot. That meant that the crushed grapes began violently to ferment as soon as they were tipped into the big vats. Too hot a fermentation is dangerous, for under such conditions harmful microbes may flourish at the expense of those that are beneficial. All day long Rachelet was busy as a doctor, watching over the seething, heaving masses in the vats, anxiously taking temperatures. He returned to his cottage late at night, longing for peace and rest.

He found Madeleine tossing and muttering under the blankets, with a high fever. He spent the remainder of the night in a chair by the bedside, and in his broken dozing he confused the fever which was threatening her life with that of the grapes which were in such a hurry to be born as wine.

Next day they took Madeleine to the hospital, and a fortnight later she died. Rachelet was with her at the end. He sat holding her hand while she lay no longer hot and restless but cold and still. He was dazed—he had scarcely slept these last two weeks—and against all reason it came into his mind that the fever which had destroyed her was in some way connected with this year's hot fermentation. Later, when he put the bottles to rest in the cellar, he had been reminded of this thought.

Once more he nosed the glass. The fumes rose into his head. But that was not why tears started to his eyes. Like one listening to a tune of poignantly sad associations, he slowly drank the wine.

Madeleine's death had only confirmed his decision to work on; but it had weakened his physical ability to do so. His young niece Jeanette with her husband Pierre Simon had moved into the cottage to look after him. They had done what they could, and he would leave them all he had in recompense. But it had not been the same. In forty-five years of marriage a man forms habits, and a new woman in the house, however willing, causes as much vexation as an unskilled cellar hand. The last seven years had been a terrible struggle. They had broken him.

And yet the feeling of being on the way out—it was the *patron* who had used that expression, the description of a wine which has passed the peak of its second, its adult fermentation and has begun to lose colour, *bouquet*, flavour and strength—this feeling had first come to him two years earlier. It was in 1943.

Rachelet's hand reached along the table. He picked up a bottle and tested it with his eyes and nose, but it was not the one he wanted. At the next attempt he was successful. He took a mouthful of the wine, and chewed it, thrusting it with tongue and indrawn cheeks into every sensitive crevice. An unusual wine, the '43. Many considered it excellent. That of La Tour-St.-Vincent had matured so rapidly that it had sold better than the other wartime vintages which had preceded it. But to Rachelet there was something false about it. Like a brilliant, charming boy who as a man becomes a nonentity or actively goes to the bad, this wine would not last. He was sure of that.

Why? He shrugged his shoulders. Perhaps the weather had been too mild throughout the previous twelve months and the vines had become soft as people do when their lives are too easy. Or perhaps it depended on some peculiarity in the yeast spores which gathered mysteriously on the skins of the grapes. Or else— was it superstition to imagine that the vines of La Tour-St.- Vincent which he had tended all their lives had been affected by what had happened to him?

All the year, from January to October, Rachelet was happy. Both he and Madeleine were so gay that often in their cottage in the evening they sang the old songs together, as well as they could. For in January they received through the underground telegraph system of the Resistance a message from Victor, their son. He had been in England, they knew, and they guessed that he must now be in occupied France. He told them only that he was well, and that he would see them again when France was free. Victor in victory—just that. But it was enough to make proud parents happy.

Never since he was a young man had Rachelet tended the vines with such joyous enthusiasm. There was very little labour to help him—children, women and old men—but the vineyard was well cared for. There was no disease. His small team, fired by his energy, had harvested the grapes in sixteen days. There was never a cloud in the September sky and the fermentation went perfectly. The new wine calmed and settled and was racked off into hogsheads, full of promise as far as taste and alcoholic content were a guide.

In October, by the same mysterious means, another message arrived. But it was not from Victor. It came from what was described as the Headquarters of the Resistance. It stated: "Victor Rachelet was arrested in February. He was tortured for information but told nothing to the enemy. In September he was executed."

The brave boy had been resisting pain all that fine summer while his parents were laughing. Where had they put the body? Rachelet wondered. Somewhere in France it had fermented and gone back into the soil. Was that all that hopeful youth was born for, to act as manure?

The wine of that cruelly mocking year was still in Rachelet's mouth. He curved back his tongue to spit the stuff violently out. ... But just in time he realized how wrong and cowardly that would have been. Victor had not put his cup aside. Nor had he, Michel, while Madeleine supported him. He must not do it now just because he was alone.

Slowly he swallowed the mouthful, tasting every drop. He put his glass back on the table, and then—although without thinking why—filled it again, right to the brim, emptying the bottle. There would be dregs in it, of course. But he and Madeleine had drunk their hope to the lees that day and he would do it again, as a festival.

When the glass had been turned upside down over his mouth he felt a new and strong emotion. It puzzled him at first but it was really quite simple. He wanted to lift from his shoulders this weight of sorrow. Was that possible? He had once experienced happiness: otherwise he would not be so capable of feeling sad. ... Surely the old wine contained something of the spirit in which it had been made. The line of bottles stretched into the shadows towards the place where he had been at the beginning of this strange evening. He got to his feet and, picking up the candle, went a pace or two along the road and dropped down in another seat.

It was fortunate that his hand then closed on the bottle of 1937. If he had picked a lesser vintage, one on the way out, it could have disappointed him out of his new mood. But this wine interested him. It was some time since he had tasted it, but it was evidently in no hurry to mature. It was one of those big, strong, slow growers with which he felt sympathy. He cocked his head and admired the colour. He made the rich liquid gyrate and warmed it to bring out the vapours—then breathed them.

This was what the connoisseur called *bouquet*. It served as a term, but it did not describe what Rachelet's ugly old nose experienced. There were varied odours in wine, certainly, but the result was not like a bunch of flowers, nothing so pretty-pretty. Wine had been born to work for its living. It had struggled as well as enjoyed itself. It had experienced frost and drought and deluge and disease. Its parent plants had been shorn of half their limbs that it might receive more of their blood. It had lived and meant to go on living.

There was the smell of fruit, of course—not only of grapes. There were odours of sweetness, of soft oils and delicate ethers.

But there was acid and bitterness as well. Those, and the smell of earth wet or dry, of damp or sunbaked vegetation. There was the tang of young skin heated by hard work. Everything was in the earth, and God created out of it each year a new wine with a new character. Its characteristics were modified as the wine grew older, but they were always recognizable. The *vigneron*, tasting every now and then, could follow its development.

The most important thing was to start it off well in life, in clean vessels so that it was not born infected. If it began life well it needed little besides care and peace. But some wines were like difficult children. This of '37 for instance—unusually soon after it had been transferred into hogsheads from the fermenting vat it had needed to be racked—drawn off into another barrel leaving the lees behind. It went on fermenting, casting out impurities. Some of them were so small and light that they would not sink. These had to be netted, dragged to the bottom under a sinking film of white of egg, and the clean wine drawn off. What a lot of wild oats it had had to sow. It was four years before the wine was clear enough for bottling. It had caused a deal of trouble, this wine!

But it was strong! (Rachelet clenched his fist.) He sipped a little of the wine and noticed once more its striking characteristic. It seemed to fill the mouth as some people seem to fill a room. With human beings you called that personality. This wine had been a personality from birth, the difficult boy of the *chai*. Rachelet had not grudged the time and trouble it cost him, because he knew the young wine had in it the possibility of greatness. Already it was proving this. But a few roughnesses remained. It needed further years of contemplation in the cool gloom of the cellar before it would be perfectly balanced.

Rachelet refilled his glass, and sipped it slowly and with enjoyment. It was curious: what the scents and flavours brought to mind was not the work in the *chai*, but a scene in the vineyards. This came to him suddenly and clearly—making him smile for the first time. He saw himself as he had been fifteen years ago, strong and upright, full of the joy of life.

The vintage of 1937 was fine, with a single day of showers. Rachelet's place was in the pressing-room, but he liked to walk into the fields on at least one occasion to see how things were going and to encourage the pickers by telling them about the wine. It happened that he chose the day of showers! He reached the distant corner of the vineyards where the harvesting was going on just as the rain came down cats and dogs. The pickers with their half-filled baskets scampered along the narrow lanes between the vines and took shelter under the big umbrellas, pressed tight together, leaning their heads inwards. The girls naturally found themselves being embraced. There was a lot of noise, laughter and mock slapping of faces. It was an unfailing source of merriment when some youth flirted with an old woman. The shouted jokes were coarse but good-humoured. Meanwhile the raindrops pattered on the black umbrellas; and the white oxen harnessed to the wagon stood patient and steaming, with their heads lowered and their sad brown eyes looking at nothing in particular. Rachelet could smell the wet leather of their hides. The rain ceased, and the pickers went back to their work, kicking the mud off their boots, trying to hit each other with it.

Rachelet with his wife and son stood watching. The true reason why he had chosen this hour to come out into the fields was that not only would he find Victor in charge but also Madeleine preparing the midday meal. Madeleine's soup was famous: it was said that she put into it everything from the château garden, including the gardener, his daughter and their cow. As a rule the harvesters returned to the kitchen to eat, but on this occasion lunch had been brought out to them since they were working so far off.

The huge tureen was being heated up over a bonfire which was hissing and spitting from the rain. Madeleine lifted the lid to stir the thick liquor and an odour came out which made the lips wet.

"How long will it be?" Rachelet asked.

"It is ready, greedy one. But your dinner is in the wine-house. You men of the *cuvier* are so proud that you eat always alone."

"Not today. I shall eat well today."

Victor called the luncheon hour and the harvesters came elbowing and chattering to receive their bowl of soup and hunk of bread and cheese. Rachelet, with his cavalryman's moustaches and his black, observant eyes, stood watching them. He liked young people and it pleased him that they should so frankly enjoy his wife's soup. But he was impatient for his own share.

"The *patron*—and a visitor," Victor said, looking along the trail which led from the château.

Rachelet could not recognize the distant figures, but he trusted his son's eyes and swore under his breath.

"No soup for you," Madeleine said. "You must take the visitor round."

Little Madeleine, although she had passed her fiftieth birthday, still had a girl's plump figure—in her husband's view at least. Her face glowed. The raindrops on her cheeks looked like tears, but her lips were curving and twitching and her eyes were bright with mischief. Rachelet smacked her hard and affectionately on the behind.

"I shall have my soup, never fear," he said.

The *patron* and the stranger joined them. The *patron* was young. He had only returned permanently to the estate since the old Marquis died the year before, and he was not yet entirely sure of himself.

"This is Mr. Waterford," he said, introducing the stranger, a thin and earnest young man who raised his hat politely. "He is the son of a friend of my father. He is writing a thesis on economics, and he wishes to ask you certain questions. I expected to find you in the *chai*—"

"It was necessary to come to the vineyards. But I am at the gentleman's disposition," Rachelet answered.

"Then I shall leave you together," the young *patron* said, and excused himself.

"Well, it's like this," Mr. Waterford began diffidently in slow and ill-pronounced French. "I am told that one person in every seven in this country earns his living in the wine industry, so I can't very well ignore it as a part of the economics of the country. But I have never studied wine myself. I do not understand it."

"What is it that Monsieur wishes to understand?" Rachelet asked. Madeleine winked at him while she and her son ostentatiously swallowed their soup, but he ignored them.

"Well, Monsieur Rachelet," Waterford said. "It is like this. Your proprietor was good enough to take me to his *chai*. He gave me half a dozen wines to taste, and he talked about *bouquet* and *velouté* and *finesse* and a lot more that was over my head—"

"Did Monsieur enjoy the wines?"

"They were really wonderful. But the prices varied by fifty per cent or more; and, after all, they came from the same grapes and vineyard. Tell me, Monsieur Rachelet, how is it you experts tell that a wine is good?"

"That is very simple, Monsieur. When it tastes good, it is good."

"Tastes—but that's just the mystery. I haven't a palate, you see."

"If Monsieur had no palate he would talk like this." (Rachelet made some guggling noises. Waterford stared—then burst out laughing.) "Would Monsieur like some soup?" Rachelet asked.

"I certainly would. I am due for luncheon at the château in an hour, but this smells too good to miss."

"You have been conscious of the *bouquet*. Do not taste yet, please. Can you tell me what is in the soup?"

Waterford nosed the bowl which Madeleine had handed to him.

"The only thing I can't tell you is what's tasty and isn't there."

"Can Monsieur be more precise?"

"Well, there's onion, and a lot of other vegetables, and a good rich stock, I'd say—and something else."

"Excellent. Now taste, Monsieur. Take a mouthful and chew it well. . . . Now what do you taste?"

Waterford swallowed. His eyes were shining behind his spectacles. "I was right about the stock. And the onion too. The other vegetables are too well mixed. But the something else was wine. Now may I eat?"

"Yes indeed, and I will eat with you. You are right to say eat, for good soup like strong wine is to be eaten. Mr. Waterford, you have a palate. Your nose warns you what to expect and your mouth confirms. If the soup had been cooked less you could have tasted all the vegetables, but the result would not have been so satisfactory. If it had been cooked more you would not have distinguished the pleasant tastes you did. It is the same with wine. Wine also draws everything from the earth, but it combines them in the cool and very slowly, not by cooking. And the flavours are far more fine. I am not clever enough to explain more, but you will understand. You like good things. You will soon learn to appreciate wine. The only important thing is to go on studying it affectionately—as one does a woman."

Mr. Waterford was easily persuaded to join the pickers. After two or three rows in the sun which was now blazing from a polished sky he was ready enough to sample the wine from the keg on the ox wagon. A few glasses later he claimed to recognize, with shouts of welcome, all the savours of the earth. After all, he was young and the harvesters encouraged him. He worked until evening, streaming with sweat—and said that he had never enjoyed himself so much.

Rachelet smiled. He had always liked young people, especially when they were modest and polite and had appreciation of the good things which God had given. It pleased him to encourage their appreciation. He himself had enjoyed life so much when this 1937 wine which he was sipping was being harvested—and in the years before. He would not have changed places with an emperor.

After all, he had been something like an emperor, or at least a prime minister, in his *chai*, which was, so to speak, the capital of the estate. What a lot of visitors there had been! But in memory these visits were little more than a procession of almost identical ceremonies not associated with any particular vintage.

The *patron* ushered a party of guests into the coolness of the great pillared building. They paused near the doorway, as if shy to leave the sunlight for the dim and solemn mystery which smelt of wine. Yet they were eager—if they were worth anything. Their voices, which had dropped at first, rose in wonder at the size of the place and at the precision of the four rows of barrels of polished oak which stretched away into the shadows. They began to make the round, leaving their tracks on the neatly raked fine gravel of the floor.

At the far end, symmetrically placed beyond the rows of barrels, was a polished walnut table. Just as the visitors reached it, Rachelet would appear with the exact number of glasses suspended bottoms upward between the fingers of his big hands. Without even glancing at the visitors, he placed them on the table and went for his *sonde*.

It was part of the tradition that the *maître de chai* could not only carry so many glasses but also that he knew precisely how many were needed.... Rachelet chuckled. That was a little trick which harmed nobody. It was connected with the fact that during the summer the youngest cellar hand was always employed cleaning out empty barrels in the courtyard, shaking a length of chain inside each.

So Rachelet, having placed the glasses on the table, went to a particular barrel. He removed the bung and thrust the *sonde*, a long tube of glass like a pipette, down through the hole. Closing the top of the tube with his thumb he drew out a purple column of wine. Easing up his thumb he dropped an exact measure into each glass. Then he stood back with folded arms to watch while the guests tasted.

He had overheard it said that a visit to the *chai* of Château La Tour-St.-Vincent was like a solemn religious ceremony. That pleased him. It was the right approach to good wine. It made even brokers start tasting in a proper mood. He had often thought what a pity it was that the Church, which knew all about ceremony, no longer owned great vineyards and so could not supply good wine for the Communion. It would have been more polite to the *bon Dieu*. That commercially concocted stuff, and what they told you to believe of it, was ... Rachelet curled down his lips and shook his head.

There had been plenty of distinguished men among the visitors to the *chai*. One was Marshal Foch. He was in civilian clothes and noticeably older than on the occasion when Rachelet had seen him during the 1914–18 War. But he had recognized him out of the corner of his eye while he was filling the *sonde*. He had muttered with the urgency of a prayer: "Little wine, be good. You are about to mix with the blood of a brave man."

Afterwards the Marshal had shaken him by the hand and thanked him—and had asked him if he were not an old soldier. They had talked for several minutes while the *patron* and his other guests stood round about in silence....

There was a burst of music as a door opened and closed; then singing, a little out of tune, which receded into the night. The first of the revellers were going home. Rachelet hoped the dance would not break up altogether. He was enjoying the sound of it now.... He reached for another bottle. He had already remembered so much and he was not yet half-way back along the road.

The next interesting wine he tasted was the 1934. He rubbed his strong hands together and settled down to enjoy the experience. For, as had been mentioned in one of the speeches, the twelve months which preceded the vintage of '34 had been quite remarkably similar to those of this last year. There had been a number of anxious moments this last year, but all had proved well in the end. The grapes were as healthy as one could wish at harvest time, and Rachelet had regretted that he could not live long enough to taste this wine in its maturity. But here it was in its model of eighteen years ago.

Rachelet remembered that year.

Between mild spells there were pricks of sharp cold in the winter, but no late frosts to shrivel the sprouting leaves. The flowering went well. The early summer was cool and rather damp. Then the dry heat came.

Apart from a few isolated cases of apoplexy—vines wilting and dying within a few days, not unexpected in these conditions of sudden change from moisture to dryness—the vineyard continued healthy. Vines with their long roots reaching down into the subsoil can put up with more dry weather than most other plants. But the drought went on too long. Men said to each other that if it would only rain it would rain good wine. The grapes were sound, but they were small. They needed pumping up.

The latter half of July was almost intolerably hot. There was no cloud in the sky and no breath of wind. The air was stale and heavy. About the farm buildings the geese lay on their bellies in the dust, their wings extended and their beaks open, panting. The horses and cattle stood under trees, swishing their tails and growing thinner every day. The vineyard was drying up.

Each morning when he left his cottage Rachelet looked anxiously at the sky. He well knew that the only way such weather could break was in a thunderstorm. And thunder often brought hail. So late in the season, hail would not only destroy the present crop but that of the next year also, for if the shoots were broken off there would be no bearers next spring for the new shoots to sprout from.

On July 20th there came news that several vineyards in Alsace had been battered to pieces by hailstones. (The same thing happened at much the same date in 1952.) Alsace—that was far enough away. But next day Rachelet heard on the radio of thunderstorms with hail in the Loire valley. They were said to be moving southwards. He wondered by what route they would come. It was far from certain that the bad weather would pass over Médoc. But it might.

When darkness fell the sky to the north glowed now and then with lightning. Rachelet estimated that the storm must be over Angoulême. He telephoned to a friend who lived there.

What he was told was not encouraging. Hailstones as large as sparrows' eggs had broken a number of windows before the storm passed on.

"In what direction was it travelling?" Rachelet asked.

"In your direction."

Rachelet hung up the receiver, picturing the vineyard bare as in midwinter except that the ground would be strewn with grapes and leaves. What made it still worse was that the *patron* was away on holiday and he would have to tell him about it when he returned.

There was nothing to be done except wait. The *vignerons* wandered aimlessly about the yard kicking the empty barrels which might not be wanted for two years, or stood in groups speculating pessimistically. Their cigarettes glowed in the darkness. Rachelet walked away and sat down alone under the cedar.

The lightning was growing brighter and the thunder more loud. There was no longer any reasonable chance that the storm would miss them. Rachelet wanted to pray, but he was ashamed to. He had never been much of a one for the forms of religion, and to call upon God only when he was in trouble seemed dishonest. At last he put it like this: "Lord, I am in Your hands. It is Your storm, but I am responsible for this vineyard. I only mention that the sea is very close and hail would do no damage there."

Then he resigned himself to wait. He must have dozed. When next he became fully conscious of his surroundings he realized that there was no lightning. Had God seen the point of his argument? But there were no stars. The night was black, and heavy as sand. When he ran his finger through his hair it crackled. Was he about to be punished? Had he offended God?

Without any warning there was a deafening explosion and a burning sword stabbed down into the heart of the vineyard. For a moment after that there was complete silence. Then it came down. It was as if the acres of crisp leaves were under heavy machine-gun fire. Scarcely knowing what he was doing, Rachelet ran out from the shelter of the cedar, his arms extended as if to protect his vines.

He stopped in his tracks. His arms dropped slowly to his sides and his head went back. He was soaked to the skin already, but nothing stung his face. It was water that was coming down, not ice—rain to fill the grapes, not hail to destroy them.

For a long time he remained at the edge of the vineyard, racking his brain for the proper words to express pious gratitude. At last he murmured: "Lord, I will drink Your health in the wine which You have saved."

Sitting at the table he now lifted his glassful to the moonlit sky. The wine was much better than it had been when he had first fulfilled his vow. After eighteen years of education in the *chai* it was nearly as good as it would ever be. Was his homage any worthier as a result? Was he himself better? He shrugged his shoulders. He felt better at the moment, but only God could judge. Dimly, half-consciously, he pictured God the Father in the image of the old *patron*, God the Son as something like the young one. He had never been obsequious to the *patron*, either the old or the young, and on certain occasions he had been downright rude. But they respected him as a good servant who worked hard for the vineyard rather than himself. He believed that God would have the same point of view. In any case, he would not be ashamed to face Him, cap in hand, when the time came.

But the time had not yet come, thank God. In fact, it was many years since he had felt so well. How was that? He tasted the wine again and remembered something else about it. While it had been in barrel it had been extremely promising and had sold well. But some years after it had been bottled it had gone off badly. Respected judges had even said that it was finished. Then—no man knew why—it had picked up again and become excellent. Wines did that sometimes—so why not human beings? Had he himself really taken a turn for the better, or was it just that travelling back along the road of vintages made him *feel* better? No matter: when a wine tasted good it was good, so presumably when he felt better he was better. The idea amused him. He got up and moved farther down the table.

But with the candle in one hand and the other hand reaching out for a bottle, he suddenly remembered something and sat down without refilling his glass. The '33 had been fair, but the three previous vintages had been terrible. He recalled this clearly enough without any stimulus of taste, for these were his first vintages as *maître de chai*. He had just taken over after his father's death and he meant to carry on the tradition—but everything went wrong.

Bad weather and disease summed it up. Cold rainy days, very little sun—that wasn't his fault. But when the disease was first noticed he made a mistake. He thought it was oïdium, of which his father had talked almost as often as of the phylloxera, and he treated the vines with sulphur. Very soon he recognized his error. The *tache d'huile* was only on the lower side of the leaves. (If it had been oïdium the mark would have been on both sides.) It was the downy mildew, and it had got a grip. The little grapes turned brown, they shrivelled and died. He was afraid the whole vineyard might be lost through the falling of the leaves. Copper sulphate and newly slaked lime was the cure, but in that wet weather a number of sprayings were necessary before it took effect.

As if that were not enough there followed in the next year *coulure*, a complete failure of fertilization, and *millerandage*, the half-way stage when only little seedless berries, round and small as peas, are born. The bad weather at the flowering time was surely part of the cause, but Rachelet wondered gloomily if he had pruned too short or manured wrongly.

He shrugged his shoulders. No use worrying now. Better find something else to think about. He moved a pace or two along the table and filled his glass from a bottle chosen at random.

He knew it immediately as the '29. He put the glass back on the table and stared at it. After a little while he involuntarily reached out his hand and took a mouthful. He kept it there, caressing its smooth fullness with his tongue, wondering at it. It was worth labouring from dawn to dusk a whole active lifetime to have been responsible for such a wine. And he had been chiefly responsible, for his father had died on the eve of the vintage, and of his retirement. The old man had been carried off by the apoplexy, as quickly and it seemed as painlessly as a vine dies of the disease.

Rachelet had loved and respected his father. He felt his loss deeply. The *chai* was a sad place without him. But Michel knew the only way in which he could show respect to the old man. He himself was in his prime, strong and eager to carry on the tradition. And God was good to him that year in other ways. Victor had completed his studies at the University. He had proved himself capable of great things in the outside world. But he had chosen to return to Château La Tour-St.-Vincent and work under his father. What a year it had been with that fine young fellow at his side, learning as he himself, Michel, had learned from his own father. And for the vines it was a wonderful year, a vintage still remembered by the whole world.

He returned to contemplation of the wine. How deeply satisfactory it was to feel it in one's mouth.... Inconsequently his memory went flying off to an entirely different period, to his childhood.

He was about six years old. On some special occasion, with his mother and a few other women and children of the estate, he had been shown over the château by the wife of the old *patron*. She had taken from its case and handed round a beautiful ruby which had belonged to Marie Antoinette. The Marquise talked about it for some time, telling its romantic history. The queen had never had it set, for she could not make up her mind how best to use so wonderful a stone.

At the end the Marquise held out her hand to take the jewel back.... It could not be found. Each person protested she had passed it on to another. Consternation! The beautiful Marquise became very pale and at last sent a servant for her husband. They waited for the *patron* in the most acute embarrassment. That one of the estate people should be a thief was unthinkable. And yet— where was the jewel?

The situation was at its worst when Madame Rachelet noticed, as mothers do, something strange about her child's expression. In her agitation she shook him violently—and the ruby fell out of his mouth on to the floor.

At home he took his punishment in silence. He could not give a reason for what he had done. Yet this wine somehow reminded him of the proud and satisfying feeling of holding that precious jewel in his mouth.

Most of the châteaux of Médoc rated the 1929 as their best vintage of the past fifty years. Rachelet considered the wine he had just tasted to be quite as good as that from any other vineyard. But he believed that Château La Tour-St.-Vincent had produced an even better one within the century—the 1900. Certainly it was the best that he himself had ever experienced. His father had said the same even when the wine was young. That made it the greatest wine of a hundred years, and last time he had tasted it, it gave the impression of improving still. Appropriately, 1900 was also the most important year of his own life. It would make a fitting climax to his pilgrimage of tastes and memories.

He would drink it at once: it would be exactly right after the 1929. He got to his feet and, picking up the candle, started the ten or twelve paces to the dark end of the table where he had begun the evening and where the old wine stood.

But he had not taken more than a couple of steps before he sat down again, shaking his head. There was no need to taste the intervening vintages: many were indifferent wines. But they had been good years of living. He would not hurry tonight. He would make the most of this journey on which all real sorrow lay behind and only the cares and happiness of youth in front.

He sat now with his back to the vineyard, looking with wrinkled forehead along the line of remaining bottles, each blurred by the shadow of the one in front. The best third of his life was there. But it was curious, the harder he tried to think of incidents, the less he seemed able to remember.

He became conscious of the music. They were playing a mixture of old tunes, strung together and fitted to a modern dance. Rachelet listened intently. Quite often an air stirred something at the back of his mind. More than once he saw Victor dancing or heard him whistling as he worked. Quite often he himself was swinging his glass at a feast at vintage time. Once he was dancing with Madeleine. But before he could get everything out of the tune it had changed to another. Music went through your head and was lost. You could not hold it in your mouth and chew it until you were sure.

As Rachelet sat listening in the black shadow of the cedar, groping for memories which slipped away like a swiftly flowing river from the eager fingers of the water-weed—as he sat there feeling half happy, half uncertain, the table in front of him became flooded with silver. The moon had found a gap between the fan-shaped branches. Half a dozen bottles were illuminated as by a spotlight. And the beam gradually moved, taking in another bottle every minute.

It became possible to read the labels. When Rachelet had first tried to do this they had been in his own writing, but now they were in the large, ill-educated yet most expressive hand of his father. His father was *maître de chai*, and it had always been his custom with these bottles destined for the *bibliothèque* to write not only the date but also a note as to the bins in which the rest of the vintage was stored.

Memories came quicker now; "1928"—a year almost as good as '29. "1924 Bins 72–81"—Rachelet could see himself in a particular corner of the cellar, stacking the bottles. The crop that year was enormous—the second largest he had known—but there had been far too much rain and the wine was thin.

But what made Rachelet smile was the manner in which the labels had been written. They showed his father's opinion of the wine. For instance, that of 1928 was written large and decorated with a scroll-like pattern. The details of a poor wine were written small and plain. One could feel that he was angry and ashamed.

What a character his father had been. People called him, Michel, a character, but he got it all from the father whom they had forgotten. He had been a hard master, treating his son more severely than any other of his assistants. He had taught him not only facts but also a principle. The good of the wine came first, human beings and their feelings second. Michel smiled, remembering the occasion when one of the *patron's* nephews, a young *beau* from Paris, had arrived to show some friends round the *chai*. Rachelet *père* had barred his way, telling him to go first and wash his hair which was dressed with some highly scented lotion.

There must be nothing in the *chai* which might even temporarily mar the wine or distract those whose duty was to watch over it by tasting. Women were excluded, even the Marquise whom the *maître de chai* adored. (She knew his rule and never challenged it, saying that she took it as a compliment.) The only woman who had ever succeeded in entering the sacred gloom was Madeleine. She had once visited her husband in the *chai*— of all reasons to collect the yolks of the eggs, the whites of which had been used for fining. She came disguised in her son's clothes and carrying a sack of corks on her shoulder. Madeleine was always up to some mischief. Everybody loved her—not least her father-in-law.

How happy they were—the aristocracy of the estate. They knew how to live—to enjoy themselves and also to work. . . . The moonlight, moving obliquely across the table, just touched a bottle marked 1919. (If they had been afraid of work it might never have been filled.) One July night that year Rachelet was strolling with his wife along a vineyard path when he saw a number of moths fly overhead. He told his father, and next morning they investigated. On the leaves of one of the first vines they looked at were patches of eggs. It might have been the *altise,* but on consideration they decided it was the rare *pyrale.*

The old *patron* joined them, and turned anxiously to his *maître de chai.* Although the *pyrale* is almost unknown in Médoc, he knew it well enough by reputation. Once the eggs hatched out the caterpillars were difficult to deal with, for if alarmed they went into the ground. And how they ate! With his own eyes, he said, he had seen a vineyard of the Midi in summer which had no leaves at all.

"That is not all," Rachelet *père* burst out, as pessimistically excited as his *patron.* "The grubs turn to moths and the moths lay again. In the autumn the young grubs go under the bark. They come out in the spring and spin their webs over the buds and eat their hearts out."

"What are we to do?" the *patron* shouted. "In Burgundy they scald the vines."

"In Burgundy they have vineyards like cottage gardens. Besides, that is in winter," Rachelet *père* shouted back. To all appearances he and the *patron* were engaged in a furious quarrel.

"Then chemicals—lead arsenate—"

"And where, *patron,* can one get lead arsenate nowadays? There is nothing to be bought this year, nothing at all."

The *patron's* anger left him. "That is true," he said. "One can get nothing at all." And then, half to himself, he added as if it were a tragic additional point: "In Germany they call this thing the *Springwurmwickler.*"

Young Rachelet burst out laughing. He had been listening, silent and worried, but the absurdly long word was too much for him.

Both men turned on him as on a common enemy.

"He discovered it, strolling in the moonlight! It is up to him to find a cure," his father said.

Rachelet was sobered immediately. He tried to think under the angry glances.

"If we could remove the eggs—" he began.

His hearers raised their eyes to heaven.

"I own, I believe, three-quarters of a million vines," the *patron* said at last. "How many leaves have they? I do not say that there are eggs on every leaf, but every leaf must be examined for eggs. And we have at most forty workmen. Is it mathematically possible for them to do what you suggest?"

Rachelet began to feel obstinate. "There are about two hundred persons available, counting women and children old enough to walk," he answered. "And we have ten days before the eggs hatch. I am not clever at mathematics, but if you give me the authority the work shall be done."

The work was done. The women left their homes and the children stayed away from school—and every infected leaf was picked and burned. A fortnight later this tremendous task was done again, just to ensure that there had been no second laying.

The crop was saved.

While Rachelet had been thinking of this incident the pool of moonlight had slipped off the side of the table, leaving the bottles once more unilluminated except by the small flame of the candle.

With the half-conscious intention of maintaining the sequence of his memories, he stretched out his hand and filled his glass.

There was something familiar in the sharp smell. He continued to breathe it, fascinated against his will, for it stung like vinegar.

At that moment there was a burst of noise. The remaining dancers were pouring out into the night behind the musicians, singing a marching song.

Rachelet brought the glass down on to the table so violently that it broke, cutting his hand. The tune was *La Madelon* and the wine the first he had drunk when he returned on leave to La Tour-St.-Vincent at Christmas, 1918.

He had loathed the war. It was not from fear: he had taken the necessary risks philosophically. It was not from the hardship: although he had the *vigneron's* standards of comfort—two good meals with wine and a dry bed at night—he had accepted the

misery of the trenches. It was not only from missing his wife, his
friends and his vineyard. What he had most loathed about the
war and what had continually horrified him was the waste.

He saw land devastated, which was bad enough. On the Marne
front it was Champagne country—a district he had pretended
to despise—but to see vine fences used for barbed wire, vineyards
ploughed up with trenches and shell-holes.... Worse still were
the bodies. They were harvested by the machine-guns and they
lay swelling and fermenting into bad smells.... He was given a
medal for bringing in wounded under fire. He was told that he
was brave. But he had only done what he considered to be his
duty. He had prevented a few young lives being picked before
their time.

Rachelet bound up his cut hand with his handkerchief, holding
one end of the knot with his teeth. Then, moving slowly but un-
hesitatingly, he took the candle to the end of the table. He would
taste the 1900 at once. He would be missing no memories, for the
years which followed belonged to it.

The bottles here were disordered, no doubt because the guests
had clustered about Rachelet to say good night. He picked up
another glass and began searching for the wine he longed for. He
could not have said how he would recognize it any more than
he could have described how he would recognize a voice. But he
never doubted that he would.

He tried three or four bottles which were almost as dead as
water under his nose. There had been bad vintages in the intervening years, as if the ground had been exhausted by what it gave
in 1900.

Sitting in the same chair where he had begun the evening, he
filled his glass once more.

With the involuntary gasp of happiness with which one recog-
nizes an old love, he became conscious that he had found what he
had been searching for. His scholar nose pressed eagerly into the
glass.... There was no doubt about it. The *bouquet* was faint
but unmistakable. He felt his heart beating against his ribs.

He sat with the glass in his cupped hands, looking out over the
vineyards and breathing this magic old wine.... Little by little
the scene in front of him appeared to change. The setting moon
became the rising sun which lit the dew-damp leaves but filled

the corridors with shadow, so that the whole vineyard was streaked alternately with silvery green and dark purple. The larks were climbing their invisible spiral staircases, singing as they went. The grasshoppers were warming up. It was as clear as that in every detail, yet somehow everything was small, as if it were a long way off.

He saw nearly a hundred people come out from the village of estate buildings and walk in scattered groups towards the southern end of the vineyard. Most of them were young. The girls wore coal-scuttle bonnets, full skirts and blouses with sleeves which bunched over their shoulders but left their forearms bare. Their clothes were full of colour. They carried wicker baskets and chattered gaily as they went along. The men wore berets, and bright handkerchiefs round their necks. Behind the last of them came a wagon drawn by two white oxen whose flanks and long-horned heads swung rhythmically with each slow stride.

When everybody had reached the chosen part of the vineyard a man began shouting, pulling and pushing at the cheerful throng until he had got each person facing a corridor between the vines. Then they began to pick.

Eight or nine men were left over. These were the foreman, the driver of the wagon, and the six strong fellows who wore the *hottes*. Rachelet himself was one of this half-dozen. He was straight and tall, with twirled moustaches, and he carried the big wooden container as a soldier carries his pack on parade.

He walked round to the other end of the plot and stood there waiting for the pickers to reach him with their full baskets. They advanced slowly, stooping almost to the ground, snip-snipping off the bunches which grew low down on the vines, now and then straightening up to ease their backs and talk and eat a grape or two. They were in no great hurry, for they had in front of them a fortnight or more of tiring work which would become monotonous if they did not make something of a game and gossip of it.

The straggling, chattering line came towards Rachelet. He knew most of the pickers: they were the families of the estate men. But about a third were strangers from Bordeaux and elsewhere. For the most part these had come in groups which kept together. He looked at them critically, wondering how useful they would prove. A party of wilful or lazy students could cause trouble, and it might not be easy to discipline them without damage to the gay spirit of the vintage.

The first of the pickers reached him—Marie Canet. It was natural that she should be first, for being the daughter of the schoolmaster she felt herself superior and therefore talked little to her companions. The second, third and fourth arrived almost together, with loud asides about the handsome *porteur*. Rachelet turned his back on them and they emptied their baskets into his *hotte*. He walked first in one direction and then in the other, receiving two or three kilos of grapes from each person—generally with a joke or a tap on the head with the empty basket. Only one picker had not reached the end, a girl. Rachelet waited for her impatiently, for the load on his back was heavy by now and he wanted to go and empty it into one of the *douils* on the ox wagon.

The girl was small—it seemed not much taller than the vines—which should have made it easier for her to pick the low bunches. She was evidently taking pains not to miss any grapes hidden by leaves. But she must be clumsy. In any case she was delaying the team.

"You are very slow," he said.

"I do my best," she answered.

On the tip of Rachelet's tongue was a sharp remark about the trouble caused by amateurs who did not appreciate the importance of a vintage at Château La Tour-St.-Vincent, and who got themselves taken on by overstating their qualifications. But the girl's tone made him hesitate. Her answer had been neither defiant nor humble: a quiet statement of fact. Her face was hidden by the rim of her bonnet.

"From where do you come?" he asked.

"From Bordeaux."

"This is your first vintage?"

"Yes. We must all start sometime. Soon I shall be as quick as anybody."

"Exactly"—Rachelet remembered why he had first spoken to her—"it is important not to dislocate the schedule. See, they are already starting on another row."

"In that case would it not be better to take my grapes without delay?"

Rachelet turned his back on her.

"You will have to stoop down," she said.

They were walking after the pickers when he noticed that the little handkerchief she held in her left hand was stained bright red.

"You have hurt yourself," he said.

"It is nothing."

"Let me see."

One of her fingers had a deep wound which was bleeding freely.

"How did this happen?" he asked.

"It was so stupid. I was holding a bunch. It was under the leaves. I cut—but it was not the bunch I cut. That is why I have been slow."

"But you did not call out? You said nothing?"

"It was so stupid."

Rachelet, who was on his knees before her, tearing his own not very clean handkerchief into strips, looked up into her face. It might have belonged to a pretty and mischievous little boy, but it was evidently very near to tears. She was biting her lip, fighting against them; but they were there, making her blue eyes glisten. Instinctively he knew that this was less from the pain than from his sympathy. He was glad—but for the sake of her pride she must not cry! He felt his heart swell. He jumped to his feet.

"It needs proper attention. Come with me, please," he said, in a businesslike voice. And as they walked together, so different in height, he went on talking to her bonnet.

"It is not serious, but it must be disinfected. I have been a soldier and you can believe I know about wounds. . . . Yes, yes, it is just two years since I finished my military service and returned to the Château. I was a cavalryman. Do you love horses? We were in Algeria, and I saw some fighting, I can tell you!"

When they reached the wagon he washed her cut finger under the tap of the wine keg, then bound it up.

"Now you will rest a little," he said.

"No, I must not dislocate the schedule."

They had returned half-way towards the pickers when she asked: "Why did you not empty that thing on your back?"

Rachelet stopped and stared down into her upturned face. For the last quarter of an hour he had been bustling about with a *hotte* containing seventy pounds weight of grapes on his shoulders— and he had not even noticed it. He burst out laughing. The girl laughed too, with the bubbling, overflowing laugh of a child.

And then they both became silent and embarrassed.

During the next few days the girl proved that she was not, as Rachelet had thought, a helpless little thing who could not be trusted even with a pair of pruning scissors. She became a quick and efficient worker. She was popular with the other pickers for her good nature and puckish humour. But she was always a little reserved—and therefore mysterious. Rachelet saw as much of her as he could. He did not mind if it caused gossip; nor, it seemed, did she. He walked with her to and from the picking plots, and they had long talks in the warm, soft evening when the work was done. Rachelet's mother, who besides running the kitchen was in general charge of the women pickers, quickly noticed what was in the air. But she could find no fault with the girl. In fact she took Madeleine—that was her name—under her special care, and learned her simple story before her son did—which perhaps prejudiced her in the girl's favour. Madeleine was the daughter of the mate of a trading vessel. They had their own house in Bordeaux and were evidently respectable. But he had been away three months on a voyage and money was running short, so she had taken this job.

After the first few days of the vintage the tempo of work considerably increased. It was evident that this would be a bumper harvest, perhaps the biggest in living memory. The weather was perfect, but it could not be expected to remain so for ever, and rain would wash the yeast spores from the skins of the grapes. Therefore both the picking and pressing must be speeded up. More pickers were drafted in, while the four best men were taken from the fields and added to the skilled team in the *cuvier*.

Rachelet was one of the chosen four. It was remarkable promotion for a young man who only a couple of years previously had returned to the Château from his conscript service. . . . But he was sorry to leave the fields just then.

He had little time, though, for thinking about Madeleine. One after another, at short intervals, the wagons came creaking into the yard and were backed against the entrance to the *cuvier*. Each wagon carried two *douils*, huge tubs piled high with several hundredweight of grapes. These tubs had to be unloaded, emptied and put back on the wagons without delay so that the oxen could return to the vineyards. The grapes had to be got off their stalks, pressed and deposited in the vats before the next relay brought in another load. Under Rachelet *père* there were no new-fangled apparatus at the Château La Tour-St.-Vincent. The *douils* were unloaded and reloaded by sheer strength. The grapes were handled and trodden and their juice transported in traditional style. The bunches were pitchforked on to the *table d'égrappage*, a table like a huge chequer-board in which the black squares were a latticing of hard wood and the white squares were holes. Six men, three on each side, moving with a rhythm like rowing, massaged the bunches on this sieve-table to make the grapes fall through the holes, leaving their stalks behind. The pitchforker continued to load the table and the massagers to stroke and press the bunches until the whole load was separated, stalks and grapes. Then the table was removed and the grapes were crushed underfoot, the half-naked men marching with high steps round and round, clasping each other's waists. Then the juice, the skins, the crushed flesh and the uncrushed pips (what together is called the must) were spooned with wooden shovels into *hottes* and carried up a twelve-foot ladder to be tipped over the head, with a sudden bowing action, into one of the five-thousand-litre vats where the juice of yesterday was already seething in the full frenzy of fermentation.

Two teams of seven men each were engaged in this work. They raced against each other for the fun of it and in the hope that they might win an interval to wash and rest. But at best they only had time to run to the pump and splash their faces before they heard the creak and rumble as the next wagon came into the yard.

They were all big fellows in the *cuvier*. The muscles rippled under their skin. But they looked like savages in war paint, their limbs spattered with the juice, their eyes red and their hair purple. They worked from dawn till dark. No one complained. Rachelet had never known a man to complain of hard work at vintage time. It was as if the bursting energy of the yeast cells got into their blood. And on this occasion they had a particular incentive, for it was evident that the vintage was going to be something quite out of the ordinary—not only in amount. From the first evening when the *maître de chai*, saccharometer in hand, had nodded approvingly over a sample of the juice, he had gone about like one who guards a tremendous secret. His team, pausing for a moment in their work, studied his face after his daily sampling of the forming wine. He had always been quick to criticize a post-phylloxera vintage, but he said nothing against this. Instead he chuckled to himself and rubbed his hands. And at the end of the first week he made a solemn announcement.

"Listen well. In the future, all over the world, men who have drunk this wine that you are making will boast about it to their grandchildren."

Word of this soon reached the pickers, and they caught the fever. Every day there was a new record of loads sent in to the *cuvier*. Excitement hung over the vineyards like the dancing haze and the shrill whistle of the grasshoppers. The symphony of the vintage rose in continuous crescendo.

Then came the final day.

The field workers gathered beside the last few acres of unharvested vines before the sun had risen. As soon as they could see they began to pick. The grapes were so fat and tightly clustered that the first wagon was soon loaded. Rachelet and his fellows stood watching at the entrance of the yard—for the pickers were working only a hundred paces from the château—until they saw the oxen come to life and start slowly towards them along the dusty track. Then the men of the *cuvier* took off their shirts, rolled up their trousers and put on sacking aprons. The calmest and most provident of them swallowed another mouthful or two of the bread and cheese and onion and wine which formed their breakfast. But most of them were too high-strung to eat. This was the climax. They would complete the harvest before they slept even if they had to work by torchlight, for although the weather was still fine it was said that rain was on the way.

From ten o'clock it began to be oppressively hot, but this slowed no one. Their streaming faces were drawn and there was little talk. But when they caught each other's eyes they smiled, sharing the secret that kept them going.

They had never worked so quickly in the *cuvier*, and yet it was all they could do to keep up with the pickers who were sending loaded wagons in at shorter and shorter intervals. It went on and on until they were dizzy with the strain of it.

They finished a pressing and turned to unload the next wagon. It was not there. They waited a minute or two and then went out to the entrance of the yard to see what had gone wrong.

Most of the pickers were sitting on the ground. The porters had put down their empty *hottes* and were staring at them. The driver was in his seat on the loaded wagon, but seemed to have lost the use of hands and voice. There was nothing more for the harvesters to do. The impression one got was of a complicated piece of machinery which has run down and stopped.

Then the *maître de chai* shouted out in his loud, cracked voice: "It is good wine. Bring in the final load!"

That set everything into violent action. But it was action of a new sort. The harvesters went racing here and there, gathering wild flowers—thyme, sage, mallow, marjoram, yarrow and verbena. Within a few minutes the *douils* were decorated and the oxen had garlands slung between their horns. Then the wagon was driven in.

The pickers danced on either side of it and crowded round it in the courtyard, singing and shouting. But the two white oxen, having backed the load against the entrance to the *cuvier*, stood still and mute with lowered heads and sad, reproachful eyes. One of them reached up with its tongue and managed to get a flower into its mouth.

There was a burst of laughter, but Rachelet, as often before, felt sorry for the beast. It had worked as hard as anybody and deserved some recompense instead of being made a fool of. Yet he hesitated what to do.

Madeleine stepped out of the throng, small, sun-browned and self-contained. Rachelet's heart bounded, for he had not seen her during these last hectic days. She went up to the ox, and taking off its garland fed it with the flowers one by one. It ate them with an expression that suggested that they were better than nothing, although not as good as grass. Rachelet could have hugged the girl. But he could not even speak to her then, for his father was calling him into the *cuvier* to press out the last of the wine.

That night there was a feast. Following tradition, a long table was set up under the cedar tree. Rachelet could see the young people round him now, their tired faces flushed with excitement, pledging each other in young wine. He was conscious of the chatter and the laughter—then the silence as the old *patron* (a young man then) and the beautiful Marquise came out with their little son between them to thank their people and tell them that they had done well. He ordered up some bottles of the 1858, the great vintage of the childhood of Rachelet *père*, and they pledged the new wine in the old.

Afterwards there was dancing in one of the buildings. It was wild. They had reached that stage of tiredness from achievement when the excited mind can keep its body dancing like a marionette as long as it does not loose the strings. Now and then, in an interval, a dancer would flop down and sit there smiling foolishly. He had let go of the strings and could not pick his tired limbs up again.

Rachelet felt superior to all the rest. He wanted to impress Madeleine with his strength. He swung her right off her feet, the mad music in his blood. She was his marionette.... No, she was not. When he put her down again she stood squarely, her hand on her side, and laughed up into his face. She was happy and friendly, but he was not impressing her at all. He felt suddenly awkward. He asked almost timidly if she would like some fresh air.

They went out of doors together. They walked a few paces and then stopped.

There was no moon, but there were more stars than there had ever been before. Every square metre of the dark blue velvet heaven was dancing with them. And how they danced! The vineyard which had been harvested, the poplars, the river, the low hills beyond—everything on earth lay watching in the soft warm air, trembling with wonder. And one felt rather than heard the high-pitched insect throbbing, something like the trembling note which a fine glass makes when its rim is stroked.

"Come and find a grasshopper," Rachelet said.

Remembering this so clearly, almost as if it were happening as it had happened fifty paces away and nearly fifty years ago, Rachelet smiled and shook his head. What does one want with grasshoppers when one's blood is seething like the forming wine? What he wanted, desperately, were words to express his feelings.

They wandered silently along the narrow paths. He must speak to her tonight or she would be gone in the morning. But he must put it in the right way to touch her heart. She was mysterious. He did not know her feelings, and he was afraid of her quick laugh.... The phrases he wanted were so slow to come!

He decided to take her to the ruined tower, a relic of the ancient days when the English owned this part of France. It was a most romantic place. They walked there slowly, and all the time he was rehearsing his declaration.

They climbed the grass knoll. She sat down on a piece of masonry. He dropped on his knees and took her hand. (He felt less awkwardly tall when kneeling.) Immediately, before his courage failed him, he began to speak. But he had got no further than the first cautious sentences when he saw that her attention was suddenly switched elsewhere. Deeply hurt, he asked her what the matter was.

"Are cattle allowed to eat the vines after the grapes have been picked?" she asked.

"What? Cattle? Where?" He jumped to his feet, looking where she pointed.

Breaking the even pattern of the vineyard were the big black silhouettes of cows.

"*Non d'un pipe!*" he shouted, and worse words too. "It is those damned pickers. They have gone spooning and left the gate open. Come!" He jerked her to her feet.

It was not easy to drive the cattle off without making them panic in the dark and break more vines. But it was done at last and the gate closed.

"I interrupted you," she said. "You were saying something."

"About those damned pickers?"

"About one of them," she answered. Her eyes were bright as stars.

"Oh yes," he said—and took her in his arms. He could not start thinking up those phrases all over again.

What it came to, Rachelet decided, was that this wine of 1900 which he was still holding under his nose was the wine of his adult life. At the age of twenty-three he had been concerned both with the harvesting and the pressing of its grapes. While it was making he had first taken Madeleine into his arms, and they had drunk a glass of it for luck at their marriage in the spring. It had played its part on every important occasion—the baptism of Victor, who was born five years later, his first communion, and his coming of age, and on every one of their wedding anniversaries. Each time the wine had tasted fuller and better balanced, as Rachelet had felt himself more mature.

He could have drunk this most famous vintage of Château Le Tour-St.-Vincent still more often, for the old *patron* gave him the freedom of it as a wedding present. But it had seemed to belong to special occasions, not to ordinary days. He had not had the heart to drink it after Madeleine died.

But he would drink it tonight. Everything was different tonight. Although Madeleine and Victor were not actually with him—although he was by himself—he was not the least bit lonely. And he had never felt better in his life. He smiled, nodding his head energetically.

He drank the wine he had been holding under his nose. By habit he drank it as a taster does, stroking it with his tongue and sucking it down in a thin stream. But even before he had completed this automatic action his expression changed. The peaceful, confident look—almost the smile of a young man thinking of yesterday—became in a moment the lined mask of disillusioned age.

It was not that the wine was bad. It had not turned to vinegar like that hard wartime vintage. It had been noble, and one could still distinguish the qualities of its greatness. But they had become so faint! Most noticeable of all, the wine had grown weak. It no longer filled the mouth: it slipped almost unnoticed down the throat. It was on the way out—a great wine, but finished.

When had it started to decline? Rachelet tried to remember when he had last tasted it. . . . It was on the evening of the young *patron's* return from the war—the second war—when he had been praised for his work and offered the house and vineyard in Anjou, but had preferred to work on another seven years. Those years had been a terrible strain. They had broken him. . . . Was he talking of the wine or of himself? It made no difference.

The wine had finished its work in life. Whenever great wines were drunk, people would be reminded of it and would talk of it, praising it perhaps even more than it deserved. But such bottles as remained would be left untouched in their bin in the museum, fading gradually into water and mud. It was the same with him. He had allowed himself to dream he was back in the days when he planned and worked with keen hope for the future. He had been wakened with a shock to find he had achieved what he had planned. He had married and begotten a fine son, he had improved the vineyard, increased the fame of Château La Tour-St.-Vincent and himself become a legend in the process. He would be talked of for a while as more remarkable than he had been. But they had put him away in his bin tonight and few people would even know when he actually died.

And what about the future of the vineyard? If he could have handed over to Victor he would have been content. Instead Pierre Simon was *maître de chai*. He was a clever fellow, but . . . Rachelet remembered how, dozing in his chair in the evenings, he had heard so many conversations about money between Pierre and Jeanette. It was not the pay packets of the *vignerons* which made the vines bear good grapes. It was that top dressing of human sweat. Would anybody give that any more? Did young people nowadays love the vines for themselves as he and his father had done?

As Rachelet stared gloomily at the vineyard he saw something moving. A small figure emerged from among the vines and came slowly and doubtfully towards the table, drawn by the candle flame.

It was a little boy of about seven years old. He was bare-footed and bare-legged, dressed only in an old shirt which was too large for him—probably the thing he slept in. With his two small hands he held against his chest an enormous bunch of grapes, and one cheek was bulging with a mouthful. He stared wonderingly at the old man, but did not seem to be afraid of him.

Rachelet believed he knew the boy by sight. He must be one of the many children of the estate. In any case he understood why he was there. How often had he himself, at that age and in this season, crept out of bed and through the window and down to the vineyard! He had liked to carry back a bunch and get into bed with it, to lie in the darkness putting one grape after another into his mouth and playing with it with his tongue until it burst against his palate. It had not been greed: he had loved grapes as his sister loved her dolls. . . . Once his father had caught him on one of these midnight excursions—but had not punished him. He had taken him up in his arms and carried him home with gentle words. It had puzzled him at the time. Now he saw a reason.

A strange emotion flooded through Rachelet, making him tremble and filling his eyes with tears. But it was not sadness. It was something else.

He refilled his glass and raised it to the fascinated child.

"We who are on the way out salute you who are on the way

in," he said softly. "There will always be good young wine coming on in the *chai* and good young fellows who love the vines. When you are a man you will sit here and drink the blood of those grapes. May the good God show you what He has made me see."

He drank the wine of his life. Then, feeling contented but very tired, he laid his head down on his forearm on the table.

From somewhere among the buildings a woman's voice began shouting shrilly: "Uncle Michel, Uncle Michel! Where are you?"

A man questioned her and she shouted back: "It is Gros Michel. We thought he had gone to bed when we went to the dance. But he is not there. He will catch his death. He never will realize how old he is."

The child looked in the direction of the voice, then at Rachelet's bowed head. Suddenly he became frightened and ran away.

WINE: A MYSTERY

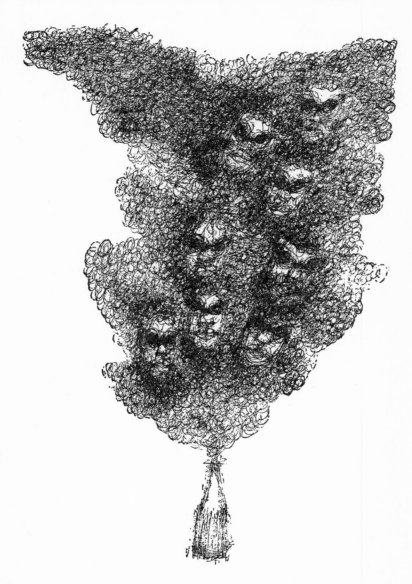

The Bibulous Business of a Matter of Taste

DOROTHY SAYERS

Dorothy Leigh Sayers (1893–1957), born in Oxford, was one of the first women to win an Oxford degree (Somerville College, 1915). Her work, whether in the field of the detective story, of translation (Dante's Inferno *and* Purgatorio*) or of Anglican drama and apologetics, bears the marks of a deeply cultivated mind, occasionally a little too conscious of its own superiority. Most critics rank her* Nine Tailors *as one of the masterpieces of the literature of detection; and I have always thought her* Gaudy Night *a magnificent, if not quite successful, attempt to burst through the conventional bounds of the detective novel. Her famous sleuth, Lord Peter Wimsey, is an elegant merger of Sherlock Holmes, D'Artagnan and Oscar Wilde. The little tale which follows is generously conceived, for it offers us not one Wimsey but three.*

"HALTE-LÀ! ... Attention! ... F—e!"

The young man in the grey suit pushed his way through the protesting porters and leapt nimbly for the footboard of the guard's van as the Paris-Evreux express steamed out of the Invalides. The guard, with an eye to a tip, fielded him adroitly from among the detaining hands.

"It is happy for monsieur that he is so agile," he remarked. "Monsieur is in a hurry?"

"Somewhat. Thank you. I can get through by the corridor?"

"But certainly. The *premières* are two coaches away, beyond the luggage-van."

The young man rewarded his rescuer, and made his way forward, mopping his face. As he passed the piled-up luggage, something caught his eye, and he stopped to investigate. It was a

57

suit-case, nearly new, of expensive-looking leather, labelled conspicuously:

LORD PETER WIMSEY,
Hôtel Saumon d'Or,
Verneuil-sur-Eure.

and bore witness to its itinerary thus:

LONDON—PARIS
(Waterloo) (Gare St. Lazare)
via Southampton-Havre.

PARIS—VERNEUIL
(Ch. de Fer de l'Ouest)

The young man whistled, and sat down on a trunk to think it out.

Somewhere there had been a leakage, and they were on his trail. Nor did they care who knew it. There were hundreds of people in London and Paris who would know the name of Wimsey, not counting the police of both countries. In addition to belonging to one of the oldest ducal families in England, Lord Peter had made himself conspicuous by his meddling with crime detection. A label like this was a gratuitous advertisement.

But the amazing thing was that the pursuers were not troubling to hide themselves from the pursued. That argued very great confidence. That he should have got into the guard's van was, of course, an accident, but, even so, he might have seen it on the platform, or anywhere.

An accident? It occurred to him—not for the first time, but definitely now, and without doubt—that it was indeed an accident for them that he was here. The series of maddening delays that had held him up between London and the Invalides presented itself to him with an air of pre-arrangement. The preposterous accusation, for instance, of the woman who had accosted him in Piccadilly, and the slow process of extricating himself at Marlborough Street. It was easy to hold a man up on some trumped-up charge till an important plan had matured. Then there was the lavatory door at Waterloo, which had so ludicrously locked itself upon him. Being athletic, he had climbed over the partition, to find the attendant mysteriously absent. And, in Paris, was it by chance that he had had a deaf taxi-driver, who mistook the direction "Quai d'Orléans" for "Gare de Lyon," and drove a mile and a half in the wrong direction before the shouts of his fare attracted his attention? They were clever, the pursuers, and circumspect. They had accurate information; they would delay him, but without taking any overt step; they knew that, if only they could keep time on their side, they needed no other ally.

Did they know he was on the train? If not, he still kept the advantage, for they would travel in a false security, thinking him to be left, raging and helpless, in the Invalides. He decided to make a cautious reconnaissance.

The first step was to change his grey suit for another of inconspicuous navy-blue cloth, which he had in his small black bag. This he did in the privacy of the toilet, substituting for his grey soft hat a large travelling-cap, which pulled well down over his eyes.

There was little difficulty in locating the man he was in search of. He found him seated in the inner corner of a first-class compartment, facing the engine, so that the watcher could approach unseen from behind. On the rack was a handsome dressing-case, with the initials P.D.B.W. The young man was familiar with Wimsey's narrow, beaky face, flat yellow hair, and insolent dropped eyelids. He smiled a little grimly.

"He is confident," he thought, "and has regrettably made the mistake of underrating the enemy. Good! This is where I retire into a *seconde* and keep my eyes open. The next act of this melodrama will take place, I fancy, at Dreux."

· · · · · · · ·

It is a rule on the Chemin de Fer de l'Ouest that all Paris-Evreux trains, whether of Grande Vitesse or what Lord Peter Wimsey preferred to call Grande Paresse, shall halt for an interminable period at Dreux. The young man (now in navy-blue) watched his quarry safely into the refreshment-room, and slipped unobtrusively out of the station. In a quarter of an hour he was back —this time in a heavy motoring-coat, helmet, and goggles, at the wheel of a powerful hired Peugeot. Coming quietly on to the platform, he took up his station behind the wall of the *lampisterie*, whence he could keep an eye on the train and the buffet door. After fifteen minutes his patience was rewarded by the sight of his man again boarding the express, dressing-case in hand. The porters slammed the doors, crying: "Next stop Verneuil!" The engine panted and groaned; the long train of grey-green carriages clanked slowly away. The motorist drew a breath of satisfaction, and, hurrying past the barrier, started up the car. He knew that he had a good eighty miles an hour under his bonnet, and there is no speed-limit in France.

.   .   .   .

Mon Souci, the seat of that eccentric and eremitical genius the Comte de Rueil, is situated three kilometres from Verneuil. It is a sorrowful and decayed château, desolate at the termination of its neglected avenue of pines. The mournful state of a nobility without an allegiance surrounds it. The stone nymphs droop greenly over their dry and mouldering fountains. An occasional peasant creaks with a single waggon-load of wood along the ill-forested glades. It has the atmosphere of sunset at all hours of the day. The woodwork is dry and gaping for lack of paint. Through the jalousies one sees the prim *salon*, with its beautiful and faded furniture. Even the last of its ill-dressed, ill-favoured women has withered away from Mon Souci, with her in-bred, exaggerated features and her long white gloves. But at the rear of the château a chimney smokes incessantly. It is the furnace of the laboratory, the only living and modern thing among the old and dying; the only place tended and loved, petted and spoiled, heir to the long solicitude which counts of a more light-hearted day had given to stable and kennel, portrait-gallery and ball-room. And below, in the cool cellar, lie row upon row the dusty bottles, each an enchanted glass coffin in which the Sleeping Beauty of the vine grows ever more ravishing in sleep.

As the Peugeot came to a standstill in the courtyard, the driver observed with considerable surprise that he was not the count's only visitor. An immense super-Renault, like a *merveilleuse* of the Directoire, all bonnet and no body, had been drawn so ostentatiously across the entrance as to embarrass the approach of any new-comer. Its glittering panels were embellished with a coat of arms, and the count's elderly servant was at that moment staggering beneath the weight of two large and elaborate suit-cases, bearing in silver letters that could be read a mile away the legend: "LORD PETER WIMSEY."

The Peugeot driver gazed with astonishment at this display,

and grinned sardonically. "Lord Peter seems rather ubiquitous in this country," he observed to himself. Then, taking pen and paper from his bag, he busied himself with a little letter-writing. By the time that the suit-cases had been carried in, and the Renault had purred its smooth way to the outbuildings, the document was complete and enclosed in an envelope addressed to the Comte de Rueil. "The hoist with his own petard touch," said the young man, and, stepping up to the door, presented the envelope to the manservant.

"I am the bearer of a letter of introduction to monsieur le comte," he said. "Will you have the obligingness to present it to him? My name is Bredon—Death Bredon."

The man bowed, and begged him to enter.

"If monsieur will have the goodness to seat himself in the hall for a few moments. Monsieur le comte is engaged with another gentleman, but I will lose no time in making monsieur's arrival known."

The young man sat down and waited. The windows of the hall looked out upon the entrance, and it was not long before the château's sleep was disturbed by the hooting of yet another motor-horn. A station taxi-cab came noisily up the avenue. The man from the first-class carriage and the luggage labelled P.D.B.W. were deposited upon the doorstep. Lord Peter Wimsey dismissed the driver and rang the bell.

"Now," said Mr. Bredon, "the fun is going to begin." He effaced himself as far as possible in the shadow of a tall *armoire normande*.

"Good evening," said the new-comer to the manservant, in admirable French, "I am Lord Peter Wimsey. I arrive upon the invitation of Monsieur le comte de Rueil. Monsieur le comte is at liberty?"

"Milord Peter Wimsey? Pardon, monsieur, but I do not understand. Milord de Wimsey is already arrived and is with monsieur le comte at this moment."

"You surprise me," said the other, with complete imperturbability, "for certainly no one but myself has any right to that name. It seems as though some person more ingenious than honest has had the bright idea of impersonating me."

The servant was clearly at a loss.

"Perhaps," he suggested, "monsieur can show his *papiers d'identité*."

"Although it is somewhat unusual to produce one's credentials on the doorstep when paying a private visit," replied his lordship, with unaltered good humour, "I have not the slightest objection. Here is my passport, here is a *permis de séjour* granted to me in Paris, here my visiting-card, and here a quantity of correspondence addressed to me at the Hôtel Meurice, Paris, at my flat in Piccadilly, London, at the Marlborough Club, London, and at my brother's house at King's Denver. Is that sufficiently in order?"

The servant perused the documents carefully, appearing particularly impressed by the *permis de séjour*.

"It appears there is some mistake," he murmured dubiously; "if monsieur will follow me, I will acquaint monsieur le comte."

They disappeared through the folding doors at the back of the hall, and Bredon was left alone.

"Quite a little boom in Richmonds to-day," he observed, "each of us more unscrupulous than the last. The occasion obviously calls for a refined subtletly of method."

After what he judged to be a hectic ten minutes in the count's library, the servant reappeared, searching for him.

"Monsieur le comte's compliments, and would monsieur step this way?"

Bredon entered the room with a jaunty step. He had created for himself the mastery of this situation. The count, a thin, elderly man, his fingers deeply stained with chemicals, sat, with a perturbed expression, at his desk. In two arm-chairs sat the two Wimseys. Bredon noted that, while the Wimsey he had seen in the train (whom he mentally named Peter I) retained his unruffled smile, Peter II (he of the Renault) had the flushed and indignant air of an Englishman affronted. The two men were superficially alike—both fair, lean, and long-nosed, with the nondescript, inelastic face which predominates in any assembly of well-bred Anglo-Saxons.

"Mr. Bredon," said the count, "I am charmed to have the pleasure of making your acquaintance, and regret that I must at once call upon you for a service as singular as it is important. You have presented to me a letter of introduction from your cousin, Lord Peter Wimsey. Will you now be good enough to inform me which of these gentlemen he is?"

Bredon let his glance pass slowly from the one claimant to the other, meditating what answer would best serve his own ends.

One, at any rate, of the men in this room was a formidable intellect, trained in the detection of imposture.

"Well?" said Peter II. "Are you going to acknowledge me, Bredon?"

Peter I extracted a cigarette from a silver case. "Your confederate does not seem very well up in his part," he remarked, with a quiet smile at Peter II.

"Monsieur le comte," said Bredon, "I regret extremely that I cannot assist you in the matter. My acquaintance with my cousin, like your own, has been made and maintained entirely through correspondence on a subject of common interest. My profession," he added, "has made me unpopular with my family."

There was a very slight sigh of relief somewhere. The false Wimsey—whichever he was—had gained a respite. Bredon smiled.

"An excellent move, Mr. Bredon," said Peter I, "but it will hardly explain—Allow me." He took the letter from the count's hesitating hand. "It will hardly explain the fact that the ink of this letter of recommendation, dated three weeks ago, is even now scarcely dry—though I congratulate you on the very plausible imitation of my handwriting."

"If *you* can forge my handwriting," said Peter II, "so can this Mr. Bredon." He read the letter aloud over his double's shoulder.

" 'Monsieur le comte—I have the honour to present to you my friend and cousin, Mr. Death Bredon, who, I understand, is to be travelling in your part of France next month. He is very anxious to view your interesting library. Although a journalist by profession, he really knows something about books.' I am delighted to learn for the first time that I have such a cousin. An interviewer's trick, I fancy, monsieur le comte. Fleet Street appears well informed about our family names. Possibly it is equally well informed about the object of my visit to Mon Souci?"

"If," said Bredon boldly, "you refer to the acquisition of the de Rueil formula for poison gas for the British Government, I can answer for my own knowledge, though possibly the rest of Fleet Street is less completely enlightened." He weighed his words carefully now, warned by his slip. The sharp eyes and detective ability of Peter I alarmed him far more than the caustic tongue of Peter II.

The count uttered an exclamation of dismay.

"Gentlemen," he said, "one thing is obvious—that there has

been somewhere a disastrous leakage of information. Which of you is the Lord Peter Wimsey to whom I should entrust the formula I do not know. Both of you are supplied with papers of identity; both appear completely instructed in this matter; both of your handwritings correspond with the letters I have previously received from Lord Peter, and both of you have offered me the sum agreed upon in Bank of England notes. In addition, this third gentleman arrives endowed with an equal facility in handwritings, an introductory letter surrounded by most suspicious circumstances, and a degree of acquaintance with this whole matter which alarms me. I can see but one solution. All of you must remain here at the château while I send to England for some elucidation of this mystery. To the genuine Lord Peter I offer my apologies, and assure him that I will endeavour to make his stay as agreeable as possible. Will this satisfy you? It will? I am delighted to hear it. My servants will show you to your bedrooms, and dinner will be at half-past seven."

. . . .

"It is delightful to think," said Mr. Bredon, as he fingered his glass and passed it before his nostrils with the air of a connoisseur, "that whichever of these gentlemen has the right to the name which he assumes is assured to-night of a truly Olympian satisfaction." His impudence had returned to him, and he challenged the company with an air. "Your cellars, monsieur le comte, are as well known among men endowed with a palate as your talents among men of science. No eloquence could say more."

The two Lord Peters murmured assent.

"I am the more pleased by your commendation," said the count, "that it suggests to me a little test which, with your kind co-operation, will, I think, assist us very much in determining which of you gentlemen is Lord Peter Wimsey and which his talented impersonator. Is it not matter of common notoriety that Lord Peter has a palate for wine almost unequalled in Europe?"

"You flatter me, monsieur le comte," said Peter II modestly.

"I wouldn't like to say unequalled," said Peter I, chiming in like a well-trained duet; "let's call it fair to middling. Less liable to misconstruction and all that."

"Your lordship does yourself an injustice," said Bredon, addressing both men with impartial deference. "The bet which you won from Mr. Frederick Arbuthnot at the Egotists' Club, when he challenged you to name the vintage years of seventeen wines blindfold, received its due prominence in the *Evening Wire.*"

"I was in extra form that night," said Peter I.

"A fluke," laughed Peter II.

"The test I propose, gentlemen, is on similar lines," pursued the count, "though somewhat less strenuous. There are six courses ordered for dinner to-night. With each we will drink a different wine, which my butler shall bring in with the label concealed. You shall each in turn give me your opinion upon the vintage. By this means we shall perhaps arrive at something, since the most brilliant forger—of whom I gather I have at least two at my table to-night—can scarcely forge a palate for wine. If too hazardous a mixture of wines should produce a temporary incommodity in the morning, you will, I feel sure, suffer it gladly for this once in the cause of truth."

The two Wimseys bowed.

"*In vino veritas,*" said Mr. Bredon, with a laugh. He at least was well seasoned, and foresaw opportunities for himself.

"Accident, and my butler, having placed you at my right hand, monsieur," went on the count, addressing Peter I, "I will ask you to begin by pronouncing, as accurately as may be, upon the wine which you have just drunk."

"That is scarcely a searching ordeal," said the other, with a smile. "I can say definitely that it is a very pleasant and well-matured Chablis Moutonne; and, since ten years is an excellent age for a Chablis—a real Chablis—I should vote for 1916, which was perhaps the best of the war vintages in that district."

"Have you anything to add to that opinion, monsieur?" enquired the count, deferentially, of Peter II.

"I wouldn't like to be dogmatic to a year or so," said that gentleman critically, "but if I must commit myself, don't you know, I should say 1915—decidedly 1915."

The count bowed, and turned to Bredon.

"Perhaps you, too, monsieur, would be interested to give an opinion," he suggested, with the exquisite courtesy always shown to the plain man in the society of experts.

"I'd rather not set a standard which I might not be able to live up to," replied Bredon, a little maliciously. "I know that it is 1915, for I happened to see the label."

Peter II looked a little disconcerted.

"We will arrange matters better in future," said the count. "Pardon me." He stepped apart for a few moments' conference with the butler, who presently advanced to remove the oysters and bring in the soup.

The next candidate for attention arrived swathed to the lip in damask.

"It is your turn to speak first, monsieur," said the count to Peter II. "Permit me to offer you an olive to cleanse the palate. No haste, I beg. Even for the most excellent political ends, good wine must not be used with disrespect."

The rebuke was not unnecessary, for, after a preliminary sip, Peter II had taken a deep draught of the heady white richness. Under Peter I's quizzical eye he wilted quite visibly.

"It is—it is Sauterne," he began, and stopped. Then, gathering encouragement from Bredon's smile, he said, with more aplomb, "Château Yquem, 1911—ah! the queen of white wines, sir, as what's-his-name says." He drained his glass defiantly.

The count's face was a study as he slowly detached his fascinated gaze from Peter II to fix it on Peter I.

"If I had to be impersonated by somebody," murmured the latter gently, "it would have been more flattering to have had it undertaken by a person to whom all white wines were *not* alike. Well, now, sir, this admirable vintage is, of course, a Montrachet of—let me see"—he rolled the wine delicately upon his tongue— "of 1911. And a very attractive wine it is, though, with all due deference to yourself, monsieur le comte, I feel that it is perhaps slightly too sweet to occupy its present place in the menu. True, with this excellent *consommé marmite*, a sweetish wine is not altogether out of place, but, in my own humble opinion, it would have shown to better advantage with the *confitures*."

"There, now," said Bredon innocently, "it just shows how one may be mislead. Had not I had the advantage of Lord Peter's expert opinion—for certainly nobody who could mistake Montrachet for Sauterne has any claim to the name of Wimsey—I should have pronounced this to be, not the Montrachet-Aîné, but the Chevalier-Montrachet of the same year, which is a trifle sweeter. But no doubt, as your lordship says, drinking it with the soup has caused it to appear sweeter to me than it actually is."

The count looked sharply at him, but made no comment.

"Have another olive," said Peter I kindly. "You can't judge wine if your mind is on other flavours."

"Thanks frightfully," said Bredon. "And that reminds me—" He launched into a rather pointless story about olives, which lasted out the soup and bridged the interval to the entrance of an exquisitely cooked sole.

The count's eye followed the pale amber wine rather thoughtfully as it trilled into the glasses. Bredon raised his in the approved manner to his nostrils, and his face flushed a little. With the first sip he turned excitedly to his host.

"Good God, sir—" he began.

The lifted hand cautioned him to silence.

Peter I sipped, inhaled, sipped again, and his brows clouded. Peter II had by this time apparently abandoned his pretensions. He drank thirstily, with a beaming smile and a lessening hold upon reality.

"Eh bien, monsieur?" enquired the count gently.

"This," said Peter I, "is certainly hock, and the noblest hock I have ever tasted, but I must admit that for the moment I cannot precisely place it."

"No?" said Bredon. His voice was like bean-honey now, sweet and harsh together. "Nor the other gentleman? And yet I fancy I could place it within a couple of miles, though it is a wine I had hardly looked to find in a French cellar at this time. It is hock, as your lordship says, and at that it is Johannisberger. Not the plebeian cousin, but the *echter* Schloss Johannisberger from the castle vineyard itself. Your lordship must have missed it (to your great loss) during the war years. My father laid some down the year before he died, but it appears that the ducal cellars at Denver were less well furnished."

"I must set about remedying the omission," said the remaining Peter, with determination.

The *poulet* was served to the accompaniment of an argument over the Lafitte, his lordship placing it at 1878, Bredon maintaining it to be a relic of the glorious 'seventy-fives, slightly over-matured, but both agreeing as to its great age and noble pedigree.

As to the Clos-Vougeôt, on the other hand, there was complete agreement; after a tentative suggestion of 1915, it was pronounced finally by Peter I to belong to the equally admirable though slightly lighter 1911 crop. The *pré-salé* was removed amid general applause, and the dessert was brought in.

"Is it necessary," asked Peter I, with a slight smile in the direction of Peter II—now happily murmuring, "Damn good wine, damn good dinner, damn good show"—"is it necessary to prolong this farce any further?"

"Your lordship will not, surely, refuse to proceed with the discussion?" cried the count.

"The point is sufficiently made, I fancy."

"But no one will surely ever refuse to discuss wine," said Bredon, "least of all your lordship, who is so great an authority."

"Not on this," said the other. "Frankly, it is a wine I do not care about. It is sweet and coarse, qualities that would damn any wine in the eyes—the mouth, rather—of a connoisseur. Did your excellent father have this laid down also, Mr. Bredon?"

Bredon shook his head.

"No," he said, "no. Genuine Imperial Tokay is beyond the opportunities of Grub Street, I fear. Though I agree with you that it is horribly overrated—with all due deference to yourself, monsieur le comte."

"In that case," said the count, "we will pass at once to the liqueur. I admit that I had thought of puzzling these gentlemen with the local product, but, since one competitor seems to have scratched, it shall be brandy—the only fitting close to a good wine-list."

In a slightly embarrassing silence the huge, round-bellied balloon glasses were set upon the table, and the few precious drops poured gently into each and set lightly swinging to release the bouquet.

"This," said Peter I, charmed again into amiability, "is, indeed, a wonderful old French brandy. Half a century old, I suppose."

"Your lordship's praise lacks warmth," replied Bredon. "This is *the* brandy—the brandy of brandies—the superb—the incomparable—the true Napoleon. It should be honoured like the emperor it is."

He rose to his feet, his napkin in his hand.

"Sir," said the count, turning to him, "I have on my right a most admirable judge of wine, but you are unique." He motioned to Pierre, who solemnly brought forward the empty bottles, un-swathed now, from the humble Chablis to the stately Napoleon, with the imperial seal blown in the glass. "Every time you have been correct as to growth and year. There cannot be six men in the world with such a palate as yours, and I thought that but one of them was an Englishman. Will you not favour us, this time, with your real name?"

"It doesn't matter what his name is," said Peter I. He rose. "Put up your hands, all of you. Count, the formula!"

Bredon's hands came up with a jerk, still clutching the napkin. The white folds spurted flame as his shot struck the other's revolver cleanly between trigger and barrel, exploding the charge, to the extreme detriment of the glass chandelier. Peter I stood shaking his paralysed hand and cursing.

Bredon kept him covered while he cocked a wary eye at Peter II, who, his rosy visions scattered by the report, seemed struggling back to aggressiveness.

"Since the entertainment appears to be taking a lively turn," observed Bredon, "perhaps you would be so good, count, as to search these gentlemen for further firearms. Thank you. Now, why should we not all sit down again and pass the bottle round?"

"You—*you* are—" growled Peter I.

"Oh, my name is Bredon all right," said the young man cheerfully. "I loathe aliases. Like another fellow's clothes, you know—never seem quite to fit. Peter Death Bredon Wimsey—a bit lengthy and all that, but handy when taken in instalments. I've got a passport and all those things, too, but I didn't offer them, as their reputation here seems a little blown upon, so to speak. As regards the formula, I think I'd better give you my personal cheque for it—all sorts of people seem able to go about flourishing Bank of England notes. Personally, I think all this secret diplomacy work is a mistake, but that's the War Office's pigeon. I suppose we all brought similar credentials. Yes, I thought so. Some bright person seems to have sold himself very successfully in two places at once. But you two must have been having a lively time, each thinking the other was me."

"My lord," said the count heavily, "these two men are, or were, Englishmen, I suppose. I do not care to know what Governments have purchased their treachery. But where they stand, I, alas! stand too. To our venal and corrupt Republic I, as a Royalist, acknowledge no allegiance. But it is in my heart that I have agreed to sell my country to England because of my poverty. Go back to your War Office and say I will not give you the formula. If war should come between our countries—which may God avert! —I will be found on the side of France. That, my lord, is my last word."

Wimsey bowed.

"Sir," said he, "it appears that my mission has, after all, failed. I am glad of it. This trafficking in destruction is a dirty kind of business after all. Let us shut the door upon these two, who are neither flesh nor fowl, and finish the brandy in the library."

The Unknown Peer

E. C. BENTLEY

*From the middle name of Edmund Clerihew Bentley (1875–
1956) is derived that of the four-line comic rhymed form
which he invented and which has become a sophisticated
competitor of the limerick. A journalist (and a first-rate one)
for most of his working life, he is known to the reading public
as the author of the epoch-making* Trent's Last Case (1913).
*Its importance is indicated by the judgment of the critic who
called Bentley "the father of the contemporary detective
novel." As a member of the Chesterton-Belloc circle of* bon-
vivants, *he, like Lord Southrop in "The Unknown Peer,"
understood wine "better than most men." And so does the
great Trent, here re-introduced.*

WHEN Philip Trent went down to Lackington, with the
mission of throwing some light upon the affair of Lord
Southrop's disappearance, it was without much hope of adding
anything to the simple facts already known to the police and
made public in the newspapers. Those facts were plain enough,
pointing to but one sad conclusion.

In the early morning of Friday, the 23rd of September, a small
touring-car was found abandoned by the shore at Merwin Cove,
some three miles along the coast from the flourishing Devonian
resort of Brademouth. It had been driven off the road over turf
to the edge of the pebble beach.

Examined by the police, it was found to contain a heavy over-
coat, a folding stool, and a case of sketching materials with a
sketching-block on the back seat; a copy of Anatole France's
Mannequin d'Osier, two pipes, some chocolate, a flask of brandy,
and a pair of binoculars in the shelves before the driving-seat; and

in the pockets a number of maps and the motoring papers of Lord Southrop, of Hingham Blewitt, near Wymondham, in Norfolk. Inquiries in the neighbourhood led to the discovery that a similar car and its driver were missing from the Crown Inn at Lackington, a small place a few miles inland; and later the car was definitely recognized.

In the hotel register, however, the owner had signed his name as L. G. Coxe; and it was in that name that a room had been booked by telephone early in the day. A letter, too, addressed to Coxe, had been delivered at the Crown, and had been opened by him on his arrival about 6:30. A large suitcase had been taken up to his room, where it still lay, and the mysterious Coxe had deposited an envelope containing £35 in banknotes in the hotel safe. He had dined in the coffee-room, smoked in the lounge for a time, then gone out again in his car, saying nothing of his destination. No more had been seen or heard of him.

Some needed light had been cast on the affair when Lord Southrop was looked up in *Who's Who*—for no one in the local force had ever heard of such a peer. It appeared that his family name was Coxe, and that he had been christened Lancelot Graham; that he was the ninth baron, was thirty-three years old, and had succeeded to the title at the age of twenty-six; that he had been educated at Harrow and Trinity, Cambridge; that he was unmarried, and that his heir was a first cousin, Lambert Reeves Coxe. No public record of any kind, nor even any "recreation" was noted in this unusually brief biography, which, indeed, bore the marks of having been compiled in the office, without any assistance from its subject.

Trent, however, had heard something more than this about Lord Southrop. Sir James Molloy, the owner of the *Record*, who had sent Trent to Lackington, had met everybody, including even the missing peer, who was quite unknown in society. Society, according to Molloy, was heartily detested and despised by Lord Southrop. His interests were exclusively literary and artistic, apart from his taste in the matter of wine, which he understood better than most men. He greatly preferred Continental to English ways of life, and spent much of his time abroad. He had a very large income, for most of which he seemed to have no use. He had good health and a kindly disposition; but he had a passion for keeping himself to himself, and had indulged it with remarkable success. One of his favourite amusements was wandering about the country alone in his car, halting here and there to make a sketch, and staying always at out-of-the-way inns under the name he had used at Lackington.

Lord Southrop had been, however, sufficiently like other men to fall in love, and Molloy had heard that his engagement to Adela Tindal was on the point of being announced at the time of his disappearance. His choice had come as a surprise to his friends; for though Miss Tindal took art and letters as seriously as himself, she was, as an authoress, not at all averse to publicity. She enjoyed being talked about, Molloy declared; and talked about she had certainly been—especially in connection with Lucius Kelly, the playwright. Their relationship had not been disguised; but a time came when Kelly's quarrelsome temper was no longer to be endured, and she refused to see any more of him.

All this was quite well known to Lord Southrop, for he and Kelly had been friends from boyhood; and the knowledge was a signal proof of the force of his infatuation. On all accounts, in Molloy's judgment, the match would have been a complete disaster; and Trent, as he thought the matter over in the coffee-room of the Crown, was disposed to agree with him.

Shortly before his arrival that day, a new fact for his first dispatch to the *Record* had turned up. A tweed cap had been found washed up by the waves on the beach between Brademouth and Merwin Cove; and the people at the Crown were sure that it was Lord Southrop's. He had worn a suit of unusually rough, very light-grey homespun tweed, the sort of tweed that, as the head-waiter at the Crown vividly put it, you could smell half a mile away; and his cap had been noted because it was made of the same stuff as the suit. After a day and a half in salt water, it had still an aroma of Highland sheep. Apart from this and its colour, or absence of colour, there was nothing by which it could be identified; not even a maker's name; but there was no reasonable doubt about its being Lord Southrop's, and it seemed to settle the question, if question there were, of what had happened to him. It was, Trent reflected, just like an eccentric intellectual—with money—to have his caps made for him, and from the same material as his clothes.

It was these garments, together with the very large horn-rimmed spectacles which Lord Southrop affected, which had made most impression on the headwaiter. Otherwise, he told Trent, there was nothing unusual about the poor gentleman, except that he seemed a bit absentminded-like. He had brought a letter to the table with him—the waiter supposed it would be the one that came to the hotel for him—and it had seemed to worry him. He had read and reread it all through his dinner, what there was of it; he didn't have only some soup and a bit of fish. Yes, sir; consommé and a nice fillet of sole, like there is this evening. There was roast fowl, but he wouldn't have that, nor nothing else. Would Trent be ordering his own dinner now?

"Yes, I want to—but the fish is just what I won't have," Trent decided, looking at the menu. "I will take the rest of the hotel dinner." An idea occurred to him. "Do you remember what Lord Southrop had to drink? I might profit by his example."

The waiter produced a fly-blown wine-list. "I can tell you that, sir. He had a bottle of this claret here, Chateau Margaux 1922."

"You're quite sure? And did he like it?"

"Well, he didn't leave much," the waiter answered. Possibly, Trent thought, he took a personal interest in unfinished wine. "Were you thinking of trying some of it yourself, sir? It's our best claret."

"I don't think I will have your best claret," Trent said, thoughtfully scanning the list. "There's a Beychevelle 1924 here, costing eighteenpence less, which is good enough for me. I'll have that." The waiter hurried away, leaving Trent to his reflections in the deserted coffee-room.

Trent had learned from the police that the numbers of the notes left in the charge of the hotel had been communicated by telephone to Lord Southrop's bank in Norwich, the reply being that these notes had been issued to him in person ten days before. Trent had also been allowed to inspect the objects, including the maps, found in the abandoned car. Lackington he found marked in pencil with a cross; and working backwards across the country he found similar crosses at the small towns of Hawbridge, Wringham, and Candley. The police, acting on these indications, had already established that "L. G. Coxe" had passed the Thursday, Wednesday and Tuesday nights respectively at inns in these places; and they had learned already of his having started from Hingham Blewitt on the Monday.

Trent, finding no more to be done at Lackington, decided to

follow this designated trail in his own car. On the morning after his talk with the waiter at the Crown he set out for Hawbridge. The distances in Lord Southrop's progress, as marked, were not great by the most direct roads; but it could be guessed that he had been straying about to this and that point of interest—not, Trent imagined, to sketch, for there had been no sketches found among his belongings. Hawbridge was reached in time for lunch; and at the Three Bells Inn Trent again found matter for thought in a conversation—much like the chat which he had already enjoyed at the Crown Inn—with the headwaiter. So it was again at the Green Man in the Wringham that evening. The next day, however, when Trent dined at the Running Stag in Candley, the remembered record of Lord Southrop's potations took a different turn. What Trent was told convinced him that he was on the right track.

The butler and housekeeper at Hingham Blewitt, when Trent spoke with them the following day, were dismally confident that Lord Southrop would never be seen again. The butler had already given to the police investigator from Devon what little information he could. He admitted that none of it lent the smallest support to the idea that Lord Southrop had been contemplating suicide; that he had, in fact, been unusually cheerful, if anything, on the day of his departure. But what, the butler asked, could a person think? Especially, the housekeeper observed, after the cap was found. Lord Southrop was, of course, eccentric in his views; and you never knew—here the housekeeper, with a despondent head-shake, paused, leaving unspoken the suggestion that a man who did not think or behave like other people might go mad at any moment.

Lord Southrop, they told Trent, never left any address when he went on one of these motoring tours. What he used to say was, he never knew where he was going till he got there. But this time he did have one object in mind, though what it was or where it was the butler did not know; and the police-officer, when he was informed, did not seem to make any more of it. What had happened was that, a few days before Lord Southrop started out, he had been rung up by some one on the phone in his study; and as the door of the room was open, the butler, in passing through the hall, had happened to catch a few words of what he said.

He had told this person he was going next Tuesday to visit the old moor; and that if the weather was right he was going to make a sketch. He had said, "You remember the church and chapel!"—the butler heard that distinctly; and he had said that it must be over twenty years. "What must be over twenty years?" Trent wanted to know. Impossible to tell: Lord Southrop had said just that.

The butler had heard nothing further. He thought the old moor might perhaps be Dartmoor or Exmoor, seeing where it was that Lord Southrop had disappeared. Trent thought otherwise, but he did not discuss the point. "There's one thing you can perhaps tell me," he said. "Lord Southrop was at Harrow and Cambridge, I believe. Do you know if he went to a preparatory school before Harrow?"

"I can tell you that, sir," the housekeeper said. "I have been with the family since I was a girl. It was Marsham House he went to, near Sharnsley in Derbyshire. The school was founded by his lordship's grandfather's tutor, and all the Coxe boys have gone there for two generations. It stands very high as a school, sir; the best families send their sons there."

"Yes, I've heard of it," Trent said. "Should you say, Mrs. Pillow, that Lord Southrop was happy as a schoolboy—popular, I mean, and fond of games, and so forth?"

Mrs. Pillow shook her head decisively. "He always hated school, sir; and as for games, he had to play them, of course, but he couldn't abide them. And he didn't get on with the other boys—he used to say he wouldn't be a sheep, just like all the other some-thing sheep—he learned bad language at school, if he didn't learn anything else. But at Cambridge—that was very different. He came alive there for the first time—so he used to say."

In Norwich, that same afternoon, Trent furnished himself with a one-inch Ordnance Survey map of a certain section of Derby-shire. He spent the evening at his hotel with this and a small-scale map of England, on which he marked the line of small towns which he had already visited; and he drew up, not for publication, a brief and clear report of his investigation so far.

The next morning's run was long. He had lunch at Sharnsley, where he made a last and very gratifying addition to his string of coffee-room interviews. Marsham House, he learnt, stood well outside Sharnsley on the verge of the Town Moor; which, as the map had already told him, stretched its many miles away to the south and west. He learnt, too, what and where were "the church and chapel," and was thankful that his inquiring mind had not taken those simple terms at their face value.

An hour later he halted his car at a spot on the deserted road that crossed the moor; a spot whence, looking up the purple slope, he could see its bareness broken by a huge rock, and another less huge, whose summits pierced the skyline. They looked, Trent told himself, not more unlike what they were called than rocks with names usually do. Away to the right of them was a small clump of trees, the only ones in sight, to which a rough cart-track led from the road; and from that point, he thought an artist might well consider that the church and chapel and their background made the best effect. He left his car and took the path through the heather.

Arrived at the clump, which stood well above the road, he looked over a desolate scene. If anyone had met Lord Southrop there, they would have had the world to themselves. Not a house or hut was in sight, and no live thing but the birds. He looked about for traces of any human visitor; and he had just decided that nothing of the sort could reasonably be expected, after the lapse of a week, when something white, lodged in the root of a fir tree, caught his eye.

It was a small piece of torn paper, penciled on one side with lines and shading the look of which he knew well. A rapid search discovered another piece near by among the heather. It was all that the wind had left undispersed of an artist's work; but for Trent, as he scanned the remnants closely, it was enough.

His eyes turned now over a wider range; for this, though to him it spelt certainty, was not what he had been looking for. Slowly following the track over the moor, he came at length to the reason for its existence—a small quarry, to all appearance long abandoned. A roughly circular pond of muddy water, some fifty yards across, filled the lower part of it; and about the margin was a confusion of stony fragments, broken and rusted implements, bits of rotting wood and smashed earthenware—a typical scene of industrial litter. With his arm bare to the shoulder Trent could feel no bottom to the pond. If it held any secret, that opaque yellow water kept it well.

There was no soil to take a footprint near the pond. For some time he raked among the débris in which the track ended, finding nothing. Then, as he turned over a broken fire-bucket, something flashed in the sunlight. It was a small, flat fragment of glass, about as large as a threepenny piece, with one smooth and two fractured edges. Trent examined it thoughtfully. It had no place in his theory; it might mean nothing. On the other hand . . . he stowed it carefully in his note-case along with the remnants of paper.

Two hours later, at the police headquarters in Derby, he was laying his report and maps, with the objects found on the moor, before Superintendent Allison, a sharp-faced, energetic officer, to whom Trent's name was well known.

It was well known also to Mr. Gurney Bradshaw, head of the firm of Bradshaw & Co., legal advisers to Lord Southrop and to his father before him. He had, at Trent's telephoned request, given him an appointment at three o'clock; and he appeared at that hour on the day after his researches in Derbyshire. Mr. Bradshaw, a courteous but authoritative old gentleman, wore a dubious expression as they shook hands.

"I cannot guess," he said, "what it is that you wish to put before me. It seems to me a case in which we should get the Court to presume death with the minimum of difficulty; and I wish I thought otherwise, for I had known Lord Southrop all his life, and I was much attached to him. Now I must tell you that I have asked a third party to join us here—Mr. Lambert Coxe, who perhaps you know is the heir to the title and to a very large estate. He wrote me yesterday that he had just returned from France, and wanted to know what the position was; and I thought he had better hear what you have to say, so I asked him for the same time as yourself."

"I know of him as a racing man," Trent said, "I had no idea he was what you say until I saw it in the papers."

The buzzer on the desk-telephone sounded, and Bradshaw put it to his ear. "Show him in," he said.

Lambert Coxe was a tall, spare, hard-looking man with a tanned, clean-shaven face, and a cordless monocle screwed into his left eye. As they were introduced he looked at the other with a keen and curious scrutiny.

"And now," Bradshaw said, "let us hear your statement, Mr. Trent."

Trent put his folded hands on the table. "I will begin by making a suggestion which may strike you gentlemen as an absurd one. It's this. The man who drove that car to Lackington, and afterwards down to the seashore, was not Lord Southrop."

Both men stared at him blankly; then Bradshaw, composing his features, said impassively, "I shall be interested to hear your reasons for thinking so. You have not a name for making absurd suggestions, Mr. Trent, but I may call this an astonishing one."

"I should damned well think so," observed Coxe.

"I got the idea originally," Trent said, "from the wine which this man chose to drink with his dinner at the Crown Inn before the disappearance. Do you think that absurd?"

"There is nothing absurd about wine," Mr. Bradshaw replied with gravity. "I take it very seriously myself. Twice a day, as a rule," he added.

"Lord Southrop, I am told, also took it seriously. He had the reputation of a first-rate connoisseur. Now this man I'm speaking of had little appetite that evening, it seems. The dinner they offered him consisted mainly of soup, fillet of sole, and roast fowl."

"I am sure it did," Bradshaw said grimly. "It's what you get nine times out of ten in English hotels. Well?"

"This man took only the soup and the fish. And with it he had a bottle of claret."

The solicitor's composure deserted him abruptly.

"Claret!" he exclaimed.

"Yes, claret, and a curious claret too. You see, mine host of the Crown kept a perfectly good Beychevelle 1924—I had some myself. But he had also a Marguax 1922; and I suppose because it was an older wine he thought it ought to be dearer, so he marked it in his list eighteenpence more than the other. That was the wine which was chosen by our traveller that evening. What do you think of it? With a fish dinner he had claret, and he chose a wine of a bad year, when he could have had a wine of 1924 for less money."

While Coxe looked his bewilderment, Mr. Bradshaw got up and began to pace the room slowly. "I will admit so much," he said. "I cannot conceive of Lord Southrop doing such a thing if he was in his right mind."

"If you still think it was he, and that he was out of his senses," Trent rejoined, "there was a method in his madness. Because the

night before, at Hawbridge, he chose one of those wines bearing
the name of a chateau which doesn't exist, and is merely a label
that sounds well; and the night before that, at Wringham, he had
two whiskies and soda just before dinner, and another inferior
claret at an excessive price on top of them. I have been to both
the inns and got these facts. But when I worked back to Candley,
the first place where Lord Southrop stayed after leaving home,
it was another story. I found he had picked out about the best
thing on the list, a Rhine wine, which hardly anybody ever asked
for. The man who ordered that, I think, was really Lord Southrop."

Bradshaw pursed up his mouth. "You are suggesting that someone in Lord Southrop's car was impersonating him at the other
three places, and that, knowing his standing as a connoisseur, this
man did his ignorant best to act up to it. Very well; but Lord
Southrop signed the register in his usual way at those places. He
received and read a letter addressed to him at Lackington. The
motor tour as a whole was just such a haphazard tour as he had
often made before. The description given of him at Lackington
was exact—the clothes, the glasses, the abstracted manner. The
cap that was washed up was certainly his. No, no, Mr. Trent. We
are bound to assume that it was Lord Southrop; and the presump-
tion is that he drove down to the sea and drowned himself. The
alternative is that he was staging a sham suicide, so as to be able
to disappear; and there is no sense in that."

"Just so," observed Lambert Coxe. "What you say about the
wine may be all right as far as it goes, Mr. Trent, but I agree with
Mr. Bradshaw. Southrop committed suicide; and if he was insane
enough to do that, he was insane enough to go wrong about his
drinks."

Trent shook his head. "There are other things to be accounted
for. I'm coming to them. And the clothes and the cap and the rest
are all part of my argument. This man was wearing Lord Southrop's tweed suit just because it was so easily identifiable. He knew
all about Lord Southrop and his ways. He had letters from Lord
Southrop in his possession, and had learnt to imitate his writing. It
was he who wrote and posted that letter addressed to L. G. Coxe;
and he made a pretence of being worried by it. He knew that
Lord Southrop's notes could be traced; so he left them at the bu-
reau to clinch the thing. And, of course, he did not drown himself.

He only threw the cap into the sea. What he may have done is to change out of those conspicuous clothes, put them in a bag which he had in the car, and which contained another suit in which he proceeded to dress himself. He may then have walked, with his bag, the few miles into Brademouth, and travelled to London by the 12:15—quite a popular train, in which you can get a comfortable sleeping-berth."

"So he may," Bradshaw agreed with some acidity, while Lambert Coxe laughed shortly. "But what I am interested in is facts, Mr. Trent."

"Well, here are some. A few days before Lord Southrop set out from his place in Norfolk, someone rang him up in his library. The door was ajar, and the butler heard a little of what he said to the caller. He said he was going on the following Tuesday to visit a place he called the old moor, as if it was a place as well known to the other as to himself. He said, 'You remember the church and the chapel,' and that it must be over twenty years; and that he was going to make a sketch."

Coxe's face darkened. "If Southrop was alive," he sneered, "I am sure he would appreciate your attention to his private affairs. What are we supposed to gather from all this keyhole business?"

"I think we can gather," Trent said gently, "that some person, ringing Lord Southrop up about another matter, was told incidentally where Lord Southrop expected to be on that Tuesday—the day, you remember, when he suddenly developed a taste for bad wine in the evening. Possibly the information gave this person an idea, and he had a few days to think it over. Also we can gather that Lord Southrop was talking to someone who shared his recollection of a moor which they had known over twenty years ago— that's to say, when he was at the prep school age, as he was thirty-three this year. And then I found that he had been at a school called Marsham House, on the edge of Sharnsley Town Moor in Derbyshire. So I went off there to explore; and I discovered that the church and chapel were a couple of great rocks on the top of the moor, about two miles from the school. If you were there with your cousin, Mr. Coxe, you may remember them."

Coxe was drumming on the table with his fingers. "Of course I do," he said aggressively. "So do hundreds of others who were at Marsham House. What about it?"

Bradshaw, who was now fixing him with an attentive eye, held up a hand. "Come, come, Mr. Coxe," he said. "Don't let us lose our tempers. Mr. Trent is helping to clear up what begins to look like an even worse business than I thought. Let us hear him out peaceably, if you please."

"I am in the sketching business myself," Trent continued, "so I looked about for what might seem the best view-point for Lord Southrop's purpose. When I went to the spot, I found two pieces of torn-up paper, the remains of a pencil sketch; and that paper is of precisely the same quality as the paper of Lord Southrop's sketching-block, which I was able to examine at Lackington. The sketch was torn from the block and destroyed, I think, because it was evidence of his having been to Sharnsley. That part of the moor is a wild, desolate place. If someone went to meet Lord Southrop there, as I believe, he could hardly have had more favourable circumstances for what he meant to do. I think it was he who appeared in the car at Wringham that evening; and I think it was on Sharnsley Moor, not at Lackington, that Lord Southrop —disappeared."

Bradshaw half rose from his chair. "Are you not well, Mr. Coxe?" he asked.

"Perfectly well, thanks," Coxe answered. He drew a deep breath, then turned to Trent. "And so that's all you have to tell us. I can't say that—"

"Oh, no, not nearly all," Trent interrupted him. "But let me tell you now what I believe it was that really happened. If the man who left the moor in Lord Southrop's car was not Lord Southrop, I wanted an explanation of the masquerade that ended at Lackington. What would explain it was the idea that the man who drove the car down to Devonshire had murdered him, and then staged a sham suicide for him three hundred miles away. That would have been an ingenious plan. It would have depended on everyone making the natural assumption that the man in the car was Lord Southrop, and how was anyone to imagine that he wasn't?

"Lord Southrop was the very reverse of a public character. He lived quite out of the world; he had never been in the news; very few people knew what he looked like. He depended on all this for maintaining his privacy in the way he did when touring in his car —staying always at small places where there was no chance of his being recognized, and pretending not to be a peer. The murderer knew all about that, and it was the essence of his plan. The people at the inns would note what was conspicuous about the traveller; all that they could say about his face would be more vague, and would fit Lord Southrop well enough, so long as there was no striking difference in looks between the two men. Those big horn-rims are a disguise in themselves."

Bradshaw rubbed his hands slowly together. "I suppose it could happen so," he said. "What do you think, Mr. Coxe?"

"It's just a lot of ridiculous guesswork," Coxe said impatiently. "I've heard enough of it, for one." He rose from his chair.

"No, no, don't go, Mr. Coxe," Trent advised him. "I have some more of what you prefer—facts, you know. They are important, and you ought to hear them. Thinking as I did, I looked about for any places where a body could be concealed. In that bare and featureless expanse I could find only one: an old, abandoned quarry in the hillside, with a great pond of muddy water at the bottom of it. And by the edge of it I picked up a small piece of broken glass.

"Yesterday evening this piece of glass was shown by a police-officer and myself to an optician in Derby. He stated that it was a fragment of a monocle, what they call a spherical lens, so that he could tell us all about it from one small bit. Its formula was not a common one—minus 5; so that it had been worn by a man very short-sighted in one eye. The police think that as very few people wear monocles, and hardly any of them would wear one of that power, an official inquiry should establish the names of those who had been supplied with such a glass in recent years. You see," Trent went on, "this man had dropped and broken his glass on the stones while busy about something at the edge of the pond. Being a tidy man, he picked up all the pieces that he could see; but he missed this one."

Lambert Coxe put a hand to his throat. "It's infernally stuffy in here," he muttered. "I'll open a window, if you don't mind." Again he got to his feet; but the lawyer's movement was quicker. "I'll see to that," he said; and stayed by the window when he had opened it.

Trent drew a folded paper from his pocket. "This is a telegram I received just before lunch from Superintendent Allison, of the Derbyshire police. I have told him all I am telling you." He unfolded the paper with deliberation. "He says that the pond was dragged this morning, and they recovered the body of a man who had been shot in the head from behind. It was stripped to the underclothing and secured by a chain to a pedal bicycle.

"That, you see, clears up the question how the murderer got to the remote spot where Lord Southrop was. He couldn't go there in a car, because he would have had to leave it there. He used a cycle, because there was to be a very practical use for the machine afterwards. The police believe they can trace the seller of the cycle, because it is in perfectly new condition, and he may give them a line on the buyer."

Bradshaw, his hands thrust into his pockets, stared at Coxe's ghastly face as he inquired, "Has the body been identified?"

"The superintendent says the inquest will be the day after to-morrow. He knows whose body I believe it is, so he will already be sending down to Hingham Blewitt about evidence of identity. He says my own evidence will probably not be required until a later stage of the inquest, after a charge has been—"

A sobbing sound came from Lambert Coxe. He sprang to his feet, pressing his hands to his temples; then crashed unconscious to the floor.

While Trent loosened his collar, the lawyer splashed water from the bottle on his table upon the upturned face. The eyelids began to flicker. "He'll do," Bradshaw said coolly. "My congratulations, Mr. Trent. This man is not a client of mine, so I may say that I don't think he will enjoy the title for long—or the money, which was what really mattered, I have reason to believe. He's dropped his monocle again, you see. I happen to know, by the way, that he has been half-blind in that eye since it was injured by a cricket ball at Marsham."

The Income Tax Mystery

MICHAEL GILBERT

If you, like Mr. Portway in Mr. Gilbert's immoral tale, would like to spend "hundreds of pounds at the wine merchant" but are a bit strapped for the necessary, you might try the pleasing swindle herein described. Mr. Portway is indeed a wine-drinker of the old school. Early Victorian, I should think, for one must go back several generations to find gentlemen enjoying their claret after lunch and their Burgundy after dinner. What did they drink with their meals? One is somehow put in mind of Ouida's fashionable guardsmen who would take curaçao at breakfast.

I QUALIFIED as a solicitor before the war and in 1937 I bought a share in a small partnership in the City. Then the War came along and I joined the Infantry. I was already thirty-five and it didn't look as if I was going to see much active service, so I cashed in on my knowledge of German and joined the Intelligence Corps.

When the War was finished, I got back to London and found our old office bombed and the other partner dead. As far as a legal practice can do so, it had vanished. I got a job without any difficulty in a firm in Bedford Row, but I didn't enjoy it. The work was easy enough but there was no real future in it. So I quit and joined the Legal Branch of Inland Revenue.

This may seem even duller than private practice, but in fact it wasn't. As soon as I had finished the subsidiary training in accountancy that all Revenue Officials have to take, I was invited to join a very select outfit known as I.B.A. or Investigation Branch, Active.

If you ask a Revenue official about I.B.A., he'll tell you it doesn't exist. This may simply mean that he hasn't heard of it. Most ordinary Revenue investigation is done by accountants who examine balance sheets, profit and loss accounts, vouchers and receipts, then ask questions and go on asking questions until the truth emerges.

Some cases can't be treated like that. They need active investigation. Someone has got to go out and find the facts. That's where I.B.A. comes in.

It isn't all big cases involving millions of pounds. The Revenue reckons to achieve the best results by making a few shrewd examples in the right places. One of our most spectacular coups was achieved when a member of the department once opened a greengrocers shop and—but that's another story.

When the name of Mr. Portway cropped up in I.B.A. records, it was natural that the dossier should get pushed across to me. For Mr. Portway was a solicitor. I can't remember exactly how he first came to our notice—you'd be surprised what casual items can set I.B.A. in motion: a conversation in a railway carriage, a hint from an insurance assessor, a bit of loud-voiced boasting in a pub. We don't go in for phone-tapping: it's inefficient and, from our point of view, quite unnecessary.

The thing about Mr. Portway was simply this: he seemed to make a very substantial amount of money without working for it.

The first real confirmation came from a disgruntled girl who had been hired to look after his books and fired for inefficiency. Mr. Portway ran a good car, she said; he dressed well, spent hundreds of pounds at the wine merchant (she'd seen one of his bills), and conducted an old-fashioned one-man practice which, by every law of economics, should have left him broke at the end of each year.

Some days he had no clients at all, she said, and spent the morning in his room reading a book (detective stories, chiefly); then he would take two hours off for lunch, snooze a little on his return, have a cup of tea, and go home. On other days a client or two would trickle in. The business was almost entirely the buying and selling of houses and the preparation of leases, mortgages, and sale agreements. Mr. Portway did it all himself. He had one girl to do the typing and look after the outer office, and another (our informant) to keep the books.

I don't suppose you know anything about solicitors' accounting, and I'm not proposing to give you a dissertation on it; but the fact is that solicitors are bound by very strict rules—rules imposed by Act of Parliament and jealously enforced by the Law Society. And quite right, too. Solicitors handle a lot of other people's money.

When we'd made a quiet check to see if Mr. Portway had any private means of his own and learned that he didn't, we decided that this was just the sort of case we ought to have a look at. It wasn't difficult. Mr. Portway knew nothing about figures. However small his staff, he had to have someone with the rudiments of accountancy, or he couldn't have got through his annual audit. We simply watched the periodicals until we saw his advertisement, and I applied for the job.

I don't know if there were any other applicants, but I'm sure I was the only one who professed to know both law and bookkeeping and who was prepared to accept the mouse-like salary he was offering.

Mr. Portway proved to be a small, round, pink-cheeked, white-haired man. One would have said Pickwickian, except that he didn't wear glasses, nor was there anything in the least owl-like about his face. So far as any comparison suggested itself, he looked more like a tortoise. He had a sardonic, leathery, indestructible face, with the long upper lip of a philosopher.

He greeted me warmly and showed me to my room. The office occupied the ground floor and basement of the house. On the right as you came in, and overlooking the paved courtyard and fountain which is all that remains of the old "Inn," was Mr. Portway's sanctum, a very nice room, on the small side, and made smaller by the rows of bookcases full of bound reports. My own room was on the left of the entrance, and even smaller and more austere. Downstairs were storerooms of old files and records and a strong-room which ran back under the pavement.

I have given you some idea of the small scale of things so that you can gather how easy I thought my job was going to be. My guess was that a week would be more than enough to detect any funny business that was going on.

I was quite wrong.

A week was enough to confirm that something *was* wrong. But by the end of a month I hadn't got a step nearer to discovering what it was.

I reported my meagre findings to my superiors.

"Mr. Portway," I said, "has a business which appears to produce, in fees, just about enough to pay the salaries of his two employees, the rent, lighting, and other outgoings, and to leave him no personal income at all. Indeed, in some instances, he has had to make up, from his own pocket, small deficiencies in the office account. Nor does his money come from private means. It is part of my duty as accountant to prepare Mr. Portway's personal tax returns"—(this, it is fair to him to say, was at his own suggestion)—"and apart from a very small holding in War Stock and occasional small earnings for articles on wine, on which he is an acknowledged expert, he has—or at least declares—no outside resources at all. Nevertheless, enjoying as he does a minus income, he lives very well, appears to deny himself little in the way of comfort. He is not extravagant, but I would not hesitate to estimate his personal expenditures at no less than three thousand pounds per annum."

My masters found this report so unsatisfactory that I was summoned to an interview. The head of the department at that time, Dai Evans, was a tubby and mercurial Welshman, like Lloyd George without the mustache. He was on Christian-name terms with all his staff; but he wasn't a good man to cross.

"Are you asking me to believe in miracles, Michael?" he said. "How can a man have an inexhaustible wallet of notes if he doesn't earn them from somewhere?"

"Perhaps he makes them," I suggested.

Dai elected to take this seriously. "A forger you mean. I wouldn't have thought it likely."

"No," I said. "I didn't quite mean that." (I knew as well as anyone that the skill and organization, to say nothing of the supplies of special paper, necessary for banknote forgery were far beyond the resources of an ordinary citizen.) "I thought he might have a hoard. Some people do, you know. There's nothing intrinsically illegal in it. Suppose he made his money before the war and stowed it away somewhere. In his strongroom downstairs, perhaps. He keeps the keys himself and that's one room no one's allowed inside. Each week he gets out a couple of dozen pound notes and spends them."

Dai grunted. "Why should he trouble to keep up an office? You say it actually costs him money. Why wouldn't he shift his hoard to a safe deposit? That way he'd save himself money and work. I don't like it, Michael. We're onto something here, boy. Don't let it go."

So I returned to Lombards Inn and kept my eyes and ears open. And as the weeks passed the mystery grew more irritating and seemingly more insoluble.

During the month which ensued I made a very careful calculation. In the course of that single month Mr. Portway acted in the purchase of one house for £5,000, and the sale of another at about the same price. He drafted the lease of an office in the City and fixed up a mortgage for an old lady with a Building Society. The income he received for these transactions totaled exactly £171.50. And that was just about five pounds *less* than he paid out—to keep his office going for the same period. . . .

One day, about three o'clock in the afternoon, I had occasion to take some papers in to him. I found him sitting in the chair beside the fireplace, the *Times* (which he read every day from first to last page) in one hand, and in the other a glass.

He said, "You find me indulging in my secret vice. I'm one of the old school who thinks that claret should be drunk after lunch and burgundy after dinner."

I am fond of French wines myself and he must have seen the quick glance I gave the bottle.

"It's a Pontet Canet," he said, "of 1943. Certainly the best of the war years, and almost the best Château of that year. You'll find a glass in the filing cabinet, Mr. Gilbert."

You can't drink wine standing up. Before I knew what I was doing, we were seated in front of the fireplace with the bottle between us. After a second glass Mr. Portway fell into a mood of reminiscence. I kept my ears open, of course, for any useful information, but only half of me, at that moment, was playing the detective. The other half was enjoying an excellent claret, and the company of a philosopher.

It appeared that Mr. Portway had come to the law late. He had studied art under Bertolozzi, the great Florentine engraver, and had then spent a couple of years in the workshops of Herr Groener, who specialized in intaglios and metal relief work. He took down from the mantelshelf a beautiful little reproduction in copper of the Papal Colophon which he had made himself. Then the first World War, most of which he had spent in Egypt, had disoriented him.

"I felt the need," he said, "of something a little more tangible in my life than the art of metal relievo." He had tried, and failed, to become an architect, and had then chosen the law, mostly to oblige an uncle who had no son.

"There have been Portways," he said, "in Lombards Inn for two centuries. I fear I shall be the last."

The telephone broke up our talk and I went back to my room.

As I thought about things that night, I came to the conclusion that Mr. Portway had presented me with the answer to one problem, in the act of setting me another.

"There have been Portways in Lombards Inn for two centuries." The tie of sentiment? Was that perhaps why he was willing to finance, from his own pocket, a practice which no longer paid him? But where did the money come from? The more you looked at it, the more impossible the whole problem became.

As cashier, remember, I received and paid out every penny the firm earned and spent. And I knew—positively and actually knew—that no money went into Mr. Portway's pocket. On the contrary, almost every month he had to draw a check on his own bank account to keep the office going. Nor did he draw, according to his bank statements, any money from that or any other account.

So from what source did the substantial wad of notes in his wallet come? As you see, I was being driven, step by step, to the only logical conclusion: that he had found some method, some perfectly safe and private method, of manufacturing money.

But not forgery, as the word is usually understood. Despite his bland admissions of an engraver's training, the difficulties were too great. Where would he get the special paper? And such notes as I had seen did not look in the least like forgeries.

I had come to one other conclusion. The heart of the secret lay in the strongroom. This was the one room that no one but Mr. Portway ever visited, the room of which he alone had the key. Try as I would, I had never even glanced inside the door. If he wanted a deed out of it, Mr. Portway would wait until I was at lunch before he went in to fetch it. And he was always the last one to leave the office.

The door of the strongroom was a heavy, old-fashioned affair, and if you have time to study it, and are patient enough, in the end you can get the measure of any lock. I had twice glimpsed the actual key, too, and that is a great help. It wasn't long before

I had equipped myself with keys which I was pretty sure would open the door. The next thing was to find an opportunity to use them.

Eventually I hit on quite a simple plan.

At about three o'clock one afternoon I announced that I had an appointment with the local Inspector of Taxes. I thought it would take an hour or ninety minutes. Would it be all right if I went straight home? Mr. Portway agreed. He was in the middle of drafting a complicated conveyance, and looked safely anchored in his chair.

I went back to my room, picked up my hat, raincoat, and brief case, and tiptoed down to the basement. Quietly I opened the door of one of the storage rooms; I had used my last few lunch breaks, when I was alone in the office, in moving a rampart of deed boxes a couple of feet out from the wall and building up the top with bundles of old papers. Now I shut the door behind me and squeezed carefully into my lair. Apart from the fact that the fresh dust I had disturbed made me want to sneeze, it wasn't too bad. Soon the dust particles resettled themselves, and I fell into a state of somnolence.

It was five o'clock before I heard Mr. Portway moving. His footsteps came down the passage outside, and stopped. I heard him open the door of the strongroom, opposite. A pause. The door shut again. The next moment my door opened and the lights sprung on.

I held my breath. The lights went out and the door closed. I heard the click of the key in the lock. Then the footsteps moved away.

He was certainly thorough. I even heard him look into the lavatory. (My first plan had been to lock myself in it. I was glad now that I had not.) At last the steps moved away upstairs; more pottering about, the big outer door slammed shut, and silence came down like a blanket.

I waited for nearly two hours. The trouble was the cleaning woman, an erratic old lady called Gertie. She had a key of her own and sometimes she came in the evening, and sometimes early in the morning. I had studied her movements for several weeks. The latest she had ever left the premises was a quarter to eight at night.

By half-past eight I felt it was safe for me to start investigating.

The storage room door presented no difficulties. The lock was on my side and I simply unscrewed it. The strongroom door was a different matter. I had got what is known in the trade as a set of "approximates"—blank keys of the type and, roughly, the shape to open most old locks. My job was to find the one that worked best, and then file it down and fiddle it until it would open the lock. (You can't do this with a modern lock, which is tooled to a hundredth of an inch, but old locks, which rely on complicated convolutions and strong springs, though they look formidable, are actually much easier.)

By half-past ten I heard the sweet click which meant success, and I swung the steel door open, turned on the light switch, and stepped in.

It was a small vault with walls of whitewashed brick, with a run of wooden shelves round two of the sides, carrying a line of black deed boxes. I didn't waste much time on them; I guessed the sort of things they would contain.

On the left, behind the door, was a table and on the table stood a heavy, brass-bound teak box—the sort of thing that might have been built to contain a microscope, only larger. It was locked—with a small, Bramah-type lock which none of my implements was designed to cope with.

I worked for some time at it, but without much hope. The only solution seemed to be to lug the box away with me—it was very heavy, but just portable—and get someone outside to work on it. I reflected that I should look pretty silly if it did turn out to contain a valuable microscope that one of old Portway's clients had left with him for safekeeping.

Then I had an idea. On the shelf inside the door was a small black tin box with *E. Portway, Personal* painted on the front. It was the sort of thing in which a careful man might keep his War Savings Certificates and Passport. It too was locked, but with an ordinary deed-box lock, which one of the keys on my ring fitted. I opened it, and sure enough, lying on top of the stacked papers inside, the first thing that caught my eye was a worn leather key-holder containing a single, brass Bramah key.

I suddenly felt a little breathless. Perhaps the ventilation in that underground room was not all it should have been. Moving with deliberation, I fitted the brass key into the tiny keyhole, pressed home, and twisted. Then I lifted the top of the box—and came face to face with Mr. Portway's secret.

At first sight it was disappointing. It looked like nothing more than a small handpress—the sort of thing you use for impressing a company seal, only a little larger. I lifted it out, picked up a piece of clean white paper off the shelf, slid the paper in, and pressed down the handle. Then I released it and extracted the paper.

Imprinted on the paper was a neat, orange, Revenue Stamp for £20. I went back to the box. Inside was a tray, and arranged in it were dies of various denominations—10s., £1, £2, £5, and upward. The largest was for £100.

I picked one of the dies out and held it up to the light. It was beautifully made. Mr. Portway had not wasted his time at Bertolozzi's Florentine atelier. There was even an arrangement of cogs behind the die by which the three figures of the date could be set —tiny, delicate wheels, each a masterpiece of the watchmaker's art.

I heard the footsteps crossing the courtyard, and Mr. Portway was through the door before I even had time to put the die down.

"What are you doing here?" I said stupidly.

"When anyone turns on the strongroom light," he said, "it also turns on the light in my office. I've got a private arrangement with the caretaker of the big block at the end who keeps an eye open for me. If he sees my light on, he telephones me at once."

"I see," I said. Once I had got over the actual shock of seeing him there, I wasn't alarmed. I was half his age and twice his size. "I've just been admiring your private work. Every man his own revenue stamp office. A lovely piece of work, Mr. Portway."

"Is it not?" agreed my employer, blinking up at me under the strong light. I could read in his chelonian face neither fear nor anger, rather a sardonic amusement at the turn of affairs. "Are you a private detective, by any chance?"

"I.B.A.—Investigation Branch of the Inland Revenue."

"And you have been admiring my little machine?"

"My only real surprise is that no one has thought of it before."

"Yes," he said. "It's very useful. To a practicing solicitor, of course. I used to find it a permanent source of irritation that my clients should pay more to the Government—who, after all, hadn't raised a finger to earn it—than they did to me. Do you realize that if I act for the purchaser of a London house for £5,000, I get about £43, whilst the Government's share is £100?"

"Scandalous," I agreed. "And so you devised this little machine to adjust the balance. Such a simple and foolproof form of forgery, when you come to think of it." The more I thought of it the more I liked it. "Just think of the effort you would have to expend —to say nothing of obtaining special stocks of paper—if you set out to forge one-hundred-pound notes. Whereas with this machine—a small die, a little pressure—"

"Oh, there's more to it than that," said Mr. Portway airily. "A man would be a fool to forge treasury notes. They have to be passed into circulation, and each one is a potential danger to its maker. Here, when I have stamped a document, it goes directly into a deed box—and it may not be looked at again for twenty years. Possibly, never."

"As a professional accountant," I said, "that is the angle which appeals to me most. Now, let me see. Take that purchase you were talking about. Your client would give you two checks, one for your fee, which goes through the books in the ordinary way, and a separate one for the stamp duty."

"Made out to cash."

"Made out to cash, of course. Which you would yourself cash at the bank, then come back here—"

"I always took the trouble to walk through the Stamp Office in case anyone should be watching me."

"Very sound precaution," I agreed. "Then you came back here, stamped the document yourself, and put the money in your pocket. It never appeared in your books at all."

"That's precisely right," said Mr. Portway. He seemed gratified at the speed with which I had perceived the finer points of his arrangements.

"There's only one thing I can't quite see," I went on. "You're a bachelor, a man with simple tastes. Could you not—I don't want to sound pompous—but by working a little harder could you not have made sufficient money legitimately for your reasonable needs?"

Mr. Portway looked at me for a moment, his smile broadening.

"I see," he said, "that you have not had time to examine the rest of this strongroom. My tastes are far from simple, Mr. Gilbert, and owing to the scandalous and confiscatory nature of modern taxation—oh, I beg your pardon, I was forgetting for the moment—"

"Don't apologize," I said. "I have often thought the same thing myself. You were speaking of your expensive tastes—"

Mr. Portway stepped over to a large, drop-fronted deed box, labeled *Lord Lampeter's Settled Estate*, and unlocked it with a key from his chain. Inside was a rack and in the rack I counted the dusty ends of a dozen bottles.

"Château Margaux. The 1934 vintage. I shouldn't say that even now it has reached its peak. Now here—" he unlocked *The Dean of Melchester, Family Affairs*—"I have a real treasure. A Mouton Rothschild of 1924."

"1924!"

"In Magnums. I know that you appreciate a good wine and since this may perhaps be our last opportunity—"

"Well—"

Mr. Portway took a corkscrew, a decanter, and two glasses from a small cupboard labeled *Estate Duty Forms, Miscellaneous*, drew the cork of the Mouton Rothschild with care and skill, and decanted it with a steady hand. Then he poured two glasses. We both held it up to the single unshaded light to note the dark, rich, almost black color, and took our first, ecstatic, mouthful. It went down like oiled silk.

"What did you say you had in the other boxes?" I inquired reverently.

"My preference has been for the great clarets," said Mr. Portway. "Of course, as I only really started buying in 1945, I have nothing that you could call a museum piece. But I picked up a small lot of 1927 Château Talbot which has to be tasted to be believed. And if a good burgundy was offered, I didn't say no to it." He gestured toward the *Marchioness of Gravesend* box in one corner. "There's a 1937 Romanée Conti—but your glass is empty—"

As we finished the Mouton Rothschild in companionable silence I looked at my watch. It was two o'clock in the morning.

"You will scarcely find any transport to get you home now," said Mr. Portway. "Might I suggest that the only thing to follow a fine claret is a noble burgundy?"

"Well—" I said.

I was fully aware that I was compromising my official position. Actually, I think my mind had long since been made up. As dawn was breaking, and the Romanée Conti was sinking in the bottle, we agreed on provisional articles of partnership.

The name of the firm is Portway & Gilbert, of 7 Lombards Inn.

If you are thinking, by any chance, of buying a house—

Red Wine

LAWRENCE G. BLOCHMAN

The author, a well-established journalist and short-story writer, tells us that "Red Wine" is his most widely known story. It has been reprinted in a dozen countries, telecast twice, broadcast by radio five times. It was during his Paris period, when he wrote for the now extinct Paris Times *a column called "Le Gourmet," that Mr. Blochman built up the gastronomic and vinous background reflected in this neatly plotted yarn. The reader will note that it employs the same device used in Dorothy Sayers' "Bibulous Business." The denouement is exceptionally well-handled, even though one might argue interminably over whether the murderer, a cool customer, would really fall into Vernier's trap.*

A RAUCOUS toot from the whistle of the yellow-funneled KPM steamer echoed from the jungle-covered headlands to arouse Heer Controleur Koert from his afternoon nap. Heer Koert did not swear; the day was too hot for any such exertion as swearing. He opened one eye and peered through the haze of his mosquito netting. Below his veranda lay a collection of glaring tin-roofed sheds, whitewashed Chinese shops, and *attap* huts clinging to the green edge of the low river bank.

Some distance offshore, beyond the muddy swirl made by the river as it pushed brown fingers into the unruffled blue of the sea, the mail steamer was smoking impatiently, the only connection between Tanjong Samar and civilization. And since Heer Koert was the official representative of civilization in Tanjong Samar, he opened the other eye.

He watched the swarm of *praus* and sampans streaking for the ship and estimated that he would have half an hour before being forced to make any further movement. In half an hour he would arise, dash tepid water on himself from a Java bath jar, drink a cup of coffee, and button his white duck jacket high about his neck. Thus he would be fit to sit at his desk and properly receive the official communications and two weeks' accumulations of the *Bataviasch Nieuwsblad* which his dusky skinned aspirant-controleur would bring ashore.

The controleur's leisurely routine was somewhat rushed, however, when he saw that the first boat ashore did not deposit his slow-moving assistant, but a brisk-walking white man he had never seen before. The stranger made such a rapid climb to the controleur's bungalow that Heer Koert had barely time to make himself dignified before there was a knock on the screen door of the veranda. He waddled ponderously to answer.

A man in a pongee suit and white topee stood there, wiping his perspiring face with a silk handkerchief. He was a well-fed-appearing man whose movements were good-natured and deliberate. His frank smile caused deep dimples to dot either side of a face that gave an impression of virile intelligence—an impression somehow strengthened by the droop of his right eyelid over a vaguely pale eye. The alert vitality of the good eye was penetrating enough for two.

"Are you Mr. Koert?" asked the man in the pongee suit. "My name is Paul Vernier. The governor-general promised me your cooperation. Has he written to you?"

"You are here before the mail," said the controleur. "But you have my cooperation anyhow. Won't you sit down, please?"

"I'll come right to the point," said Vernier, sinking into a high, fan-backed Bilibid chair. "I'm looking for a killer."

"Dayaks, maybe?" said the rotund controleur. "You must go far up the river to find them. And they are not killing so much any more. Instead of letting them hunt new heads for marriage ceremonies, we are persuading them to use old heads—"

"Dayaks don't interest me," said Vernier. "I'm looking for an American—an American murderer named Jerome Steeks. I've traced him to Tanjong Samar."

Koert clapped his hands and shouted something in Malay, which was answered by a grunt in another room.

"I am offering you coffee," he explained. "This is coffee time. Later is gin time. Where is your baggage?"

"I have all the baggage I need in my inside pocket—extradition papers for Jerome Steeks, approved by the governor-general in Batavia. I'll pick up Steeks as soon as you tell me where he is, and I'll take him aboard the steamer before she sails."

"You can't do that," said the controleur simply.

"Why not? I'm positive Jerome Steeks is in Tanjong Samar."

"There is nobody with that name in my district."

"Naturally he wouldn't be using his own name. But it shouldn't be so hard to locate my man in this bustling metropolis. Isn't there an American here?"

"There are three Americans." Vernier's eyebrows raised slightly as Koert continued, "All three are on the Kota Bharu rubber estate up the river. The round trip to the plantation will take two hours, not counting time for looking for the Americans. The steamer leaves in one hour. Shall I send out for your baggages?"

Vernier's gaze fixed Koert for a moment. Then his pursed lips spread into a smile.

"All right," he said. "If it won't be too much trouble."

Koert clapped his hands again and muttered more Malay. A servant appeared with a tray.

"They will get it for you," said the controleur. "And now we can drink our coffee."

There was no coffee pot on the tray—only cups, sugar bowl, a pitcher of hot milk, and a small jug. Vernier watched Koert pour a spoonful of black essence from the jug into each cup, then add the steaming milk. The resultant liquid looked and smelled a little like coffee.

"And now," said Koert, passing a cup, "tell me about this man you want to arrest. Does he know you?"

"No."

"Good. In that case he will not suspect. You can arrest him a few hours before the next ship calls. That will save unpleasant makeshifts. We have no good jail here. You will recognize this American? You have his photograph?"

"Jerome Steeks is a very clever man," said Vernier. "He planned a perfect escape from a nearly perfect crime. There isn't a single picture or set of fingerprints of him in existence. I know him only by description: medium height, slight build, pale complexion, dark hair, and small black mustache."

The controleur suddenly grasped his ample girth with both hands, threw back his head, opened his mouth wide, and emitted loud cackling sounds. After a moment Vernier decided Heer Koert was laughing.

"You must have come to the wrong *dessa*," said the controleur. "All three men are medium height, but all are quite strong-looking, cleanshaven, brown as coffee by the sun, and none has dark hair."

"I told you Steeks was clever." Vernier smiled a little wistfully. "But I'm positive he is here. He came here from Batavia six months ago."

"All three men came from Batavia six months ago, by the same boat. The estate changed hands and the new owner wanted Americans to run it, because American planters know how to bud the trees and double the rubber yield. What sort of man is the murderer?"

Vernier gulped the bitterish coffee. "Utterly ruthless," he said, "yet a polished gentleman. Strange combination. He has lived a great deal in Europe, where he was known as a connoisseur of music, women, good cooking, and fine wines. I heard of him first when I was in France."

"Ah, France," said Heer Koert, looking steadfastly at Vernier's drooping eyelid. "Then it was in France that you—"

He made a vague gesture, as though afraid to touch a delicate subject. Vernier saw the gesture and smiled.

"Yes," he said. "A piece of shrapnel. It started me on my present career, I guess. One eye isn't enough for the infantry, so they took me off the line and put me into the intelligence. I made so many French contacts that after the armistice I followed them up. Stayed on in Paris to study Bertillon methods with the French Sûreté. Just before I came home I remember reading of Jerome Steeks attending the annual banquet of Paris vintners, entering the usual wine-tasting contest, and identifying by taste unlabeled vintages as capably as the oldest professional taster."

Heer Koert made clucking sounds with his tongue. "A gourmet," he commented.

"He was rich. Nobody questioned the source of his money, which was undoubtedly—well, extralegal. Three years ago he married a San Francisco heiress, took her to Europe, brought her back to California. Shortly after their return, Mrs. Steeks's body was found lying on the end of a little-used pier, a bullet in the brain. Tire marks on the pier led to a search for Steeks's car, which was found in the bay. Steeks was supposed to have been drowned in the plunge. A note told of a suicide pact. They had run through the heiress's fortune, lost staggering sums at Monte Carlo, and decided on death rather than poverty. Although Steeks's body was never found, in view of the tides, the discovery of two empty shells in a revolver, and the fact that Mrs. Steeks's fortune was indeed dissipated, the police accepted the double-suicide theory."

"And of course it was false?"

"Of course. It was a case of coldblooded murder for profit. A year later a prominent shyster lawyer got into a jam, was arrested, and in his safe cops found a letter from Steeks, written from Batavia. The lawyer had apparently been salting away the wife's missing fortune and was to notify Steeks when he could come back safely. Well, the Secretary of State asked for extradition right away, and I slid out to Batavia to pick up the trail. Clues can get pretty cold in a year, and evidence can be camouflaged. But I've got Mr. Steeks here now. With no steamer for two weeks, he can't very well get away from me."

Controleur Koert shook his head in a puzzled manner. "I am not so sure," he said. "There is no gourmet and no polished gentleman at Kota Bharu estate. There is just Americans."

"One of them is a murderer. When can we go and pick him out, Mr. Koert?"

The controleur scratched himself behind the ear. "First I must attend to the steamer," he said. "Then I will talk with you about best methods."

"In the meantime I'll walk about the town a bit," said Vernier, arising. "It's cooler now. Maybe I can learn something."

"Mr. Vernier, please don't open that screen door yet," cried Koert, rushing after the detective in a panic. "Wait."

He rolled a newspaper into a small torch, lighted it, and waved the flame against the screen to cremate whatever mosquitoes had gathered on the outside, awaiting a chance to enter.

"Now," he said. "Go. And shut the door quickly. In an hour and a half come back. We will have gin *pahits* and discuss methods."

The controleur persuaded Paul Vernier to wait until next morning before starting his manhunt. The sun glinted with hard brilliance on the coffee-colored river when the two men—Koert in whites, Vernier in khaki—walked down to the shore. They threaded their way among carved, high-stemmed *praus* drawn up on the beach, with red and blue demons grinning from their leaning masts. The two white men crawled under the palm-thatched canopy shading the middle of a long narrow sampan. Paddles dug into the brown water, churning the current. The craft swung upstream.

The sampan slid between low banks of mangrove and nipa palms, behind which arose mountains of verdure, cliffs of tangled palms and creepers, slashed by the broad fresh green blades of plantains, flecked by the white puffs of ripe tree cotton, the yellow of cannas, and the flame of *lantana*.

Four naked mahogany torsos glistened as four paddles swung in unison. The steersman aft of the canopy chanted.

After a few minutes on the river Vernier drew Koert's attention to another sampan following them, stroke for stroke.

"Yes," said Koert. "That is your baggages. I had them sent by another sampan because we are already crowded in this one."

"But I don't need baggage," said Vernier. "I won't have to stay at the plantation. I'll pick my man and come back to stay with you—if you don't mind."

"I would be more than pleased. But I am afraid you will have to stay longer. I know the three Americans. None of them fits your description. You will have to study them closer. The governor-general said I should help you, so I sent word ahead that we would come for *makan* at noon today and that you might want to stay on for a few days to see how rubber is made."

The round-faced detective's dimples appeared. "I wouldn't like to do that—accept a man's hospitality and then clamp the bracelets on him. If I find I have to stay there to complete my identification, I'll tell them so right out. Not likely that my man will escape from this place. That way it will make it an open battle of wits, and I'll feel better about staying with the men."

"Oh, no, no!" exclaimed the controleur. "You can't do that.

I have already said you were a stockholder and for that reason wished to stay on the plantation. You can not contradict the controleur."

Vernier's dimples disappeared. "Can't you say you misunderstood me?" he inquired.

"Should the governor-general hear I was misunderstanding people, I might not get my promotion to be sub-resident in Java. Besides, it will be easier for you to work quietly like I plan."

"Well, all right. We'll try it for a while," said Vernier soberly. A pucker grew between his eyebrows.

A rickety little pier, two tin-roofed sheds, and a clearing of the jungle to make way for the symmetrical rows of *hevea* trees marked the place where the Kota Bharu rubber plantation reached the river. From the river it was a five-minute walk to the large bungalow, raised on piles, which served as quarters for the white plantation-managers.

The three managers puzzled Vernier as they were introduced —Prale, Wilmerding, and Doran.

The controleur had been right. There was nothing of a cultured *bon vivant* among these rough-and-ready Americans, and all were light. Prale was a bland-looking, sandy-haired fellow with a smart-aleck twist to the corners of his mouth and a turned-up nose. Wilmerding was blond, almost towheaded, with a vigorous handshake. Doran, keen-eyed and restless, had light reddish hair. Which one of the trio was the black-haired Jerome Steeks? None of them, Vernier would have said, had he not definite information that the murderer was here. One of them *must* be Steeks.

"Hope you don't object to *rystaffel*," said Doran as they filed into a darkened room for lunch. "That's all our cook ever gives us for noon."

"From what I had of it in Java," said Vernier, "I rather like it."

"I don't," said Wilmerding. "*Rystaffel*'s enough to give dyspepsia to a herd of buffaloes."

Whatever the reaction of buffaloes to the national dish of the Dutch colonial in the Indies, Wilmerding was apparently not afraid of dyspepsia for himself. He heaped his plate high with rice and proceeded to decorate it with all the accessories which two servants brought to the table: curried eggs, fried bananas, onions, chutneys, shredded coconut, tiny red dried fish, peppers,

and various unidentified spiced meats and vegetables. Vernier
watched Wilmerding mix the conglomeration in approved Dutch
East Indies style. Wilmerding caught Vernier's eye, guessed his
judgment on the score of inconsistency, and said, "Well, we
have to eat something."

"*Rystaffel's* not bad with a glass of beer," said Vernier.

"We never have any real cold beer out here," Wilmerding
complained. "No ice. And warm beer is nasty."

Vernier studied Wilmerding a moment. He was attacking his
rystaffel with as much gusto as his two companions, but for
a flash, Vernier thought he had detected a styled movement in
the lifting of a fork. Perhaps not, inasmuch as Wilmerding wiped
his mouth with the back of his hand after taking a draft of beer.
Still—

"I ran across some pretty good wine down in Batavia and
Surabaya. Why don't you fellows get some of it sent up?"
Vernier suggested.

"Never learned to drink wine," said Wilmerding. "We got
plebeian tastes. Just beer—and a little gin or scotch at night.
Prale over there talks a lot about the wine he drank, but if you
ask me he'd a lot rather have an ice-cream soda. A lot of us
would, I guess."

He ran his fingers through his blond hair, thoughtfully sipped
some beer, then went after his rice with renewed vigor.

Talk ranged from baseball back in the States to the classic
argument as to which is worse, mosquitoes or citronella oil; the
amours of the contract Javanese laborers and reports of a head-
hunting expedition by Dayaks in a neighboring district occupied
some of the conversation. It wasn't until an amazing amount of
rice had been consumed, however, that Vernier saw his first indication as to which of the three might be the cultured murderer.
The detective pricked up his ears when Wilmerding suggested
that Doran give him some music.

"Music?" echoed Vernier.

"Yeah. Doran plays," said Prale. "He plays a mean phonograph."

Yes, the phonograph was his, Doran admitted. What would
Mr. Vernier like to hear? Probably nothing, because it was
damned hard to keep up a decent repertoire out there in Borneo,

where the new records had to be shipped in and half the time arrived broken.

"May I look?" said Vernier.

He slid back the disks, one after the other, expecting to find recordings of operas, symphonies, and other more serious compositions—probably French composers dominating. He found only jazz numbers, out-of-date sentimental ballads, Irving Berlin, pre-Gershwin dance music. No trained, cosmopolitan taste here.

"Play anything," he said.

The phonograph squealed, sang, and strummed away. Wilmerding sat smoking a pipe with Heer Koert. Prale walked to the edge of the veranda and looked through the screen toward the river. Doran was sorting over his precious records. Vernier walked slowly about the room, taking in details with his one alert eye. He stopped in front of a bookcase and began reading the titles.

"Hello," he said. "Who owns the French books?"

"They were here when we came," said Wilmerding. "There was a French planter on the estate before us. He left the books."

"Anybody here read them?" Vernier inquired, taking down a volume bound in yellow paper covers.

"Prale practically invented the French language," said Doran. "Just ask him."

Vernier was holding the French book close to his face, slowly turning pages. "I studied French," he said, as if to himself. Then, watching the room over the top of his book, he said, as though reading, "*Il y a un meurtrier dans cette maison.*"

He paused, watching for a reaction to his announcement in French that there was a murderer in the house. He was disappointed. Prale looked stupidly sheepish as the others overwhelmed him with banter.

"What's it all about, Prale?" demanded Wilmerding.

"Translate for us," ordered Doran.

"Why, it's all about houses," said Prale. "*Maison*—that's French for 'house.'"

When the laughter had subsided, Heer Controleur Koert arose and mopped his ruddy face. "You will excuse me, I have to return to the *dessa* for important official business," he said, with as much equanimity as if everyone present did not know that the important business was his daily siesta. "And you, Mr. Vernier? Are you going to pay a visit of some days to this estate?"

"If I'm not in the way," said Vernier. The drooping lid of his sightless eye quivered just a trifle.

"Plenty of room," said Wilmerding.

"Even if there wasn't, we'd make room by putting Doran out to sleep with the mosquitoes," said Prale.

"Which would spare me from listening to Prale's wisecracks," countered Doran.

"I would like very much to have a chance to see how you fellows get a dozen golf balls and a set of balloon tires out of a tree," said Vernier. "But I warn you"—he paused and looked at Koert—"I warn you that you'll have me prowling all over the place, asking questions like a woman at a ball game. I'm curious —about all sorts of things."

He worked his curiosity overtime during the next few days. He prowled and asked questions at all hours. He would follow Prale down the estate in the misty dawn at tapping time, listening as he offered profane suggestions, half English, half broken Malay, to the Javanese who were shaving the diagonal scars on the trunks of the *hevea* trees so that the milky latex would ooze out into grooves, through a spigot into tiny porcelain cups. After the sun had become hot enough to stop the flow of sap he would make the rounds with Wilmerding, watching Javanese women in gay sarongs collecting latex in buffalo-drawn tank carts. Then he would stand where Doran, at the chemical shack, received the latex, pouring it into vats to be coagulated into rubber.

But in three days he got nowhere. He still believed that one of the planters was Jerome Steeks. And he still did not know whether it was Prale, Doran, or Wilmerding. One thing he did know for certain: Steeks's hair had changed color in the last eighteen months. The dark murderer of San Francisco had become a blond. Hydrogen peroxide or some other bleaching agent must have been in use here—in use constantly, too, because for three days Vernier had looked closely to find one head of hair that was darker at the roots. Vain search. The new growth was apparently being bleached as fast as it came out. This might be a clue.

The following day, when the three planters had gone out into the steamy morning, Vernier remained at the bungalow, pleading a headache. He lay on his springless tropical bed until he no longer heard the servants stirring about. Then he arose, went directly to Prale's room, and started systematically to examine every corner of it. He ran hurriedly through a chest of drawers and a steamer trunk green with the quick mold of the tropics. He had little expectation that a man as clever as Jerome Steeks would leave telltale papers around, but he hoped to find that bleaching agent. As a matter of fact he found nothing but clothes, a photograph of an old woman in a moldly leather case, a catalog from a Chicago mail-order house. . . .

He repeated the procedure in Wilmerding's room. As he was opening a trunk he thought he heard steps outside the door. He arose quickly, listened, looked out. He saw no one. He returned to his task; again fruitless. Doran's room was equally devoid of evidence.

But Doran was in the chemical shack most of the day! Just the place to hide a bleach and a little henna dye. A bottle more or less among the other chemicals would not be noticed. So Vernier went out to do a little noticing. He asked questions of Doran, who was busy with the latex. He picked up bottles and tapped metal drums. Doran gave a satisfactory explanation for everything. Another blind clue.

Prale? Wilmerding? Doran? He shut himself up alone that afternoon to reflect, to work out some plan of attack. He was so wrapped in thought that he was late for dinner. An animated conversation was in progress before he reached the table, but it stopped suddenly as he appeared in the doorway. As he sat down conversation was resumed on trivial matters, obviously forced in an effort by the planters to cover up a change of subject. Vernier knew they had been talking about him.

After dinner there was a poker game. The four men sat about a table on the veranda. Perspiration glistened on faces and naked arms, golden in the lamplight.

A cloud of insects buzzed and flickered about the lamp, one occasionally diving into the flame with an odorous sizzle, sometimes falling among the cards in a wing-beating frenzy. Vernier was unusually quiet. He was studying his three opponents.

Jerome Steeks had been somewhat of a gambler. He might

betray himself at the game. One of the three planters did, in fact, display considerably more card sense than the others—Prale. Luck was against him, however, and the chips piled up in front of Vernier. The trio were not good sports about losing, either. At least Vernier attributed a certain tensity in the hot atmosphere to his consistent winnings. Conversation seemed strained tonight, and what little talk there was was rarely directed at him.

Finally, when he had raked in a jackpot with four sixes over Prale's ace full, Doran tossed his cards to the center of the table and cleared his throat.

"Say, Vernier," he began, looking the detective full in the face, "Just exactly what are you doing in Borneo, anyhow?"

"I thought Koert explained," said Vernier. "I'm—"

"We mean the real reason," said Wilmerding. "Of course the stockholder story is out, because there aren't any stockholders in Kota Bharu rubber. The whole estate belongs to one man. I know that for certain."

Vernier laughed. It was a genuine laugh, for although he felt the situation rapidly growing more uneasy, he could appreciate the joke he had played on himself by accepting the controleur's suggestion to act the role of stockholder.

"Do you boys think I'm out here to sell you gold bricks or something?" he said genially.

His joviality was not reflected by the three planters. There was an embarrassed silence for several seconds. Then Prale said with a drawl, "What kind of gold bricks were you looking for in my room this morning?"

Again a leaden moment of silence. All eyes were fixed on Vernier. The detective held the deck of cards between his hands and was ruffling the edge of the pack with his thumb. It made a sharp crackling noise, repeated several times as he scanned the three faces around the lamp. He was thinking about the footsteps he had heard while he was in Wilmerding's room that morning. A spying servant, seeking to ingratiate himself by bearing tales to his employer?

"In your room?"

"Yes," said Wilmerding. "We understand you did a little prospecting today—to cure your headache."

"I don't like this business—your coming here lying to us,

Vernier," put in Doran. "How do we know what crooked game you're up to? You're probably a spy of some kind."

"Don't be ridiculous."

"He's not ridiculous." It was Wilmerding speaking. "We're living on the frayed edge of civilization here. We've got to look out for ourselves. We've got a perfect right to be suspicious of strangers. There's nothing ridiculous in a man protecting himself against potential enemies."

"How did you just happen to come to Tanjong Samar, which most people never heard of?" demanded Prale. "Why did you pick Kota Bharu estate out of the hundreds of rubber plantations in the East Indies?"

Vernier was still ruffling the pack of cards with his thumb. The three men about the table looked at him in ominous silence. They were serious, these faces that perspired in the lamplight; suspicious, challenging, and perhaps just a bit contemptuous. Vernier dropped the cards to the table carelessly. A *gecko* in some dark corner of the veranda uttered a series of explosive cries that sounded uncannily like human words. Insects continued their monotonous buzzing about the lamp. Vernier leaned forward easily on his elbows.

"I'll tell you why I came to Tanjong Samar," he said at last. "I came here to arrest a murderer."

There was a little movement by each of the three planters. Surprise, perhaps. Resentment—

"I'll be quite frank with you boys," Vernier continued. "I told the controleur he'd better pass me off as a stockholder until I found out which one of you three was the man I wanted. I had definite information that the murderer was on the Kota Bharu rubber estate."

Vernier's smile again flashed, and his one eye shone so with frankness that the planters leaned back in their chairs. The tension was eased for a moment.

"I'll bet Doran is the guy you're after," said Prale.

"If you stick around long enough, you can pick me up for killing Prale. I feel it coming on," said Doran.

"What's the murderer's name?" asked Wilmerding.

"Jerome Steeks."

Vernier's keen glance shifted from one face to another, but he detected not so much as the flicker of an eyelash.

"Never heard of him."

"Sounds like a vegetable to me."

"Which one of us is he?"

Vernier leisurely lighted a cigarette over the lamp chimney before he replied.

"None of you," he said. "I hadn't been here long before I decided that the tip I had was wrong. Jerome Steeks had dark hair. You men are all naturally light—nothing phony about your wigs. So I'm going to go back to Java on the next KPM steamer. Then home. I kick myself, though, for having had you all under false suspicion, even if it wasn't my fault. To put myself right, to show there's no ill will on my part, I want to throw a party for you boys. We'll make it on steamer day, and you can declare a holiday, because I know the captain of the *Van Laar* is a real epicure. He has a fine cellar aboard—specializes in Chambertin —and has a great cook. I'll have him lend me the cook and a few rare old bottles for the occasion. You're invited to take a rest from *rystaffel* and have a real feed. How about it?"

There was no immediate response to the invitation. The planters seemed a little bit wary. Wilmerding spoke first.

"Sure, we'll eat your chow," he said.

"Fine," said Vernier. "I'll promise you a banquet you won't forget. How would boar with Madeira and mushroom sauce do for the roast? I'll furnish the wine sauce if there's boar to be had around here. I'll shoot one myself if someone will lend me a gun."

"I'll shoot you a pig," said Doran. "I don't like strangers using my gun."

Next morning Vernier went down the river to Tanjong Samar and called on the controleur.

"Mr. Koert," he said, "when does the East Borneo steamer leave Batavia?"

The controleur studied red lines on a wall map and consulted books.

"Is there any way for me to get through a communication to the ship before she leaves Java?" said Vernier, while Koert turned pages.

The controleur stroked his two chins a moment before replying. "There is a wireless at Balik Papan," he said. "For twenty-

five guilders I can get an *Orang Laut* to paddle up the coast to
Balik Papan to the wireless station. He could get there in time.
Why?"

"I want the United States consul in Batavia to get some things
on that boat for me. The consul knows a good cellar in Batavia.
I want him to get me some Chambertin of the same vintage he
produced when I was there. And I'll want other wines, and a
cook. He can get me a cook from the Hôtel des Indes and put
him on the boat, too, with ingredients for a menu I'm going to
indicate. And ice. We must have ice—"

He sat down and began drafting the message.

"Very good," said the controleur. "If you will give me the
twenty-five guilders, and the price of the message, I will see it
goes at once. And in the meantime I am glad you are here. If
you had not come, I should have gone after you this afternoon.
You must stay with me until your steamer comes."

"Why so?"

"Because your life is no longer safe on the plantation."

"What makes you think so?"

"I know. I hear from natives. Servants talk. Talk travels. In
the end it always reaches me. You told the planters at Kota
Bharu of your mission—"

"I protected you. The governor-general will never know anything derogatory."

"But your man will certainly kill you before steamer day."

"Oh, no," said Vernier, smiling. "We're all good friends now.
I'm giving this dinner to show there's no hard feelings. Besides,
I must go back to the estate. Everything depends upon my being
there."

"Well, suit yourself; but remember I warned you."

"I consider myself warned. And in the meantime hurry that
SOS for food, wine, and ice. You're invited, of course."

Cordial relations were apparently re-established when Vernier
returned to the rubber estate. The three planters gave no outward evidence that they had not accepted Vernier's profession
of good faith, yet the detective sensed an undercurrent of
suspicion. He had an idea one of the trio was fomenting ill feelings, or at least keeping them alive, for his own private ends.
And for that reason Vernier slept lightly and kept his loaded

automatic under his "Dutch Wife"—the cylindrical bolster found beneath every mosquito netting in the East Indies, used as an aid to ventilation of the body and to reduce perspiration during sleep.

During the entire week that preceded the arrival of the KPM steamer Vernier acted as enthusiastic press agent for his farewell dinner. He outlined his menu and told of the wines he would serve with each course—particularly the Chambertin, king of red Burgundies, robust, fragrant, heady, Napoleon's favorite wine. . . .

"Any Chambertin is fine," Vernier would tell the planters, "but nineteen-eleven Chambertin is beyond comparison. It is the superlative in wine. Burgundy produced real nectar that year. You'll see."

Three days before the arrival of the steamer the matter of boar again came up. All three planters decided to go shooting.

"Come with us," said Prale to Vernier.

"I haven't a gun," said Vernier, looking at Doran.

Doran looked away and did not reply.

"I have two rifles," said Wilmerding. "You can take one."

At the last minute, however, Wilmerding found that the packing of smoked crepe for shipment on the next boat was not going rapidly enough. He decided to stay on the estate to push the coolies a bit.

Prale and Doran accompanied Vernier into the jungle beyond the limits of the plantation. Vernier noticed casually that he was the only one wearing a white topee. The other two wore khaki sun helmets.

"We won't have to go far," said Prale. "Sometimes they come right down in the trees. Just keep plugging straight ahead."

That was the plan. Vernier was to keep on straight ahead, while Prale and Doran were to oblique to the right and left. Several Malays were out in front.

As a matter of fact, as soon as the two men were out of sight in the chest-high thicket, Vernier stopped walking. He wanted those two men ahead of him, not behind. Jerome Steeks was a ruthless person. . . .

The detective took off his white topee and perched it atop a *lantana* bush. Then he walked several paces away and squatted down in the damp growth, his rifle between his knees. They could not possibly see him there, but they could see his sun helmet—a flash of white in the dense greenery.

For twenty minutes he waited, whisking away flies and insects. Then he heard a shot, followed by two more, a fourth shot, and his sun helmet leaped spinning into the air, struck a tree, bounded to the ground at his feet. Jerome Steeks could shoot, too. Which was he? Vernier picked up the helmet. Did the shot come from the left—Prale—or the right—Doran? He turned the helmet in the direction it had been facing atop the bush. He looked at the holes. Then he looked again. The shot had come from neither left nor right. It had come from behind. One of the pair had succeeded in circling around behind him, despite his precautions. But which one?

Putting on his helmet, he started back toward the estate. He hoped to cross the trail of the man who had fired behind. But he was disappointed. He reached the bungalow without meeting anyone. It was half an hour later that Prale and Doran came back, with their Malays carrying the dead pig.

There was no more stray shooting before steamer day, and when the yellow-funneled steamer again hove to off the river mouth Vernier was still in the dark as to who had fired the shot.

The ship arrived one gray, sweltering afternoon, and the controleur got the skipper to lay over until nearly midnight instead of making the usual hurried call. He could be in Balik Papan by dawn, anyhow.

The cook imported from Batavia came ashore in a sampan loaded with crates, boxes, and a huge cake of ice wrapped in burlap. He repaired immediately to the bungalow of Heer Koert, where he shooed his Chinese predecessor into a corner and began to exercise his art. In view of the controleur's superior kitchen, and the time that would have been lost by transporting the supplies up the river, the three planters had agreed to come down to the *dessa*.

In deference to Dutch colonial custom, the dinner was preceded by a few rounds of gin *pahits* on the veranda. Vernier proudly produced a menu written in French, which he passed around, watching the expression on the faces of the three Americans as they read:

FOIE GRAS AU PORTO

HOMARD À L'ARMORICAINE

TRUFFES SOUS LA CENDRE

SANGLIER À LA MADÈRE

POMMES SOUFFLÉES

ZABAGLIONE

PETIT FOURS   ROQUEFORT

DEMI-TASSE

MONTRACHET 1904   CHAMBERTIN-CRÉSIGNY 1911

CHAMPAGNE IRROY 1919

The eyes of the Dutch controleur and the steamship captain, who also was a guest, grew large and bright as they scanned the menu. Those of the three Americans did not show a flicker of comprehension.

The planters smacked their lips over the goose liver in port wine jelly, however, and breathed noisily in unison— "Ah-h-h"—when the lobster appeared, steaming in its savory fumes of white wine, brandy, essence of tomatoes.

Paul Vernier, as he presided over the table glittering with the crystal ware and cutlery from Batavia, seemed to be thoroughly enjoying himself. At times he could be as boisterous as the three Americans. Yet when he mentioned his wines he spoke reverently in low tones.

"This Montrachet," he said, as he poured the fragrant golden wine that accompanied the lobster, "beats any other white wine in the world. Can't compete with Chambertin, of course, but in nineteen-four it was as good as white Burgundy ever was or will be."

The planters approved profanely. There was plenty of white wine, so they drank plenty. And Montrachet is a heady wine. They probably did not fully appreciate the truffles. Each truffle had been embedded in a potato and baked in live coals. One had only to peel off the charred potato to find the truffle in all its succulence. . . .

Then came the boar, bathed in its mauve wine sauce, studded with mushrooms, exhaling a glorious aroma.

"And now," announced Vernier, "the king of wines. There never was a better wine than Chambertin, and there never was a better Chambertin than nineteen-eleven. Look!"

Carefully cradled in a special basket with a handle at one end, the bottle was passed around. Vernier called attention to the cobwebs on the bottle. Then he poured a little in his own glass, holding it up to be admired.

"Look at that color!" he said. "Rubies. Clear, leaping flame. The fire of a thousand sunsets. And the bouquet! Just have a whiff of it. Sheer poetry! That's wine for you—Chambertin!"

He held out the glass to the nostrils of each of the guests, watching them as they breathed the spirituous fragrance.

"And now, pass me your large wineglasses, please. Thanks."

Scarcely moving the bottle, he poured each glass three-fourths full. His one keen eye darted quick glances about the table. Then he suddenly plunged a spoon into a dish of cracked ice and began to tinkle the crystal chunks into each glass of red wine.

Wilmerding instantly half rose from his chair directly opposite, his mouth open as though he had witnessed something horrible.

"My God, man! Don't put ice in that Chambertin!" he said in low, shocked tones.

Vernier dropped the spoon, made a swipe for his pocket, and lunged across the table before Wilmerding could sit down again. There was a metallic click, a grunt—and a pair of handcuffs glistened around Wilmerding's wrists.

Straightening up, Vernier said quietly, "Jerome Steeks!"

The room was immediately in an uproar. The diners were on their feet, shouting, gesticulating. The controleur was yelling in Dutch at the steamship captain, who was nodding his head furiously. Prale was pounding the table and hurling pyrotechnic language at Vernier. Doran had an arm around Wilmerding and was assuring him that everything was all right. Wilmerding continued to stare at Vernier, his mouth open.

"Jerome Steeks!" repeated Vernier.

"Liar!" yelled Doran.

"You can't get away with that stuff!" Prale was advancing toward Vernier with a chair swung above his head.

"Wait!" Vernier made a pacific gesture with both hands. Prale paused. "I'll tell you how I know this man is Jerome Steeks." Prale put down the chair. "Only an epicure, a gourmet such as Jerome Steeks, would have been shocked by my putting ice in Chambertin. Only a man who knows thoroughly how to eat and drink appreciates wines enough to understand that the bouquet of Chambertin would be destroyed, frozen up, by cold. Steeks knows that red wine should always be drunk at the temperature of the room. This, gentlemen, is Jerome Steeks, epicure—wanted in San Francisco for murder."

"How about it, Willy? What's the inside?" demanded Prale.

Steeks, lately Wilmerding, did not turn his head. He was looking forlornly at a growing purple stain on the table cloth. In his excitement of snapping on the handcuffs, Vernier had upset three glasses of wine.

"Say, Vernier," said the manacled man at last. "Will you do me one last and quite reasonable favor?"

"Sure," said Vernier, "if you'll do me one. Tell me how you kept your hair blond without bleaching agents."

Wilmerding-Steeks smiled faintly. "It was always blond," he said. "When I started living by my wits I figured I'd probably have to hide out someday. So I dyed it black and kept it that way, knowing I could let it grow out blond when I wanted to. And now, will you do me that favor?"

"What is it?" asked Vernier.

"Pour me a glass of your Chambertin," came the reply, "without ice."

The Widow

MARGERY ALLINGHAM

*Margery Allingham (1904–   ) is perhaps most nearly en-
titled to inherit the crown of Dorothy Sayers. She is one of
the three or four most literate of English detective-story
writers, and her creation, Mr. Campion, one of the most ingratiating of contemporary sleuths. Born in London, she was
from the age of seven trained in the writing craft by her
father, the feuilletonist H. J. Allingham. Her most ambitious
novel,* The Tiger in the Smoke, *was quite properly reviewed
not only as good entertainment but as a serious work of fiction.* "The Widow" *is not about wine but about wine carried
to a higher power, to wit: liqueur brandy. And a most high-
spirited tale it is too—though one regrets that Miss Allingham,
like Miss Sayers, should fall into the "true Napoleon" trap.*

THE second prettiest girl in Mayfair was thanking Superintendent Stanislaus Oates for the recovery of her diamond
bracelet and the ring with the square-cut emerald in it, and Mr.
Campion, who had accompanied her to the ceremony, was admiring her technique.

She was doing it very charmingly; so charmingly, in fact, that
the Superintendent's depressing little office had taken on an air
of garden-party gaiety which it certainly did not possess in the
ordinary way, while the Superintendent himself had undergone
an even more sensational change.

His long dyspeptic face was transformed by a blush of smug
satisfaction and he quite forgot the short lecture he had prepared
for his visitor on The Carelessness Which Tempts the Criminal,
or its blunter version, Stupidity Which Earns Its Own Reward.

It was altogether a most gratifying scene, and Mr. Campion,

seated in the visitor's chair, his long thin legs crossed and his pale eyes amused behind his horn-rimmed spectacles, enjoyed it to the full.

Miss Leonie Peterhouse-Vaughn raised her remarkable eyes to the Superintendent's slightly sheepish face and spoke with deep earnestness.

"I honestly think you're wonderful," she said.

Realizing that too much butter can have a disastrous effect on any dish, and not being at all certain of his old friend's digestive capabilities, Mr. Campion coughed.

"He has his failures too," he ventured. "He's not omnipotent, you know. Just an ordinary man."

"Really?" said Miss Peterhouse-Vaughn with gratifying surprise.

"Oh, yes; well, we're only human, miss." The Superintendent granted Mr. Campion a reproachful look. "Sometimes we have our little disappointments. Of course on those occasions we call in Mr. Campion here," he added with a flash of malice.

Leonie laughed prettily and Mr. Oates's ruffled fur subsided like a wave.

"Sometimes even he can't help us," he went on, encouraged, and, inspired no doubt by the theory that the greater the enemy the greater the honour, launched into an explanation perhaps not altogether discreet. "Sometimes we come up against a man who slips through our fingers every time. There's a man in London to-day who's been responsible for more trouble than I can mention. We know him, we know where he lives, we could put our hands on him any moment of the day or night, but have we any proof against him? Could we hold him for ten minutes without getting into serious trouble for molesting a respectable citizen? Could we? Well, we couldn't."

Miss Peterhouse-Vaughn's expression of mystified interest was very flattering.

"This is incredibly exciting," she said. "Who is he?—or mustn't you tell?"

The Superintendent shook his head.

"Entirely against the regulations," he said regretfully, and then, on seeing her disappointment and feeling, no doubt, that his portentous declaration had fallen a little flat, he relented and made a compromise between his conscience and a latent vanity which

Mr. Campion had never before suspected. "Well, I'll show you this," he conceded. "It's a very curious thing."

With Leonie's fascinated eyes upon him, he opened a drawer in his desk and took out a single sheet torn from a week-old London evening paper. A small advertisement in the Situations Vacant column was ringed with blue pencil. Miss Peterhouse-Vaughn took it eagerly and Mr. Campion got up lazily to read it over her shoulder.

WANTED: *Entertainer suitable for children's party. Good money offered to right man. Apply in person any evening. Widow, 13 Blakenham Gardens, W1.*

Leonie read the lines three times and looked up.

"But it seems quite ordinary," she said.

The Superintendent nodded. "That's what any member of the public would think," he agreed, gracefully keeping all hint of condescension out of his tone. "And it would have escaped our notice too except for one thing, and that's the name and address. You see, the man I was telling you about happens to live at 13 Blakenham Gardens."

"Is his name Widow? How queer!"

"No, miss, it's not." Oates looked uncomfortable, seeing the pitfall too late. "I ought not to be telling you this," he went on severely. "This gentleman—and we've got nothing we can pin on him, remember—is known as 'The Widow' to the criminal classes. That's why this paragraph interested us. As it stands it's an ad for a crook, and the fellow has the impudence to use his own address! Doesn't even hide it under a box number."

Mr. Campion eyed his old friend. He seemed mildly interested.

"Did you send someone along to answer it?" he enquired.

"We did." The Superintendent spoke heavily. "Poor young Billings was kept there singing comic songs for three-quarters of an hour while W— I mean this fellow—watched him without a smile. Then he told him he'd go down better at a police concert."

Miss Peterhouse-Vaughn looked sympathetic.

"What a shame!" she said gravely, and Mr. Campion never admired her more.

"We sent another man," continued the Superintendent, "but when he got there the servant told him the vacancy had been filled. We kept an eye on the place, too, but it wasn't easy. The

whole crescent was a seething mass of would-be child enter-
tainers."

"So you haven't an idea what he's up to?" Mr. Campion seemed
amused.

"Not the faintest," Oates admitted. "We shall in the end,
though; I'll lay my bottom dollar. He was the moving spirit in
that cussed Featherstone case, you know, and we're pretty certain
it was he who slipped through the police net in the Barking business."

Mr. Campion raised his eyebrows. "Blackmail and smuggling?"
he said. "He seems to be a versatile soul, doesn't he?"

"He's up to anything," Oates declared. "Absolutely anything.
I'd give a packet to get my hands on him. But what he wants with
a kids' entertainer—if it is an entertainer he's after—I do not
know."

"Perhaps he just wants to give a children's party?" suggested
Miss Peterhouse-Vaughn and while the policeman was considering this possibility, evidently the one explanation which had not
crossed his mind, she took her leave.

"I must thank you once again, Mr. Oates," she said. "I can't tell
you how terribly, terribly clever I think you are, and how awfully
grateful I am, and how frightfully careful I'll be in future not to
give you any more dreadful trouble."

It was a charming little speech in spite of her catastrophic adjectives and the Superintendent beamed.

"It's been a pleasure, miss," he said.

As Mr. Campion handed her into her mother's Daimler he regarded her coldly.

"A pretty performance," he remarked. "Tell me, what do you
say when a spark of genuine gratitude warms your nasty little
heart? My poor Oates!"

Miss Peterhouse-Vaughn grinned.

"I did do it well, didn't I?" she said complacently. "He's rather
a dear old goat."

Mr. Campion was shocked and said so.

"The Superintendent is a distinguished officer. I always knew
that, of course, but this afternoon I discovered a broad streak
of chivalry in him. In his place I think I might have permitted
myself a few comments on the type of young woman who leaves
a diamond bracelet and an emerald ring in the soap-dish at a pub-

lic restaurant and then goes smiling to Scotland Yard to ask for it back. The wretched man had performed a miracle for you and you call him a dear old goat."

Leonie was young enough to look abashed without losing her charm.

"Oh, but I am grateful," she said. "I think he's wonderful. But not so absolutely brilliant as somebody else."

"That's very nice of you, my child." Mr. Campion prepared to unbend.

"Oh, not you, darling." Leonie squeezed his arm. "I was talking about the other man— The Widow. He's got real nerve, don't you think?—using his own address and making the detective sing and all that. . . . So amusing!"

Her companion looked down at her severely.

"Don't make a hero out of *him*," he said.

"Why not?"

"Because, my dear little hideous, he's a crook. It's only while he remains uncaught that he's faintly interesting. Sooner or later your elderly admirer, the Superintendent, is going to clap him under lock and key and then he'll just be an ordinary convict, who is anything but romantic, believe me."

Miss Peterhouse-Vaughn shook her head.

"He won't get caught," she said. "Or if he does—forgive me, darling—it'll be by someone much cleverer than you or Mr. Oates."

Mr. Campion's professional pride rebelled.

"What'll you bet?"

"Anything you like," said Leonie. "Up to two pounds," she added prudently.

Campion laughed. "The girl's learning caution at last!" he said. "I may hold you to that."

The conversation changed to the charity matinée of the day before, wherein Miss Peterhouse-Vaughn had appeared as Wisdom, and continued its easy course, gravitating naturally to the most important pending event in the Peterhouse-Vaughn family, the christening of Master Brian Desmond Peterhouse-Vaughn, nephew to Leonie, son to her elder brother, Desmond Brian, and godson to Mr. Albert Campion.

It was his new responsibility as a godfather which led Mr. Campion to take part in yet another elegant little ceremony some few days after the christening and nearly three weeks after Leonie's sensational conquest of Superintendent Oates's susceptible heart.

Mr. Campion called to see Mr. Thistledown in Cheese Street, EC, and they went reverently to the cellars together.

Mr. Thistledown was a small man, elderly and dignified. His white hair was inclined to flow a little and his figure was more suited, perhaps, to his vocation than to his name. As head of the small but distinguished firm of Thistledown, Friend and Son, Wine Importers since 1798, he very seldom permitted himself a personal interview with any client under the age of sixty-five, for at that year he openly believed the genus *homo sapiens*, considered solely as a connoisseur of vintage wine, alone attained full maturity.

Mr. Campion, however, was an exception. Mr. Thistledown thought of him as a lad still, but a promising one. He took his client's errand with all the gravity he felt it to deserve.

"Twelve dozen of port to be laid down for Master Brian Desmond Peterhouse-Vaughn," he said, rolling the words round his tongue as though they, too, had their flavour. "Let me see, it is now the end of '36. It will have to be a '27 wine. Then by the time your godson is forty—he won't want to drink it before that age, surely?—there should be a very fine fifty-year-old vintage awaiting him."

A long and somewhat heated discussion, or, rather, monologue, for Mr. Campion was sufficiently experienced to offer no opinion, followed. The relative merits of Croft, Taylor, Da Silva, Noval and Fonseca were considered at length, and in the end Mr. Campion followed his mentor through the sacred tunnels and personally affixed his seal upon a bin of Taylor, 1927.

Mr. Thistledown was in favour of a stipulation to provide that Master Peterhouse-Vaughn should not attain full control over his vinous inheritance until he attained the age of thirty, whereas Mr. Campion preferred the more conventional twenty-one. Finally a compromise of twenty-five was agreed upon and the two gentlemen retired to Mr. Thistledown's consulting-room glowing with the conscious virtue of men who had conferred a benefit upon posterity.

The consulting-room was comfortable. It was really no more than an arbour of bottles constructed in the vault of the largest cellar and was furnished with a table and chairs of solid ship's timber. Mr. Thistledown paused by the table and hesitated before speaking. There was clearly something on his mind and Campion, who had always considered him slightly inhuman, a sort of living port crust, was interested.

When at last the old gentleman unburdened himself it was to make a short speech.

"It takes an elderly man to judge a port or a claret," he said, "but spirits are definitely in another category. Some men may live to be a hundred without ever realizing the subtle differences of the finest rums. To judge a spirit one must be born with a certain kind of palate. Mr. Campion, would you taste a brandy for me?"

His visitor was startled. Always a modest soul, he made no pretensions to connoisseurship and now he said so firmly.

"I don't know." Mr. Thistledown regarded him seriously. "I have watched your taste for some years now and I am inclined to put you down as one of the few really knowledgeable younger men. Wait for me a moment."

He went out, and through the arbour's doorway Campion saw him conferring with the oldest and most cobwebby of the troglodyte persons who lurked about the vaults.

Considerably flattered in spite of himself, he sat back and awaited developments. Presently one of the younger myrmidons, a mere youth of fifty or so, appeared with a tray and a small selection of balloon glasses. He was followed by an elder with two bottles, and at the rear of the procession came Mr. Thistledown himself with something covered by a large silk handkerchief. Not until they were alone did he remove the veil. Then, whipping the handkerchief aside, he produced a partly full half-bottle with a new cork and no label. He held it up to the light and Mr. Campion saw that the liquid within was of the true dark amber.

Still with the ritualistic air, Mr. Thistledown polished a glass and poured a tablespoonful of the spirit, afterwards handing it to his client.

Feeling like a man with his honour at stake, Campion warmed the glass in his hand, sniffed at it intelligently, and finally allowed a little of the stuff to touch his tongue.

Mr. Thistledown watched him earnestly. Campion tasted again and inhaled once more. Finally he set down his glass and grinned.

"I may be wrong," he said, "but it tastes like the real McKay."

Mr. Thistledown frowned at the vulgarism. He seemed satisfied, however, and there was a curious mixture of pleasure and discomfort on his face.

"I put it down as a Champagne Fine, 1835," he said. "It has not, perhaps, quite the superb caress of the true Napoleon—but a brave, yes, a brave brandy! The third best I have ever tasted in my life. And that, let me tell you, Mr. Campion, is a very extraordinary thing."

He paused, looking like some old white cockatoo standing at the end of the table.

"I wonder if I might take you into my confidence?" he ventured at last. "Ah—a great many people do take you into their confidence, I believe? Forgive me for putting it that way."

Campion smiled. "I'm as secret as the grave," he said, "and if there's anything I can do I shall be delighted."

Mr. Thistledown sighed with relief and became almost human.

"This confounded bottle was sent to me some little time ago," he said. "With it was a letter from a man called Gervaise Papulous; I don't suppose you've ever heard of him, but he wrote a very fine monograph on brandies some years ago which was greatly appreciated by connoisseurs. I had an idea he lived a hermit's life somewhere in Scotland, but that's neither here nor there. The fact remains that when I had this note from an address in Half Moon Street I recognized the name immediately. It was a very civil letter, asking me if I'd mind, as an expert, giving my opinion of the age and quality of the sample."

He paused and smiled faintly.

"I was a little flattered, perhaps," he said. "After all, the man is a well-known authority himself. Anyway, I made the usual tests, tasted it and compared it with the oldest and finest stuff we have in stock. We have a few bottles of 1848 and one or two of the 1835. I made the most careful comparisons and at last I decided that the sample was a '35 brandy, but not the same blend as our own. I wrote him; I said I did not care to commit myself, but I gave him my opinion for what it was worth and I appended my reasons for forming it."

Mr. Thistledown's precise voice ceased and his colour heightened.

"By return I received a letter thanking me for mine and asking me whether I would care to consider an arrangement whereby I could buy the identical spirit in any quantity I cared to name at a hundred and twenty shillings a dozen, excluding duty—or, in other words, ten shillings per bottle."

Mr. Campion sat up. "Ten shillings?" he said.

"Ten shillings," repeated Mr. Thistledown. "The price of a wireless licence," he added with contempt. "Well, as you can imagine, Mr. Campion, I thought there must be some mistake. Our own '35 is listed at sixty shillings a bottle and you cannot get finer value anywhere in London. The stuff is rare. In a year or two it will be priceless. I considered this sample again and reaffirmed my own first opinion. Then I re-read the letter and noticed the peculiar phrase—'an arrangement whereby you will be able to purchase.' I thought about it all day and finally I put on my hat and went down to see the man."

He glanced at his visitor almost timidly. Campion was reassuring.

"If it was genuine it was not a chance to be missed," he murmured.

"Exactly." Mr. Thistledown smiled. "Well, I saw him, a younger man than I had imagined but well informed, and I received quite a pleasant impression. I asked him frankly where he got the brandy and he came out with an extraordinary suggestion. He asked me first if I was satisfied with the sample, and I said I was or I should hardly have come to see him. Then he said the whole matter was a secret at the moment, but that he was asking certain well-informed persons to a private conference and something he called a scientific experiment. Finally he offered me an invitation. It is to take place next Monday evening in a little hotel on the Norfolk coast where Mr. Papulous says the ideal conditions for his experiment exist."

Mr. Campion's interest was thoroughly aroused.

"I should go," he said.

Mr. Thistledown spread out his hands.

"I had thought of it," he admitted. "As I came out of the flat at Half Moon Street I passed a man I knew on the stairs. I won't mention his name and I won't say his firm is exactly a rival of ours, but—well, you know how it is. Two or three old firms get the reputation for supplying certain rare vintages. Their names are equally good and naturally there is a certain competition between them. If this fellow has happened on a whole cellar full of this brandy I should like to have as good a chance of buying it as the next man, especially at the price. But in my opinion and in my experience that is too much to hope for, and that is why I have ventured to mention the matter to you."

A light dawned upon his client.

"You want me to attend the conference and make certain everything's above-board?"

"I hardly dared to suggest it," he said, "but since you are such an excellent judge, and since your reputation as an investigator—if I may be forgiven the term—is so great, I admit the thought did go through my mind."

Campion picked up his glass and sniffed its fragrance.

"My dear man, I'd jump at it," he said. "Do I pass myself off as a member of the firm?"

Mr. Thistledown looked owlish.

"In the circumstances I think we might connive at that little inexactitude," he murmured. "Don't you?"

"I think we'll have to," said Mr. Campion.

When he saw the "little hotel on the Norfolk coast" at half-past six on the following Monday afternoon the thought came to him that it was extremely fortunate for the proprietor that it should be so suitable for Mr. Papulous's experiment, for it was certainly not designed to be of much interest to any ordinary winter visitor. It was a large country public-house, not old enough to be picturesque, standing by itself at the end of a lane some little distance from a cold and sleepy village. In the summer, no doubt, it provided a headquarters for a great many picnic parties, but in winter it was deserted.

Inside it was warm and comfortable enough, however, and Campion found a curious little company seated round the fire in the lounge. His host rose to greet him and he was aware at once of a considerable personality.

He saw a tall man with a shy ingratiating manner, whose clothes were elegant and whose face was remarkable. His deep-set eyes were dark and intelligent and his wide mouth could smile disarmingly, but the feature which was most distinctive was the way in which his iron-grey hair drew into a clean-cut peak in the centre of his high forehead, giving him an odd, Mephistophelean appearance.

"Mr. Fellowes?" he said, using the alias Campion and Mr. Thistledown had agreed upon. "I heard from your firm this morning.
Of course I'm very sorry not to have Mr. Thistledown here. He
says in his note that I am to regard you as his second self. You
handle the French side, I understand?"

"Yes. It was only by chance that I was in England yesterday
when Mr. Thistledown asked me to come."

"I see." Mr. Papulous seemed contented with the explanation.
Campion looked a mild, inoffensive young man, even a little
foolish.

He was introduced to the rest of the company round the fire
and was interested to see that Mr. Thistledown had been right in
his guess. Half a dozen of the best-known smaller and older wine
firms were represented, in most cases by their senior partners.

Conversation, however, was not as general as might have been
expected among men of such similar interests. On the contrary,
there was a distinct atmosphere of restraint, and it occurred to
Mr. Campion that they were all close rivals and each man had not
expected to see the others.

Mr. Papulous alone seemed happily unconscious of any discomfort. He stood behind his chair at the head of the group and
glanced round him with satisfaction.

"It's really very kind of you all to have come," he said in his
deep musical voice. "Very kind indeed. I felt we must have experts, the finest experts in the world, to test this thing, because it's
revolutionary—absolutely revolutionary."

A large old gentleman with a hint of superciliousness in his
manner glanced up.

"When are we going to come to the horses, Mr. Papulous?"

His host turned to him with a deprecatory smile.

"Not until after dinner, I'm afraid, Mr. Jerome. I'm sorry to
seem so secretive, but the whole nature of the discovery is so
extraordinary that I want you to see the demonstration with your
own eyes."

Mr. Jerome, whose name Campion recognized as belonging to
the moving spirit of Bolitho Brothers, of St. Mary Axe, seemed
only partly mollified. He laughed.

"Is it the salubrious air of this particular hotel that you need
for your experiment, may I ask?" he enquired.

"Oh no, my dear sir. It's the stillness." Mr. Papulous appeared to be completely oblivious of any suggestion of a sneer. "It's the utter quiet. At night, round about ten o'clock, there is a lack of vibration here, so complete that you can almost feel it, if I may use such a contradiction in terms. Now, Mr. Fellowes, dinner's at seven-thirty. Perhaps you'd care to see your room?"

Campion was puzzled. As he changed for the meal—a gesture which seemed to be expected of him—he surveyed the situation with growing curiosity. Papulous was no ordinary customer. He managed to convey an air of conspiracy and mystery while appearing himself as open and simple as the day. Whatever he was up to, he was certainly a good salesman.

The dinner was simple and well cooked and was served by Papulous's own man. There was no alcohol and the dishes were not highly seasoned, out of deference, their host explained, to the test that was to be put to their palates later on.

When it was over and the mahogany had been cleared of dessert, a glass of clear water was set before each guest and from the head of the table Mr. Papulous addressed his guests. He made a very distinguished figure, leaning forward across the polished wood, the candle-light flickering on his deeply lined face and high heart-shaped forehead.

"First of all let me recapitulate," he said. "You all know my name and you have all been kind enough to say that you have read my little book. I mention this because I want you to realize that by asking you down here to witness a most extraordinary demonstration I am taking my reputation in my hands. Having made that point, let me remind you that you have, each of you, with the single exception of Mr. Fellowes, been kind enough to give me your considered views on a sample of brandy which I sent you. In every case, I need hardly mention, opinion was the same—a Champagne Fine of 1835."

A murmur of satisfaction not untinged with relief ran round the table and Mr. Papulous smiled.

"Well," he said, "frankly that would have been my own opinion had I not known—mark you, I say 'known'—that the brandy I sent you was a raw cognac of nearly a hundred years later—to be exact, of 1932."

There was a moment of bewilderment, followed by an explosion from Mr. Jerome.

"I hope you're not trying to make fools of us, sir," he said severely. "I'm not going to sit here, and—"

"One moment, one moment." Papulous spoke soothingly. "You really must forgive me. I know you all too well by repute to dare to make such a statement without following it immediately by the explanation to which you are entitled. As you're all aware, the doctoring of brandy is an old game. Such dreadful additions as vanilla and burnt sugar have all been used in their time and will, no doubt, be used again, but such crude deceptions are instantly detected by the cultured palate. This is something different."

Mr. Jerome began to seethe.

"Are you trying to interest us in a fake, sir?" he demanded. "Because, if so, let me tell you I, for one, am not interested."

There was a chorus of hasty assent in which Mr. Campion virtuously joined.

Gervaise Papulous smiled faintly.

"But of course not," he said. "We are all experts. The true expert knows that no fake can be successful, even should we so far forget ourselves as to countenance its existence. I am bringing you a discovery—not a trick, not a clever fraud, but a genuine discovery which may revolutionize the whole market. As you know, time is the principal factor in the maturing of spirits. Until now time has been the one factor which could not be artificially replaced. An old brandy, therefore, is quite a different thing from a new one."

Mr. Campion blinked. A light was beginning to dawn upon him.

Mr. Papulous continued. There seemed to be no stopping him. At the risk of boring his audience he displayed a great knowledge of technical detail and went through the life history of an old liqueur brandy from the time it was an unripe grapeskin on a vine outside Cognac.

When he had finished he paused dramatically, adding softly:

"What I hope to introduce to you to-night, gentlemen, is the latest discovery of science, a method of speeding up this long and wearisome process so that the whole business of maturing the spirit takes place in a few minutes instead of a hundred years. You have all examined the first-fruits of this method already and have been interested enough to come down here. Shall we go on?"

The effect of his announcement was naturally considerable. Everybody began to talk at once save Mr. Campion, who sat

silent and thoughtful. It occurred to him that his temporary colleagues were not only interested in making a great deal of money
but very much alarmed at the prospect of losing a considerable
quantity also.

"If it's true it'll upset the whole damned trade," murmured his
next-door neighbour, a little thin man with wispy straw-coloured
hair.

Papulous rose. "In the next room the inventor, M. Philippe
Jessant, is waiting to demonstrate," he said. "He began work on
the idea during the period of prohibition in America and his researches were assisted there by one of the richest men in the
world, but when the country was restored to sanity his patron
lost interest in the work and he was left to perfect it unassisted.
You will find him a simple, uneducated, unbusiness-like man, like
many inventors. He came to me for help because he had read
my little book and I am doing what I can for him by introducing
him to you. Conditions are now ideal. The house is perfectly still.
Will you come with me?"

The sceptical but excited little company filed into the large
"commercial" room on the other side of the passage. The place
had been stripped of furniture save for a half-circle of chairs and
a large deal table. On the table was a curious contraption, vaguely
resembling two or three of those complicated coffee percolators
which seemed to be designed solely for the wedding-present
trade.

An excitable little man in a long brown overall was standing
behind the table. If not an impressive figure, he was certainly an
odd one, with his longish hair and gold-rimmed pince-nez.

"Quiet, please. I must beg of you quiet," he commanded, holding up his hand as they appeared. "We must have no vibration,
no vibration at all, if I am to succeed."

He had a harsh voice and a curious foreign accent, which
Campion could not instantly trace, but his manner was authoritative and the experts tiptoed gently to their seats.

"Now," said M. Jessant, his small eyes flashing, "I leave all
explanations to my friend here. For me, I am only interested in
the demonstration. You understand?"

He glared at them and Papulous hastened to explain.

"M. Jessant does not mean the human voice, of course," he
murmured. "It is vibration, sudden movement, of which he is
afraid."

"Quiet," cut in the inventor impatiently. "When a spirit matures in the ordinary way what does it have?—quiet, darkness, peace. These conditions are essential. Now we will begin, if you please."

It was a simple business. A clear-glass decanter of brandy was produced and duly smelt and sampled by each guest. Papulous himself handed round the glasses and poured the liquid. By unanimous consent it was voted a raw spirit. The years 1932 and 1934 were both mentioned.

Then the same decanter was emptied into the contraption on the table and its progress watched through a system of glass tubes and a filter into a large retort-shaped vessel at the foot of the apparatus.

M. Jessant looked up.

"Now," he said softly. "You will come, one at a time, please, and examine my invention. Walk softly."

The inspection was made and the man in the brown overall covered the retort with a hood composed of something that looked like black rubber. For a while he busied himself with thermometers and a little electric battery.

"It is going on now," he explained, suppressed excitement in his voice. "Every second roughly corresponds to a year—a long, dark, dismal year. Now—we shall see."

The hood was removed, fresh glasses were brought, and the retort itself carefully detached from the rest of the apparatus.

Mr. Jerome was the first to examine the liquid it contained and his expression was ludicrous in its astonishment.

"It's incredible!" he said at last. "Incredible! I can't believe it. ... There are certain tests I should like to make, of course, but I could swear this is an 1835 brandy."

The others were of the same opinion and even Mr. Campion was impressed. The inventor was persuaded to do his experiment again. To do him justice he complied willingly.

"It is the only disadvantage," he said. "So little can be treated at the one time. I tell my friend I should like to make my invention foolproof and sell the machines and the instructions to the public, but he tells me no."

"No indeed!" ejaculated Mr. Campion's neighbour. "Good heavens! it would knock the bottom out of half my trade. . . ."

When at last the gathering broke up in excitement it was after midnight. Mr. Papulous addressed his guests.

"It is late," he said. "Let us go to bed now and consider the whole matter in the morning when M. Jessant can explain the theory of his process. Meanwhile, I am sure you will agree with me that we all have something to think about."

A somewhat subdued company trooped off upstairs. There was little conversation. A man does not discuss a revolutionary discovery with his nearest rival.

Campion came down in the morning to find Mr. Jerome already up. He was pacing the lounge and turned on the young man almost angrily.

"I like to get up at six," he said without preamble, "but there were no servants in the place. A woman, her husband and a maid came along at seven. It seems Papulous made them sleep out. Afraid of vibration, I suppose. Well, it's an extraordinary discovery, isn't it? If I hadn't seen it with my own eyes I should never have believed it. I suppose one's got to be prepared for progress, but I can't say I like it. Never did."

He lowered his voice and came closer.

"We shall have to get together and suppress it, you know," he said. "Only thing to do. We can't have a thing like this blurted out to the public and we can't have any single firm owning the secret. Anyway, that's my opinion."

Campion murmured that he did not care to express his own without first consulting Mr. Thistledown.

"Quite, quite. There'll be a good many conferences in the City this afternoon," said Mr. Jerome gloomily. "And that's another thing. D'you know there isn't a telephone in this confounded pub?"

Campion's eyes narrowed.

"Is that so?" he said softly. "That's very interesting."

Mr. Jerome shot him a suspicious glance.

"In my opinion . . . ," he began heavily, but got no further. The door was thrust open and the small wispy-haired man, who had been Campion's neighbour at dinner, came bursting into the room.

"I say," he said, "a frightful thing! The little inventor chap has been attacked in the night. His machine is smashed and the plans and formula are stolen. Poor old Papulous is nearly off his head."

Both Campion and Jerome started for the doorway and a moment later joined the startled group on the landing. Gervaise

Papulous, an impressive figure in a long black dressing-gown, was standing with his back to the inventor's door.

"This is terrible, terrible!" he was saying. "I beseech you all, go downstairs and wait until I see what is best to be done. My poor friend has only just regained consciousness."

Jerome pushed his way through the group.

"But this is outrageous," he began.

Papulous towered over him, his eyes dark and angry.

"It is just as you say, outrageous," he said, and Mr. Jerome quailed before the suppressed fury in his voice.

"Look here," he began, "you surely don't think ... you're not insinuating. . . ."

"I am only thinking of my poor friend," said Mr. Papulous.

Campion went quietly downstairs.

"What on earth does this mean?" demanded the small wispy-haired gentleman, who had remained in the lounge.

Campion grinned. "I rather fancy we shall all find that out pretty clearly in about an hour," he said.

He was right. Mr. Gervaise Papulous put the whole matter to them in the bluntest possible way as they sat dejectedly looking at the remains of what had proved a very unsatisfactory breakfast.

M. Jessant, his head in bandages and his face pale with exhaustion, had told a heart-breaking story. He had awakened to find a pad of chloroform across his mouth and nose. It was dark and he could not see his assailant, who also struck him repeatedly. His efforts to give the alarm were futile and in the end the anaesthetic had overpowered him.

When at last he had come to himself his apparatus had been smashed and his precious black pocket-book, which held his calculations and which he always kept under his pillow, had gone.

At this point he had broken down completely and had been led away by Papulous's man. Mr. Gervaise Papulous then took the floor. He looked pale and nervous and there was an underlying suggestion of righteous anger and indignation in his manner which was very impressive.

"I won't waste time by telling you how appalled I am by this monstrous attack," he began, his fine voice trembling. "I can only tell you the facts. We were alone in this house last night. Even my own man slept out in the village. I arranged this to ensure ideal conditions for the experiment. The landlady reports that the doors were locked this morning and the house had not been entered from the outside. Now you see what this means? Until last night only the inventor and I knew of the existence of a secret which is of such great importance to all of you here. Last night we told you, we took you into our confidence, and now ..." he shrugged his shoulders. "Well, we have been robbed and my friend assaulted. Need I say more?"

An excited babble of protest arose and Mr. Jerome seemed in danger of apoplexy. Papulous remained calm and a little contemptuous.

"There is only one thing to do," he said, "but I hesitated before calling in the police, because, of course, only one of you can be guilty and the secret must still be in the house, whereas I know the publicity which cannot be avoided will be detrimental to you all. And not only to yourselves personally, but to the firms you represent."

He paused and frowned.

"The Press is so ignorant," he said. "I am so afraid you may all be represented as having come here to see some sort of faking process—new brandy into old. It doesn't sound convincing, does it?"

His announcement burst like a bomb in the quiet room. Mr. Jerome sat very still, his mouth partly open. Somebody began to speak, but thought better of it. A long unhappy silence supervened.

Gervaise Papulous cleared his throat.

"I am sorry," he said. "I must either have my friend's note-book back and full compensation, or I must send for the police. What else can I do?"

Mr. Jerome pulled himself together.

"Wait," he said in a smothered voice. "Before you do anything rash we must have a conference. I've been thinking over this discovery of yours, Mr. Papulous, and in my opinion it raises very serious considerations for the whole trade."

There was a murmur of agreement in the room and he went on.

"The one thing none of us can afford is publicity. In the first place, even if the thing becomes generally known it certainly won't become generally believed. The public doesn't rely on its palate; it relies on our labels, and that puts us in a very awkward position. This final development precipitates everything. We must clear up this mystery in private and then decide what is best to be done."

There was a vigorous chorus of assent, but Mr. Papulous shook his head.

"I'm afraid I can't agree," he said coldly. "In the ordinary way M. Jessant and I would have been glad to meet you in any way, but this outrage alters everything. I insist on a public examination unless, of course," he added deliberately, "unless you care to take the whole matter out of our hands."

"What do you mean?" Mr. Jerome's voice was faint.

The tall man with the deeply lined face regarded him steadily.

"Unless you care to club together and buy us out," said Mr. Papulous. "Then you can settle the matter as you like. The sum M. Jessant had in mind was fifteen thousand pounds, a very reasonable price for such a secret."

There was silence after he had spoken.

"Blackmail," said Mr. Campion under his breath and at the same moment his glance lighted on Mr. Papulous's most outstanding feature. His eyebrows rose and an expression of incredulity, followed by amazement, passed over his face. Then he kicked himself gently under the breakfast table. He rose.

"I must send a wire to my principal," he said. "You'll understand I'm in an impossible position and must get in touch with Mr. Thistledown at once."

Papulous regarded him.

"If you will write your message my man will despatch it from the village," he said politely and there was no mistaking the implied threat.

Campion understood he was not to be allowed to make any private communication with the outside world. He looked blank.

"Thank you," he said and took out a pencil and a loose-leaf note-book.

"Unexpected development," he wrote. "Come down immediately. Inform Charlie and George cannot lunch Tuesday. A. C. Fellowes."

Papulous took the message, read it and went out with it, leaving a horrified group behind him.

Mr. Thistledown received Mr. Campion's wire at eleven o'clock and read it carefully. The signature particularly interested him.

Shutting himself in his private room, he rang up Scotland Yard and was fortunate in discovering Superintendent Oates at his desk. He dictated the wire carefully and added with a depreciatory cough:

"Mr. Campion told me to send on to you any message from him signed with his own initials. I don't know if you can make much of this. It seems very ordinary to me."

"Leave all that to us, sir." Oates sounded cheerful. "Where is he, by the way?"

Mr. Thistledown gave the address and hung up the receiver. At the other end of the wire the superintendent unlocked a drawer in his desk and took out a small red manuscript book. Each page was ruled with double columns and filled with Mr. Campion's own elegant handwriting. Oates ran a forefinger down the left-hand column on the third page.

"Carrie . . . Catherine . . . Charles. . . ."

His eye ran across the page.

"Someone you want," he read and looked on down the list.

The legend against the word "George" was brief. "Two," it said simply.

Oates turned to the back of the book. There were several messages under the useful word "lunch." "Come to lunch" meant "Send two men." "Lunch with me" was translated "Send men armed," and "Cannot lunch" was "Come yourself."

"Tuesday" was on another page. The superintendent did not trouble to look it up. He knew its meaning. It was "hurry."

He wrote the whole message out on a pad.

"Unexpected developments. Come down immediately. Someone you want (two). Come yourself. Hurry. Campion."

He sighed. "Energetic chap," he commented and pressed a bell for Sergeant Bloom.

As it happened, it was Mr. Gervaise Papulous himself who caught the first glimpse of the police car which pulled up outside the lonely little hotel. He was standing by the window in an upper room whose floor was so flimsily constructed that he could listen with ease to the discussion taking place in the lounge below. There the unfortunate experts were still arguing. The only point on which they all agreed was the absolute necessity of avoiding a scandal.

As the car stopped and the superintendent sprang out and

made for the door Papulous caught a glimpse of his official-looking figure. He swung round savagely to the forlorn little figure who sat hunched up on the bed.

"You peached, damn you!" he whispered.

"Me?" The man who had been calling himself "Jessant" sat up in indignation. "Me peach?" he repeated, his foreign accent fading into honest South London. "Don't be silly. And you pay up, my lad. I'm fed up with this. First I do me stuff, then you chloroform me, then you bandage me, then you keep me shut up 'ere, and now you accuse me of splitting. What you playing at?"

"You're lying, you little rat." Papulous's voice was dangerously soft and he strode swiftly across the room towards the man on the bed, who shrank back in sudden alarm.

"Here—that'll do, that'll do. What's going on here?"

It was Oates who spoke. Followed by Campion and the sergeant he strode across the room.

"Let the fellow go," he commanded. "Good heavens, man, you're choking him."

Doubling his fist, he brought it up under the other man's wrists with a blow which not only loosed their hold but sent their owner staggering back across the room.

The man on the bed let out a howl and stumbled towards the door into the waiting arms of Sergeant Bloom, but Oates did not notice. His eyes were fixed upon the face of the tall man on the other side of the room.

"The Widow!" he ejaculated. "Well I'll be damned!"

The other smiled.

"More than probably, my dear Inspector. Or have they promoted you?" he said. "But at the moment I'm afraid you're trespassing."

The superintendent glanced enquiringly at the mild and elegant figure at his side.

"False pretences is the charge," murmured Mr. Campion affably. "There are certain rather unpleasant traces of blackmail in the matter, but false pretences will do. There are six witnesses and myself."

The man whose alias was The Widow stared at his accuser.

"Who are you?" he demanded, and then, as the answer dawned upon him, he swore softly. "Campion," he said. "Albert Campion ... I ought to have recognized you from your description."

Campion grinned. "That's where I had the advantage of you," he said.

Mr. Campion and the superintendent drove back to London together, leaving a very relieved company of experts to travel home in their own ways. Oates was jubilant.

"Got him," he said. "Got him at last. And a clear case. A pretty little swindle, too. Just like him. If you hadn't been there all those poor devils would have paid up something. They're the kind of people he goes for, folk whose business depends on their absolute integrity. They all represent small firms, you see, with old, conservative clients. When did you realize that he wasn't the real Gervaise Papulous?"

"As soon as I saw him I thought it unlikely." Campion grinned as he spoke. "Before I left town I rang up the publishers of the Papulous monograph. They had lost sight of him, they said, but from their publicity department I learned that Papulous was born in '72. So as soon as I saw our friend The Widow I realized that he was a good deal younger than the real man. However, like a fool I didn't get on to the swindle until this morning. It was when he was putting on that brilliant final act of his. I suddenly recognized him and, of course, the whole thing came to me in a flash."

"Recognized him?" Oates looked blank. "I never described him to you."

Mr. Campion looked modest. "Do you remember showing off to a very pretty girl I brought up to your office, and so far forgetting yourself as to produce an advertisement from an evening paper?" he enquired.

"I remember the ad," Oates said doggedly. "The fellow advertised for a kids' entertainer. But I don't remember him including a photograph of himself."

"He printed his name," Campion persisted. "It's a funny nickname. The significance didn't occur to me until I looked at him this morning, knowing that he was a crook. I realized that he was tricking us, but I couldn't see how. Then his face gave him away."

"His face?"

"My dear fellow, you haven't spotted it yet. I'm glad of that. It didn't come to me for a bit. Consider that face. How do crooks get their names? How did Beaky Doyle get his name? Why was

Cauliflower Edwards so called? Think of his forehead, man. Think of his hair."

"Peak," said the superintendent suddenly. "Of course, a widow's peak! Funny I didn't think of that before. It's obvious when it comes to you. But even so," he added more seriously, "I wonder you cared to risk sending for me on that alone. Plenty of people have a widow's peak. You'd have looked silly if he'd been on the level."

"Oh, but I had the advertisement as well," Campion objected. "Taken in conjunction, the two things are obvious. That demonstration last night was masterly. Young brandy went in at one end of the apparatus and old brandy came out at the other, and we saw, or thought we saw, the spirit the whole time. There was only one type of man who could have done it—a children's party entertainer."

Oates shook his head.

"I'm only a poor demented policeman," he said derisively. "My mind doesn't work. I'll buy it."

Campion turned to him. "My good Oates, have you ever been to a children's party?"

"No."

"Well, you've been a child, I suppose?"

"I seem to remember something like that."

"Well, when you were a child what entertained you? Singing? Dancing? *The Wreck of the Hesperus?* No, my dear friend, there's only one kind of performer who goes down well with children and that is a member of the brotherhood of which Jessant is hardly an ornament. A magician, Oates. In other words, a conjurer. And a damned good trick he showed us all last night!"

He trod on the accelerator and the car rushed on again.

The superintendent sat silent for a long time. Then he glanced up.

"That *was* a pretty girl," he said. "Nice manners, too."

"Leonie?" Campion nodded. "That reminds me, I must phone her when we get back to town."

"Oh?" The superintendent was interested. "Nothing I can do for you, I suppose?" he enquired archly.

Campion smiled. "Hardly," he said. "I want to tell her she owes me two pounds."

The Wine Glass

A. A. MILNE

*Alan Alexander Milne (1882–1956) transmuted a small bear
into one of the world's most beloved animals. Winnie has
even been successfully re-incarnated* (Winnie Ille Pu) *in
classical (more or less) Latin. Humorist, playwright, and the
most popular writer for children in the century's second
quarter, Milne also authored a brilliant masterpiece of detection,* The Red House Mystery *(1921). His feeling for original plot comes to the fore in this miniature gem of sleuthery.
It starts with a bottle of Tokay modified by prussic acid and
concludes with a bombshell of a surprise ending.*

I AM in a terrible predicament, as you will see directly. I don't
know what to do. . . .

"One of the maxims which I have found most helpful in my
career at Scotland Yard," the superintendent was saying, "has
been the simple one that appearances are not always deceptive. A
crime may be committed exactly as it seems to have been committed and exactly as it was intended to be committed." He
helped himself and passed the bottle.

"I don't think I follow you," I said, hoping thus to lead him on.

I am a writer of detective stories. If you have never heard of
me, it can only be because you don't read detective stories. I
wrote "Murder on the Back Stairs" and "The Mystery of the
Twisted Eglantine," to mention only two of my successes. It was
this fact, I think, which first interested Superintendent Frederick
Mortimer in me, and, of course, me in him. He is a big fellow
with the face of a Roman Emperor; I am the small neat type. We
gradually became friends and so got into the habit of dining together once a month. He liked talking about his cases, and natu-

rally I liked listening. But this evening the wine seemed to be making itself felt.

"I don't think I follow you," I said again.

"I mean that the simple way of committing a murder is often the best way. This doesn't mean that the murderer is a man of simple mind. On the contrary. He is subtle enough to know that the simple solution is too simple to be credible."

This sounded anything but simple, so I said, "Give me an example."

"Well, take the case of the bottle of wine which was sent to the Marquis of Hedingham on his birthday. Have I never told you about it?"

"Never," I said, and I helped myself and passed the bottle.

He filled his glass and considered. "Give me a moment to get it clear," he said. "It was a long time ago." While he closed his eyes and let the past drift before him, I ordered up another bottle of the same.

"Yes," said Mortimer, opening his eyes. "I've got it now."

I leaned forward, listening eagerly. This is the story he told me.

The first we heard of it at the Yard (said Mortimer) was a brief announcement over the telephone that the Marquis of Hedingham's butler had died suddenly at His Lordship's town house in Brook Street, and that poison was suspected. This was at seven o'clock. We went around at once. Inspector Totman had been put in charge of the case; I was a young detective sergeant at the time, and I generally worked under Totman. He was a brisk, military sort of fellow, with a little prickly ginger mustache, good at his job in a showy, orthodox way, but he had no imagination, and he was thinking all the time of what Inspector Totman would get out of it. Quite frankly I didn't like him. Outwardly we kept friendly, for it doesn't do to quarrel with one's superiors; indeed, he was vain enough to think that I had a great admiration for him; but I knew that he was just using me for his own advantage, and I had a shrewd suspicion that I should have been promoted before this, if he hadn't wanted to keep me under him so that he could profit by my brains.

We found the butler in his pantry, stretched out on the floor. An open bottle of Tokay, a broken wine glass with the dregs of the liquid still in it, the medical evidence of poisoning, all helped to build up the story for us. The wine had arrived about an hour before, with the card of Sir William Kelso attached to it. On the card was a typewritten message, saying, "Bless you, Tommy, and here's something to celebrate with." I can't remember the exact words, of course, but that was the idea. Apparently it was His Lordship's birthday, and he was having a small family party of about six people for the occasion. Sir William Kelso, I should explain, was his oldest friend and a relation by marriage, Lord Hedingham having married his sister; in fact, Sir William was to have been one of the party present that evening. He was a bachelor, about fifty, and a devoted uncle to his nephew and nieces.

Well, the butler had brought up the bottle and the card to His Lordship—this was about six o'clock; and Lord Hedingham, as he told us, had taken the card, said something like, "Good old Bill. We'll have that tonight, Perkins," and Perkins had said, "Very good, My Lord," and gone out again with the bottle. The card had been left lying on the table. Afterwards, there could be little doubt what had happened. Perkins had opened the bottle with the intention of decanting it but had been unable to resist the temptation to sample it first. I suspect that in his time he had sampled most of His Lordship's wine but had never before come across a Tokay of such richness. So he had poured himself out a full glass, drunk it, and died almost immediately.

"Good heavens!" I interrupted. "But how extremely providential—I mean, of course, for Lord Hedingham and the others."

"Exactly," said Mortimer, as he twirled his own wine glass.

The contents of the bottle were analyzed (he went on) and found to contain a more-than-fatal dose of prussic acid. Of course we did all the routine things. With young Roberts, a nice young fellow who often worked with us, I went around to all the chemists' shops in the neighborhood. Totman examined everybody from Sir William and Lord Hedingham downwards.

Roberts and I took the bottle around to all the wine merchants in the neighborhood. At the end of a week all we could say was this:

One: The murderer had a motive for murdering Lord Hedingham; or, possibly, somebody at his party; or, possibly, the whole party. In accordance with the usual custom, His Lordship would be the first to taste the wine. A sip would not be fatal, and in a wine of such richness the taste might not be noticeable; so that the whole party would then presumably drink His Lordship's health. He would raise his glass to them, and in this way they would all take the poison, and be affected according to how deeply they drank. On the other hand, His Lordship might take a good deal more than a sip in the first place, and so be the only one to suffer. My deduction from this was that the motive was revenge rather than gain. The criminal would avenge himself on Lord Hedingham if His Lordship or *any* of his family were seriously poisoned; he could only profit if *definite* people were definitely *killed*. It took a little time to get Totman to see this, but he did eventually agree.

Two: The murderer had been able to obtain one of Sir William Kelso's cards, and knew that John Richard Mervyn Plantaganet Carlow, tenth Marquis of Hedingham, was called "Tommy" by his intimates. Totman deduced from this that he was therefore one of the Hedingham-Kelso circle of relations and friends. I disputed this. I pointed out: (a) that it was to strangers rather than to intimate friends that cards were presented, except in the case of formal calls, when they were left in a bowl or tray in the hall, and anybody could steal one; (b) that the fact that Lord Hedingham was called Tommy must have appeared in society papers and be known to many people; and, most convincing of all, (c) that the murderer did *not* know that Sir William Kelso was to be in the party that night. For obviously some reference would have been made to the gift, either on his arrival or when the wine was served; whereupon he would have disclaimed any knowledge of it, and the bottle would immediately have been suspected. As it was, of course, Perkins had drunk from it before Sir William's arrival. Now both Sir William and Lord Hedingham assured us that they *always* dined together on each other's birthday, and they were convinced that any personal friend of theirs would have been aware of the fact. I made Totman question them about this, and he then came round to my opinion.

Three: There was nothing to prove that the wine in the bottle corresponded to the label; and wine experts were naturally reluctant to taste it for us. All they could say from the smell was that it was a Tokay of sorts. This, of course, made it more difficult for us. In fact I may say that neither from the purchase of the wine nor the nature of the poison did we get any clue.

We had, then, the following picture of the murderer. He had

a cause of grievance, legitimate or fancied, against Lord Hedingham, and did not scruple to take the most terrible revenge. He
knew that Sir William Kelso was a friend of His Lordship and
called him Tommy, and that he might reasonably give him a bottle of wine on his birthday. He did *not* know that Sir William
would be dining there that night; that is to say, *even as late as six
o'clock that evening, he did not know.* He was not likely, therefore, to be anyone at present employed or living in Lord Hedingham's house. Finally, he had had an opportunity to get hold of a
card of Sir William's.

As it happened, there was somebody who fitted completely
into this picture. It was a fellow called—wait a bit—Merrivale,
Medley—oh, well, it doesn't matter. Merton, that was it. Merton.
He had been His Lordship's valet for six months, had been suspected of stealing and had been dismissed without a character
reference. Just the man we wanted. So for a fortnight we
searched for Merton. And then, when at last we got on to him,
we discovered that he had the most complete alibi imaginable.
(*The superintendent held up his hand, and it came into my mind
that he must have stopped the traffic as a young man with just
that gesture.*) Yes, I know what you're going to say, what you
detective-story writers always say—the better an alibi, the worse
it is. Well, sometimes, I admit; but not in this case. For Merton
was in jail, under another name, and he had been inside for the
last two months. And what do you think he was suspected of, and
was waiting trial for? Oh, well, of course you guess; I've as good
as told you. He was on a charge of murder—and murder, mark
you, by poison.

"Good heavens!" I interjected. I seized the opportunity to refill
my friend's glass. He said, "Exactly," and took a long drink.

You can imagine (he went on) what a shock this was to us.
You see, a certain sort of murder had been committed; we had
deduced that it was done by a certain man, without knowing
whether he was in the least capable of such a crime; and now,
having proved to the hilt that he *was* capable of it, we had simul-
taneously proved that he didn't do it.

I said to Totman, "Let's take a couple of days off, and each of
us think it out, then pool our ideas and start afresh."

Totman frisked up his little mustache and laughed in his con-
ceited way. "You don't think I'm going to admit myself wrong,

do you, when I've just proved I'm right?" (Totman saying "I," when he had got everything from me!) "Merton's my man. He'd got the bottle ready, and somebody else delivered it for him. That's all. He had to wait for the birthday, you see, and when he found himself in prison, his wife or somebody—"

"—took round the bottle, all nicely labeled 'Poison; not to be delivered till Christmas Day.'" I had to say it, I was so annoyed with him.

"Don't be more of a damned fool than you can help," he shouted, "and don't be insolent, or you'll get into trouble."

I apologized humbly and told him how much I liked working with him. He forgave me, and we were friends again. He patted me on the shoulder.

"You take a day off," he said kindly, "you've been working too hard. Take a bus into the country and make up a good story for me; the story of that bottle, and how it came from Merton's lodging to Brook Street, and who took it and why. I admit I don't see it at present, but that's the bottle, you can bet your life. I'm going down to Leatherhead. Report here on Friday morning, and we'll see what we've got. My birthday as it happens, and I feel I'm going to be lucky." Leatherhead was where an old woman had been poisoned. That was the third time in a week he'd told me when his wretched birthday was.

I took a bus to Hampstead Heath. I walked round the Leg of Mutton Pond twenty times. And each time that I went round, Totman's theory seemed sillier than the last time. And each time I felt more and more strongly that we were being *forced* into an entirely artificial interpretation of things. It sounds fantastic, I know, but I could almost feel the murderer behind us, pushing us along the way he wanted us to go.

I sat down on a seat and filled a pipe, and I said, "Right! The murderer's a man who wanted me to believe all that I have believed. When I've told myself that the murderer intended to do so-and-so, he intended me to believe that, and therefore he didn't do so-and-so. When I've told myself that the murderer wanted to mislead me, he wanted me to think he wanted to mislead me, which meant that the truth was exactly as it seemed to be. Now then, Fred, you'll begin all over again, and you'll take things as they are and won't be too clever about them. Because the murderer expects you to be clever, and wants you to be clever, and from now on you aren't going to take your orders from *him*."

And of course, the first thing which leaped to my mind was that the murderer *meant* to murder the butler!

It seemed incredible now that we could ever have missed it. Didn't every butler sample his master's wines? Why, it was an absolute certainty that Perkins would be the first victim of a poisoned bottle of a very special vintage. What butler could resist pouring himself out a glass as he decanted it?

Wait, though. Mustn't be in a hurry. Two objections. One: Perkins might be the one butler in a thousand who wasn't a wine-sampler. Two: Even if he were like any other butler, he might be out of sorts on that particular evening and have put by a glass to drink later. Wouldn't it be much too risky for a murderer who only wanted to destroy Perkins, and had no grudge against Lord Hedingham's family, to depend so absolutely on the butler drinking first?

For a little while this held me up, but not for long. Suddenly I saw the complete solution.

It would *not* be risky if (a) the murderer had certain knowledge of the butler's habits; and (b) could, if necessary, at the last moment, prevent the family from drinking. In other words, if he were an intimate of the family, were himself present at the party, and, without bringing suspicion on himself, could bring the wine under suspicion.

In other words, only if he were Sir William Kelso! For Sir William was the only man in the world who could say, "Don't drink this wine. I'm supposed to have sent it to you, and I didn't, so that proves it's a fake." The *only* man.

Why hadn't we suspected him from the beginning? One reason, of course, was that we had supposed the intended victim to be one of the Hedingham family, and of Sir William's devotion to his sister, brother-in-law, nephew and nieces, there was never any doubt. But the chief reason was our assumption that the last thing a murderer would do would be to give himself away by sending his own card with the poisoned bottle. "The *last* thing a murderer would do"—and therefore the *first* thing a really clever murderer would do.

To make my case complete to myself, for I had little hope as yet of converting Totman, I had to establish motive. Why should Sir William want to murder Perkins? I gave myself the pleasure of having tea that afternoon with Lord Hedingham's housekeeper. We had caught each other's eye on other occasions when I had been at the house, and—well, I suppose I can say it now—I had a way with the women in those days. When I left, I knew two things. Perkins had been generally unpopular, not only downstairs, but upstairs. "It was a wonder how they put up with him." And Her Ladyship had been "a different woman lately."

"How different?" I asked.

"So much younger, if you know what I mean, Sergeant Mortimer. Almost like a girl again, bless her heart."

I did know. And that was that. Blackmail.

What was I to do? What did my evidence amount to? Nothing. It was all corroborative evidence. If Kelso had done one suspicious thing, or left one real clue, then the story I had made up would have convinced any jury. As it was, in the eyes of a jury he had done one completely unsuspicious thing and had left one real clue to his innocence—his visiting card. Totman would just laugh at me.

I disliked the thought of being laughed at by Totman. I wondered how I could get the laugh on him. I took a bus to Baker Street, and walked into Regent's Park, not minding where I was going, but just thinking. And then, as I got opposite Hanover Terrace, who should I see but young Roberts.

"Hallo, young fellow, what have *you* been up to?"

"Hallo, Sarge," he grinned. "Been calling on my old school chum, Sir William Kelso—or rather, his valet. Tottie thought he might have known Merton. Speaking as one valet to another, so to speak."

"Is Inspector Totman back?" I asked.

Roberts stood to attention, and said, "No, Sergeant Mortimer, Inspector Totman is not expected to return from Leatherhead, Surrey, until a late hour tonight."

You couldn't be angry with the boy. At least I couldn't. He had no respect for anybody, but he was a good lad. And he had an eye like a hawk. Saw everything and forgot none of it.

I said, "I didn't know Sir William lived up this way."

Roberts pointed across the road. "Observe the august mansion. Five minutes ago you'd have found me in the basement, talking to a housemaid who thought Merton was a town in Surrey. As it is, of course."

I had a sudden crazy idea.

"Well, now you're going back there," I said. "I'm going to call on Sir William, and I want you handy. Would they let you in at the basement again, or are they sick of you?"

"Sarge, they just love me. When I went, they said, 'Must you go?'"

We say at the Yard, "Once a murderer, always a murderer." Perhaps that was why I had an absurd feeling that I should like young Roberts within call. Because I was going to tell Sir William Kelso what I'd been thinking about by the Leg of Mutton Pond. I'd only seen him once, but he gave me the idea of being the sort of man who wouldn't mind killing, but didn't like lying. I thought he would give himself away . . . and then—well, there might be a roughhouse, and Roberts would be useful.

As we walked in at the gate together, I looked in my pocket-book for a card. Luckily I had one left, though it wasn't very clean. It was a bit ink-stained, in fact. Roberts, who never missed anything, said, "Personally I always use blotting paper," and went on whistling. If I hadn't known him, I shouldn't have known what he was talking about. I said, "Oh, do you?" and rang the bell. I gave the maid my card and asked if Sir William could see me, and at the same time Roberts gave her a wink and indicated the back door. She nodded to him, and asked me to come in. Roberts went down and waited for her in the basement. I felt safer.

Sir William was a big man, as big as I was. But of course a lot older. He said, "Well, Sergeant, what can I do for you?" twiddling my card in his fingers. He seemed quite friendly about it. "Sit down, won't you?"

I said, "I think I'll stand, Sir William. I want just to ask you one question, if I may?" Yes, I know I was crazy, but somehow I felt inspired.

"By all means," he said, obviously not much interested.

"When did you first discover that Perkins was blackmailing Lady Hedingham?"

He was standing in front of his big desk, and I was opposite him. He stopped fiddling with my card and became absolutely still; and there was a silence so complete that I could feel it in every nerve of my body. I kept my eyes on his, you may be sure. We stood there, I don't know how long.

"Is that the only question?" he asked. The thing that frightened me was that his voice was just the same as before. Ordinary.

"Well, just one more. Have you a typewriter in your house?" Just corroborative evidence again, that's all. But it told him that I knew.

He gave a long sigh, tossed the card into the wastepaper basket and walked to the window. He stood there with his back to me, looking out but seeing nothing. Thinking. He must have stood there for a couple of minutes. Then he turned around, and to my amazement he had a friendly smile on his face. "I think we'd both better sit down," he said. We did.

"There is a typewriter in the house which I sometimes use," he began. "I daresay you use one too."

"I do."

"And so do thousands of other people—including, it may be, the murderer you are looking for."

"Thousands of people, including the murderer," I agreed.

He noticed the difference, and smiled. "People" I had said, not "other people." And I didn't say I was looking for him. Because I had found him.

"And then," I went on, "there was the actual wording of the typed message."

"Was there anything remarkable about it?"

"No. Except that it was exactly right."

"Oh, my dear fellow, anyone could have got it right. A simple birthday greeting."

"Anyone in your own class, Sir William, who knew you both. But that's all. It's Inspector Totman's birthday tomorrow." I added to myself: As he keeps telling us, damn him! "If I sent him a bottle of whisky, young Roberts—that's the constable who's in on this case; you may have seen him about, he's waiting for me now down below"—I thought this was rather a neat way of getting that in—"Roberts could make a guess at what I'd say, and so could anybody at the Yard who knows us both, and they wouldn't be far wrong. But *you* couldn't, Sir William."

He looked at me. He couldn't take his eyes off me. I wondered what he was thinking. At last he said, "You'd probably say, 'A long life and all the best, with the admiring good wishes of—' How's that?"

It was devilish. First that he had really been thinking it out when he had so much else to think about, and then that he'd got it so right. That "admiring" which meant that he'd studied Totman just as he was studying me, and knew how I'd play up to him.

"You see," he smiled, "it isn't really difficult. And the fact that my card was used is in itself convincing evidence of my innocence, don't you think?"

"To a jury perhaps," I said, "but not to me."

"I wish I could convince *you*," he murmured to himself. "Well, what are you doing about it?"

"I shall, of course, put my reconstruction of the case in front of Inspector Totman tomorrow."

"Ah! A nice birthday surprise for him. And, knowing your Totman, what do you think he will do?"

He had me there, and he knew it.

"I think *you* know him too, Sir," I said.

"I do," he smiled.

"And me, I daresay, and anybody else you meet. Quick as lightning. But even ordinary men like me have a sort of sudden understanding of people sometimes. As I've got of you, Sir. And I've a sort of feeling that, if ever we get you into a witness box, and you've taken the oath, you won't find perjury so much to your liking as murder. Or what the law calls murder."

"But *you* don't?" he said quickly.

"I think," I said, "that there are a lot of people who *ought* to be killed. But I'm a policeman, and what I think isn't evidence. You killed Perkins, didn't you?"

He nodded; and then said, almost with a grin at me, "A nervous affection of the head, if you put it in evidence. I could get a specialist to swear to it."

My God, he was a good sort of man. I was really sorry when they found him next day, after he'd put a bullet through his head. And yet what else could he do? He knew I should get him.

I was furious with Fred Mortimer. That was no way to end a story. Suddenly, like that, as if he were tired of it. I told him so.

"My dear little friend," he said, "it isn't the end. We're just coming to the exciting part. This will make your hair curl."

"Oh!" I said sarcastically. "Then I suppose all that you've told me so far is just introduction?"

"That's right. Now you listen. On Friday morning, before we heard of Sir William's death, I went in to report to Inspector Totman. He wasn't there. Nobody knew where he was. They rang up his apartment house. Now hold tight to the leg of the table or something. When the porter got into his flat, he found Totman's body. Poisoned."

"Good heavens!" I ejaculated.

"You may say so. There he was, and on the table was a newly opened bottle of whisky, and by the side of it a visiting card. And whose card do you think it was? *Mine!* And what do you think it said? 'A long life and all the best, with the admiring good wishes of—' *me!* Lucky for me I had had young Roberts with me. Lucky for me he had this genius for noticing and remembering. Lucky for me he could swear to the exact shape of the smudge of ink on that card. And I might add, lucky for me that they believed me when I told them word for word what had been said at my interview with Sir William, as I have just told you. I was reprimanded, of course, for exceeding my duty, as I most certainly had, but that was only official. Unofficially they were very pleased with me. We couldn't prove anything, naturally, and Sir William's suicide was left unexplained. But a month later I was promoted to Inspector."

Mortimer fixed his glass and drank, while I revolved his extraordinary story in my mind.

"The theory," I said, polishing my glasses thoughtfully, "was, I suppose, that Sir William sent the poisoned whisky, not so much to get rid of Totman, from whom he had little to fear, as to discredit you by bringing you under suspicion, and to discredit entirely your own theory of the other murder."

"Exactly."

"And then, at the last moment he realized that he couldn't go on with it, or the weight of his crimes became suddenly too much for him, or—"

"Something of the sort. Nobody ever knew, of course."

I looked across the table with sudden excitement; almost with awe.

"Do you remember what he said to you?" I asked, giving the words their full meaning as I slowly quoted them. " 'The fact that my card was used is in itself convincing evidence of my innocence....' And you said, 'Not to me.' And he said, 'I wish

I could convince *you*.' *And that was how he did it!* The fact
that your card was used *was* convincing evidence of your innocence!"

"With the other things. The proof that he was in possession
of the particular card of mine which was used, and the certainty that he had committed the other murder. Once a poisoner,
always a poisoner."

"True . . . yes. . . . Well, thanks very much for the story, Fred.
All the same, you know," I said, shaking my head at him, "it
doesn't altogether prove what you set out to prove."

"What was that?"

"That the simple explanation is generally the true one. In the
case of Perkins, yes. But not in the case of Totman."

"Sorry, I don't follow."

"My dear fellow," I said, putting up a finger to emphasize
my point, for he seemed a little hazy with the wine suddenly;
"the *simple* explanation of Totman's death—surely?—would have
been that *you* had sent him the poisoned whisky."

Superintendent Mortimer looked a little surprised, "But I did,"
he said.

So now you see my terrible predicament. I could hardly listen
as he went on dreamily: "I never liked Totman, and he stood
in my way; but I hadn't seriously thought of getting rid of him
until I got that card into my hands again. As I told you, Sir
William dropped it into the basket and turned to the window,
and I thought: Damn it, *you* can afford to chuck about visiting
cards, but I can't. It's the only one I've got left, and if you don't
want it, I do. So I bent down very naturally to tie my shoelace
and felt in the basket behind me, because, of course, it was
rather an undignified thing to do, and I didn't want to be seen;
and just as I was putting it into my pocket I saw that ink smudge
again, and I remembered that Roberts had seen it. And in a
flash the whole plan came to me; simple; foolproof. And from
that moment everything I said to him was in preparation for it.
Of course we were quite alone, but you never knew who might
be listening, and besides"—he twiddled the stem of his wine
glass—"p'raps I'm like Sir William, rather tell the truth than not.
And it was true, all of it—how Sir William came to know about
Totman's birthday, and knew that those were the very words
I should have used.

"Don't think I wanted to put anything on to Sir William that wasn't his. I liked him. But he as good as told me he wasn't going to wait for what was coming to him, and he'd done one murder anyway. That was why I slipped down with the bottle that evening and left it outside Totman's flat. Didn't dare wait till the morning, in case Sir William closed his account that night." He stood up and stretched himself. "Ah, well, it was a long time ago. Good-by, old man, I must be off. Thanks for a grand dinner. Don't forget, you're dining with *me* next Tuesday. I've got a new Burgundy for you. You'll like it."

He drained his wine glass and swaggered out, leaving me to my thoughts.

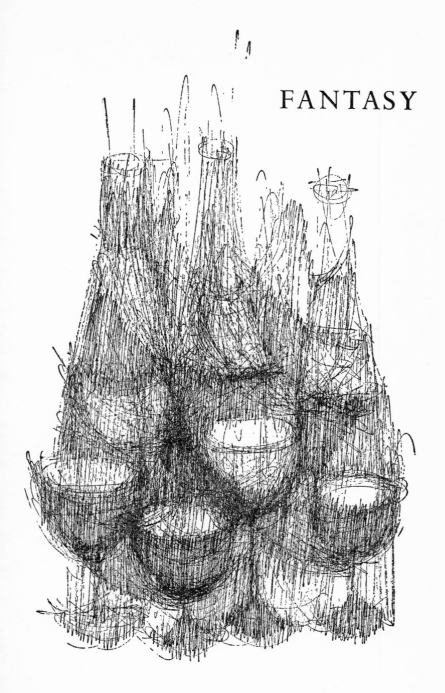

FANTASY

The 2003 Claret

KINGSLEY AMIS

*Kingsley Amis (1922–), English novelist and poet, is
London-born and a product of St. John's College, Oxford.
From 1948 he lectured in English literature at the University
College of Swansea. His second novel,* Lucky Jim *(1954),
a successful variation on the comic-picaresque, won him a
considerable reputation in England, a more moderate one in
America. He has also written* That Uncertain Feeling *(1956)
and* I Like It Here *(1958). His* New Maps of Hell *(1960)
proposes a highly serious interpretation of science-fiction.
Presumably "The 2003 Claret" represents an offshoot of his
interest in the subject. Starting with a machine known as
TIOPEPE, it kids wine-snobs and super-gourmets with wit
and wackiness.*

H OW long to go now?" the Director asked for the tenth
time.

I compared the main laboratory chronometer with the dial on
the TIOPEPE (Temporal Integrator, Ordinal Predictor and
Electronic Propulsion Equipment. "He should be taking the
trance-pill in a few seconds, sir," I said. "Then there's only the
two minutes for it to take effect, and we can bring him back."

"Supposing he hasn't taken the pill?"

"I'm sure he'd survive the time-shift even if he were fully
conscious, sir. It's instantaneous, after all."

"I know, but being snatched back from fifty years in the
future can't do a man's mind any good, can it? We just don't
know what we're up against, Baker. I wish those blasted politi-
cians had let us go slow on this project. But no, there mustn't
be any delay or the Russians will have developed time-travel

before the Atlantic Powers, so we bundle Simpson off to the
year 2010 and if we lose him or he turns up a raving lunatic it's
our fault." The Director sat moodily down on a work-bench.
"What happens if he gets tight?"

"He won't have done that, sir. Simpson's one of the Knights of
Bordeaux. They never get drunk—isn't it a rule of the society?"

"I believe so, yes." The Director cheered up a little. "He'll
probably have a good deal to tell us, with any luck. The Douro
growers are making this a vintage year, you know, Baker. Imagine what that stuff must be like where Simpson is. Just one
glass—"

"Did you actually tell Simpson to sample the wines in 2010?"

The Director coughed. "Well, I did just make the suggestion
to him. After all, part of our terms of reference was to report
on social conditions, in addition to the political situation. And
drinking habits are a pretty good guide to the social set-up,
aren't they? Find out how people treat their port and you've
found out a lot about the kind of people they are."

"Something in that, sir." I'm a beer man myself, which made
me a bit of an outsider in the team. There were only the four
of us in the lab. that night—the V.I.P.s and the press boys had
been pushed into the Conference Room, thank heaven—and all
the other three were wine-bibbers of one sort or another. The
Director, as you will have gathered, was fanatical about port;
Rabaiotti, my senior assistant, belonged to a big Chianti family;
and Schneider, the medical chap, had written a book on hock.
Simpson was reputedly on the way to becoming a sound judge
of claret, though I had sometimes wondered whether perhaps
tactical considerations played their part in his choice of hobby.
Anyway, I considered I was lucky to have got the job of Chief
Time-Engineer, against competition that included a force-field
expert who doubled as an amateur of old Madeira and an elec-
tronics king named Sandeman—no relation, it turned out, but
the Director couldn't have known that at the time.

"The receiver is tuned, Dr. Baker."

"Thank you, Dr. Rabaiotti. Would you like to operate the
recall switch, sir?"

"Why, that's extremely kind of you, Baker." The Director
was shaking with excitement. "It's this one here, isn't it?" His
hand brushed the trigger of a relay that would have sent Simpson

shooting back to about the time of Victoria's accession. This may have been half-deliberate: the Director often got wistful about what pre-phylloxera stuff might or might not have tasted like.

"No, this one, sir. Just press it gently down."

The switch clicked and instantly the figure of Simpson—tallish, forty-ish, baldish—appeared in the receiver. We all gave a shout of triumph and relief. Rabaiotti killed the power, Schneider hurried forward and there was tension again. "I'd give a case of Croft 1919 to see him conscious and mentally sound," the Director muttered at my side.

"Everything all right so far," Schneider called. "I've given him a shot that'll pull him round in a minute or two."

We lit cigarettes. "Pity conditions wouldn't allow of him bringing anything back," the Director said. "Just think of a forty-year-old 1970 all ready to drink. But I suppose it would have cost too much anyway. Next time we must find a better way of handling the currency problem. Very risky giving him raw gold to pawn. And we're restricted to a lump small enough not to arouse too much suspicion. Oh, well, he should have been able to afford a few glasses. I hope that champagne's all right, by the way?"

"Oh, yes, I put it in the molecular-motion-retarder myself, with the setting at point-three. It'll be nicely chilled by now."

"Splendid. I do want the dear boy to get a decent livener inside him before he faces all those cameras and interviews. I should have preferred a dry port myself, or possibly a Bittall, but I know what the occasion demands, of course. It's a Clicquot 1952 I've got for him. I don't understand these things myself, but the Director of Lunal Projectiles swears by it."

"He's coming round now," Schneider shouted, and we all pressed forward.

There was an intense silence while Simpson blinked at us, sat up and yawned. His face was absolutely impassive. Very slowly he scratched his ear. He looked like a man with a bad hang-over.

"Well?" the Director demanded eagerly. "What did you see?"

"Everything. At least, I saw enough."

"Had there been a war? Is there going to be a war?"

"No. Russia joined the Western Customs Union in 1993, China some time after 2000. The R.A.F.'s due to be disbanded in a few months."

Then everyone hurled questions at once: about flying saucers, the Royal Family, the sciences, the arts, interplanetary travel, climatic conditions in the Rheingau—all sorts of things. Simpson seemed not to hear. He just sat there with the same blank look on his face, wearily shaking his head.

"What's the matter?" I asked finally. "What was wrong?"

After a moment, he said in a hollow voice, "Better if there had been a war. In some ways. Yes. Much better."

"What on earth do you mean?"

Simpson gave a deep sigh. Then, hesitantly, to a silent audience and with the bottle of champagne quite forgotten, he told the following story.

The landing went off perfectly. Hyde Park was the area selected, with a thousand-square-yard tolerance to prevent Simpson from materialising inside a wall or half-way into a passer-by. Nobody saw him arrive. He changed his gold into currency without difficulty, and in a few minutes was walking briskly down Piccadilly, looking into shop-windows, studying dress and behaviour, buying newspapers and magazines, and writing busily in his notebook. He had several fruitful conversations, representing himself according to plan as a native of Sydney. This brought him some commiseration, for England had just beaten Australia at Lord's by an innings and 411 runs. Yes, everything seemed normal so far.

His political report and much of his social report were complete by six-thirty, and his thoughts started turning to drink: after all, it was a positive duty. As he strolled up Shaftesbury Avenue he began looking out for drink advertisements. The beer ones had much in common with those of 1960, but were overshadowed in prominence by those recommending wines. MOUTON ROTHSCHILD FOR POWER, BREEDING AND GRANDEUR, one said. ASK FOR OESTRICHER PFAFFENBERG—THE HOCK WITH THE CLEAN FINISH, enjoined another. MY GOLLY, MY ST. GYOERGYHEGYI FURMINT, bawled a third. Well, practical experiment would soon establish what was what. Simpson slipped quietly through the doorway of an establishment clearly devoted to drink.

The interior was surprising. If some French provincial café had not been gutted of décor and furnishings to get this place up, then a good job of duplication had been done. Men in neat, sombre clothing sat at the tables talking in low tones, wine-glasses and wine-bottles before them, while aproned waiters moved silently about. One of them was decanting a red wine from a bottle that was thick with dust and cobwebs, watched critically by all the nearby drinkers. Simpson crept to a seat in an unfrequented part of the room.

A waiter approached. "What can I bring you, monsieur?"

Here it must be explained that Simpson was not quite the claret-fancier the Director thought him. He enjoyed claret all right, but he also enjoyed other French wines, and German wines, and Italian wines, and Iberian wines, and Balkan wines, and fortified wines, and spirits, and liqueurs, and *apéritifs*, and cocktails, and draught beer, and bottled beer, and stout, and cider, and perry—all the way down to Fernet Branca. (There were some drinks he had never drunk—*arak, kava,* Gumpolds-kirchner Rotgipfler, methylated spirits—but they were getting fewer all the time.) Anyway, feeling dehydrated after his walk round the streets, he unreflectingly ordered a pint of bitter.

"I'm sorry, monsieur, I don't understand. What is this bitter?"

"Bitter beer, ale; you know. Haven't you got any?"

"Beer, monsieur?" The waiter's voice rose in contempt. "*Beer?* I'm afraid you're in the wrong district for that."

Several men turned round, nudged one another and stared at Simpson, who blushed and said, "Well ... a glass of wine, then."

"France, Germany, Luxembourg, Austria...."

Simpson tried to think. "A claret, please. Let's say—a nice St. Emilion."

"Château Le Couvent, Château Puyblanquet, Château Belcier, Château Grand Corbin Despagne...."

"Oh ... I leave it to you."

"*Bien,* monsieur. And the year? Will you leave that to me too?"

"If you don't mind."

The waiter swept away. Conscious that all eyes were upon him, Simpson tried to sink into his chair. Before he could compose himself, a middle-aged man from a nearby table had come over and sat down next to him. "Well, who are you?" this man asked.

"A—a traveller. From Sydney."

"These days that's no excuse for not knowing your wines,

friend. Some of them Rubicons and Malbecks are as firm and
fully rounded as all bar the greatest Burgundies. And I found
a Barossa Riesling on holiday this year that was pretty near as
gay as a Kreuznacher Steinweg. You well up on the Barossas,
friend?"

"No, not really, I'm afraid."

"Thought not, somehow. Otherwise you wouldn't stalk in here
and screech out for *beer*. Ger, ought to be ashamed of yourself,
you ought."

"I'm awfully sorry."

"Should hope so and all. Now, I'm an honest working man,
see? I'm a DRIP, I am."

"A drip?"

"Domestic Reactor Installation Practitioner. Don't they go in
for them down under? Now you listen to me. When I come in
here to meet my colleagues and crack a bottle or two after the
daily round, I don't want my palate soured by some toff yelling
out about beer, especially not when we got a really elegant
Gevrey Chambertin or Chambolle Musigny or something of
that in front of us. It's psychosomatic, like. Just the idea of beer's
enough to cut off some of the subtler overtones, get me?"

"I'm sorry," Simpson said again. "I didn't realise. But tell me:
don't you eat while you're drinking these wines?"

"What, and foul up the taste-buds with fat and sauces and
muck? You got a nerve even mentioning food in a place like this.
We're oenophiles in here, I'll have you know, not a bunch of
pigs. Ah, here's your claret." The stranger held the glass up to
the light, then sniffed it delicately. "Right, now let's see what you
got to say about this. And get on with it."

Simpson drank. It was the most wonderful wine he had ever
known, with a strange warm after-taste that seemed to seep
upwards and flood his olfactory centres. He sighed deeply.
"Superb," he said at last.

"Come on, come on, we want more than that; you got to do
better than that. Give us a spot of imagery, kind of style, a
reference to art, that type of stuff."

"It's—I don't know—it's the richness of summer, all the glory
of . . . of love and lyric poetry, a whole way of life, profound
and . . . some great procession of—"

"Ah, you turn me up," the man said violently. "This is a 2003

Château La Bouygue, reconstituted pre-phylloxera of course. Now, light and free, not rich in association but perfectly assured without any insincerity, instrumental where the 'ois are symphonic, the gentleness of a Braque rather than the bravura of a Matisse. That's as far as you can go with it. Love and lyric poetry indeed. I never heard such slop in my life. You aren't fit to come in here, friend. You get off out to one of the pubs with your boss-class pals, that's where you belong."

Simpson threw down some coins and ran, a gust of ill-natured laughter sounding in his ears. He felt like walking the streets for the two hours in 2010 that still remained to him, but a nagging curiosity emboldened him to ask to be directed to a pub.

The place he finally made his way to was on the corner of a narrow street on the edge of Soho. It was a red-brick affair like a miniature grammar school or a suburban bank. As he approached, a bus drew up and a crowd of young people got off, chattering loudly to one another in what Simpson made out as a version of the upper-class tones current in his own time. He was more or less swept in through the front door of the pub, and had no time to puzzle out the significance of a notice above the entrance, painted by hand with what seemed deliberate inelegance, and bearing the legend: CRACKED UP BY THE WALLOP AND SCOFF MOB.

He found himself in a large, ill-lighted and crowded room of which the main feature was a long counter that ran from end to end zigzag-wise, as if to accommodate as many as possible of the tall stools that were closely packed along it. What were evidently glass sandwich cupboards stood every couple of feet along the red plastic top. A group of people, half-crowd, half-queue, was clustered round the entrance, and Simpson mingled with them. He noticed that most of the stools were occupied by persons drinking beer or some such liquid out of pint glasses and eating rolls or sandwiches. Conversations were bawling away around him.

"My dear, simply nobody goes to the Crown these days. Simon and I were given fresh crisps the last time we went."

"It doesn't surprise me. We had some mustard that couldn't have been more than a day old."

"The wallop's first-class down at the George, and as for the scoff—the bluest piece of ham you ever saw. A really memorable thrash. I'm getting the secretary of the Mob to crack them up in the next issue of the *Boozer Rag*."

"Have you bagged stools, sir?"

"I beg your pardon?"

"Sorry, mate. Have you bagged, mate?"

"No, I'm afraid not. May I see the head potman?"

"I'll get him over directly, mate."

"Shall we start thinking about what we're going to have? Pickled onions to start? With a glass of mild?"

"Nuts for me. Mixed and salted."

"Right, that's three onions, one nuts. And then I can recommend the cheese rolls. They know me here and always see that I get the three-day-old, with plenty of rind."

After some time, Simpson obtained a stool and ordered a pint of bitter from the grubby barmaid.

"Certainly, love. A fresh barrel has just come on."

"Oh, I'll have mild instead, then."

"By all means, love, if you wish for it. Your taste is your own. And what will you have in the way of scoff, love?"

"Oh, er—nothing to eat, thank you."

"If I may say so, love, with all due respect, you might perhaps do better at the wine-bar if you don't wish for any scoff. We have standards to maintain here, love."

"I'm awfully sorry. What . . . scoff do you recommend?"

"Our gherkins have frequently been cracked up, love. Not a dish is sold till it's two days old."

"They sound delightful. One dish, please."

"Very good, love. With cigarette-ash garnishings, of course."

The beer came. It was horrible. The gherkins came. Simpson took no notice of them. Dazedly he watched and listened to those around him. A kind of ritual seemed to be being enacted by a group of four immediately next to him. The two couples raised their pints in concert, intoned the word "Cheers" in a liturgical manner, poured a few drops on to the front of their greasy pullovers, and sank their drinks in one swallow. Afterwards they all sighed loudly, wiped their mouths with their hands, banged the empty glasses down on the counter, and spoke in turn.

"Lovely drop of wallop."

"First today."

"I needed that."

"Lays the dust."

"You can't beat a decent pint."

"Full of goodness."

"Keeps your insides working."

"It's a real drink."

When this point was reached, all four shouted "Let's have another" in unison, and were immediately served with fresh drinks and small plates of sandwiches. The bread on these was curled up at the corners, revealing purple strips of meat criss-crossed with gristle. One of the men felt the texture of the bread and nodded approvingly. "I told you this place was good," his friend said. Then the party got down to what was clearly the *pièce de résistance*, alternately biting at the sandwiches and taking pulls of beer, chewing the resulting mush with many a belch of appreciation. Simpson lowered his head into his hands. The talk went on.

"What's the fighting like here?"

"Oh, excellent. The governor of the boozer gets it under way at ten-thirty sharp, just outside on the corner. I did hear a whisper that he's going to allow broken bottles for the last five minutes tonight. The police should be with us by then. They're very keen round here."

"At the Feathers, you know, they kick off at ten-fifteen inside the bar. Don't know whether I agree with that."

"No. After all, it's only the finale of the evening."

"Absolutely. Shouldn't make it too important."

"Definitely not. Getting tight's the object of the exercise."

"Quite. By the way, who's that fellow next to you?"

"No idea. Wine-bar type, if you ask me."

"Hasn't touched his gherkins. Refused fresh butter. Shouldn't be here at all."

"Couldn't agree more. I mean, look at his clothes."

"Wonder how long since they were slept in."

"If they ever have been."

"Disgusting."

"And what would you like to follow, love?"

This last was the barmaid. Simpson raised his head and gave a long yell of fury, bewilderment, horror and protest. Then he ran from the room and went on running until he was back at the point where the TIOPEPE was to pick him up. With shaking fingers he put the trance-pill into his mouth.

The Director broke the silence that followed the end of Simpson's story. "Well, it's a long time ahead, anyway," he said with an attempt at cheerfulness.

"Is it?" Simpson shouted. "Do you think that sort of situation develops in a couple of weeks? It's starting to happen already. Wine-snobbery spreading, more and more of this drinking what you ought to drink instead of what you like. Self-conscious insistence on the virtues of pubs and beer because the wrong people are beginning to drink wine. It'll be here in our time, don't you worry. You just wait."

"Ah, now, Simpson, you're tired and overwrought. A glass of champagne will soon make you see things in a different light."

"Slip away with me afterwards," I murmured. "We'll have a good go at the beer down in town."

Simpson gave a long yell—much like the one, probably, he vented at the end of his visit to 2010. Springing to his feet, he rushed away down the lab. to where Schneider kept the medical stores.

"What's he up to?" the Director puffed as we hurried in pursuit. "Is he going to try and poison himself?"

"Not straight away, sir, I imagine."

"How do you mean, Baker?"

"Look at that bottle he's got hold of, sir. Can't you see what it is?"

"But ... I can't believe my eyes. Surely it's...."

"Yes, sir. Surgical spirit."

Dead Man's Bottles

ROBERT GRAVES

*To put it simply, Robert Ranke Graves (1895–   ) is one
of the finest poets now using English, as well as an historical
novelist of formidable powers. Son of the Irish poet and
song-writer Alfred Perceval Graves, he was educated at
Charterhouse and temporarily interrupted his college career
in order to join the Royal Welch Fusiliers during World War
I. His war and post-war experiences supplied the matrix for
his now classic autobiography,* Goodbye to All That, *recently reprinted in up-dated form. Graves belongs to the
populous English school of creative cranks (Samuel Butler
offers another example). His anthropological, mythological
and theological theories have upset the academy and won
him a reputation as an original if cross-grained scholar. For
its weird narrative "Dead Man's Bottles" draws on the generally unrelated fields of kleptomania and oenophilia.*

I WAS more amused than shocked when I first realized that
I was a matchbox- and pencil-pocketer: it seemed a harmless
enough form of absent-mindedness. Why matchbox- and pencil-
pocketers—the aberrancy is quite a common one—should not
also take cigarette lighters and fountain pens, no psychologist has
been able to explain, but in practice they never do. Another odd
thing about them is that, however slow and stupid on other
occasions, they are quick as lightning and as cunning as weasels
when they go into action.

"Sign, please!" the errand boy would call at the door of my
flat in Hammersmith Mall, and when I came out, fumbling half-
heartedly in my pockets for a pencil, he would offer me his.
Then, after scribbling my name on the chit, I would perform

some ingenious sleight of hand—but exactly how and what must remain unknown, because I never caught myself at it. All I can say is that he went off whistling, convinced that the pencil was back behind his ear, while I retired indoors with a clear conscience; and that, when I emptied my pockets before going to bed, the nasty chewed stub of indelible was there, large as life, along with other more handsome trophies. As for matches: I would stop a stranger in the street, politely ask for a light, strike a match on the box he offered and, after hypnotizing him (and myself) into the belief that I had returned it, thank him and stroll slowly off. I often wonder what a film-take of the incident would have shown.

Pencils are cheap, matches are cheaper still. My friends remained seemingly unaware of my depredations, or at any rate never accused me of them, until one Easter I went to stay at Kirtlington, near Oxford, with one F. C. C. Borley, a Wadham don who lectured on moral philosophy and was an expert on French literature and wine.

Borley was youngish, with an unwholesome complexion, lank hair, and so disagreeable a voice and manner that he literally had not a friend in the world—unless one counted me, and neither of us really liked the other. His fellow dons couldn't stand him, though he had a well-stored and accurate mind, praiseworthy loyalty to the College, and no obvious vices—except to dress like a stage Frenchman and always to be in the right. He gave them the creeps, they said, and agreed that his election had been a major disaster. I had met him by chance on a walking tour in Andalusia, where I nursed him through an illness because nobody else was about; and now I was helping him with the typescript of a book he had written on drinking-clubs at the English Universities. I never pretended to compete with him in vintage scholarship or to share his rhetorical raptures over such and such a glorious port-wine year—Borley always chose to call it "port wine"—or the peculiar and Elysian bouquet of this or that little-known *Château*. And never let on that, in fact, I considered port primarily an invalid's drink and preferred an honest Spanish red wine or brandy to the most cultivated French. The only subject on which I claimed to be knowledgeable was sherry, a wine singled out for praise in the Fellows' grace at Wadham, and therefore not to be lightly disregarded by Borley, even though it meant nothing to his palate.

He had a Savoyard chef called Plessis whose remarkable ragouts and crêmes and soufflés these elegant wines served well enough to wash down. Out of respect for Plessis I never contradicted Borley or listened with anything but close attention to his endless dissertations on food, wine, the French classics, and eighteenth-century drinking habits. In exchange, he accepted my suggested amendments to his book readily enough wherever style, not fact, was in question; but that was because I had left him his affectations and perverse punctuation and everything else that gave the book its unpleasant, personal flavour, and concentrated merely on cutting out irrelevancies and repetitions and taking him up on the finer points of grammar.

Over coffee and brandy one evening, when our work on the book was all but finished, he suddenly unmasked his batteries. "Fellow drinker," he said—he had a nauseating habit of calling people "fellow drinker" at table and "fellow gamester" at cards —"I have a crow to pluck with you, and what could be a more suitable time than this?"

"Produce your bird," I answered, and then in a pretty good imitation of Borley himself: "When we've plucked, singed, and gutted it like good scullions, and set aside the tail feathers for pipe-cleaners, we'll summon Plessis from his cabinet and leave him to the fulfilment of his genius. I have no doubt but he'll stuff the carrion with prunes soaked in rose water, chopped artichoke hearts, paprika, and grated celeriac—then stew gently in a swaddling of cabbage leaves and serve with hot *mousseron* sauce. . . . What wine shall we say, fellow drinker? *Maître Corbeau, 1921?* Or something with even more body?"

But Borley was not to be sidetracked. "Frankly," he continued, jutting out his pointed chin with its silly black imperial, "it goes against my conscience as a host to make the disclosure, but *in vino veritas*, you know: you're a damned thief!"

I flushed. "Go and count your German-silver teaspoons, check your forged fore-edge paintings, send Mme Plessis upstairs to go through my linen in search of your absurd Sulka neckties. There's not an object in this house that I'd accept as a gift, except some of your sherry—though not all of that. Your taste in fur-

nishings and *objets d'art* is almost as bad as your manners, or
your English grammar."

He was prepared for some such comeback and met it calmly.
"Yesterday, friend Reginald Massie," he said pompously, "you
stole every match I possessed. Today I sent to the grocer for
another packet of a dozen boxes. Tonight there's only a single
box left, that one on the mantelpiece.... Just Heavens, and now
that too has disappeared! It was there two minutes ago, I'd stake
my reputation—and I never saw you leave your chair! However, nobody's come in, so pray hand it over!"

He was trembling with passion. Caught on the wrong foot, I
began emptying my trouser pockets, and out came the matchboxes; but, I was glad to see, no more than seven of them.

"There," I said, "count! You lie; I did not take the whole
dozen. Where are the other five? I believe you're a match-
pocketer yourself."

"You were courteous enough to change for dinner," he reminded me. "The rest of the loot will be found in your tennis
trousers. And now for the pencils!"

I felt in my breast pocket and pulled out eight or nine. "The
perquisites of my profession," I explained lightly. "Think of the
trouble I've taken in correcting your illiterate English, not to
mention your more than sketchy Spanish. I needed a whole
fistful of pencils. You'd probably have had them all back before
I left."

"Tell me, how often in your life have you either returned a
borrowed pencil or bought a new one?"

"I can't say offhand. But once, at a Paddington book stall, I
remember...."

"Yes, felonious Massie, I can well picture the scene. Just before
the train started you asked the attendant to show you an assortment of propelling-pencils, drew your purse, made a couple of
passes and, hey presto, levanted with the whole tray."

"I have never in my life pocketed a propelling-pencil. That
would be theft. You insult me."

"It's about time someone did, fellow drinker! What a petti-
fogging rogue you are, to be sure. Convinced that nobody's
going to haul you into Court for the sake of a penny pencil or
a ha'penny matchbox, you lose all sense of decency and filch
wholesale. Now, if you were to set your covetous eyes on

something only a little larger and more valuable, such as, as—
let us say this corkscrew—"

"I wouldn't be found dead with that late-Victorian mon-
strosity!"

"—I repeat, with this corkscrew, I'd have a trifle more respect
for you. But you stick to your own mean lay. In the criminal
world, *on dit*, William Sikes, the master burglar, looks down his
nose at the ignoble sneak thief and tuppenny tapper. William's
scorn for you, O lower than Autolycus, would be an easterly
blast to wither every flower in the summer's garden of your
self-esteem." He leaned back in his ornate chair, placed the tips
of his fingers together and eyed me malevolently.

It is a fallacy that good wine makes one less drunk than bad
wine. Borley would never have dared to talk to me like that if
he hadn't had a skinful of his special Pommard; and if I hadn't
been matching him glass for glass I should probably have kept
my temper. I'd once heard him remark after a post-mortem at
a North Oxford bridge table: "...*And if* the King of Hearts
had worn a brassière and pink bloomers, he'd have been a Queen!
So what, fellow gamesters?" But there was no *And if* on this
occasion.

Frowning, I poured myself another brandy, tossed it over his
shirt front, and then tweaked his greasy nose until it bled. I
ought to have remembered that he had a weak heart; but then, of
course, so ought he.

Borley died ten days later, after a series of heart attacks. Nobody knew about the tweaked nose—it isn't the sort of thing
the victim boasts about—and though I think Plessis and his wife
guessed from the brandy on their master's clothes that there had
been a brawl, they did not bring the matter up. They benefited
unexpectedly from the will: a legacy of a thousand pounds, free
of death duties. To me, in spite of my disparagement of his wine,
Borley left "the Worser Part" of his cellar—it was another of his
affectations to capitalize almost every other word—while "the
Better" was to go to Wadham Senior Common Room. I had also
been appointed his sole executor, which entailed a great deal of
tiresome work: it fell to me to organize his funeral and act as
chief mourner. The bulk of his estate went to a second cousin,
a simple-minded Air Force officer at Banbury, who took one

look at the Kirtlington house, pulled a comic face, and took the next train back. The will, I should mention, had been a last-minute scrawl on the flyleaf of a cookery book, which was grudgingly accepted for probate because the nurse and doctor had witnessed it and the intentions were clear enough.

I felt a bit guilty about Borley. Once or twice in the course of the next few weeks I had a novel twinge of conscience when I stowed away my day's catch of pencils and matches in the bottom drawer of my desk. Then one day a letter came from Dick and Alice Semphill reminding me that I was to spend a yachting holiday with them in August, and that *Psyche* would be found moored in Oulton Broad on the fifteenth, if that suited me. I wrote back that I'd be there without fail, accompanied by a dozen of Borley's burgundies and clarets which, though the "Worser Part" of his cellar, were well worth drinking; and a bottle or two of my own Domecq Fundador brandy.

Psyche is a comfortable craft, though rather slow, and the Semphills were glad to see me again. Both of them are mad on sailing. Dick's an architect and Alice and I once nearly got married when we were both under age; we're still a little more than friends. I think that's all I need say about them here.

The first night in the saloon, just before supper, eight-year-old Bunny Semphill watched me produce a bottle of Beaujolais and offered to uncork it. But he found the job too stiff for him, so I had to finish it.

As I was twisting the cork from the corkscrew, I started as though I had been stung. "Bunny," I asked, "where the deuce did this come from?"

He stared at me. "I don't know, Mr. Massie. I took it from the rack behind you."

"Dick," I called, trying not to sound scared, "where did you get this ivory-handled corkscrew?"

Dick, busy mixing the salad in the galley, called back: "I didn't know we possessed such a thing. I always use the one on my pocket knife."

"Well, what's this?" And I showed it to him.

"Never set eyes on it until now."

Neither, it proved, had Alice Semphill or Captain Murdoch, an Irish Guardsman who was the fifth member of the party.

"You look as though you'd seen a ghost," said Alice. "What's so extraordinary about the corkscrew, Reggie? Have you come across it before?"

"Yes: it belonged to the chap who bequeathed me the wine. But the trouble is that it wasn't part of the bequest. I can't make out how it got here."

"You must have brought it along by mistake. Perhaps it got stuck into one of the bottle covers."

"I'd have seen it when I packed them."

"Not necessarily."

"Besides, who put it on the rack?"

"Probably yourself. You know, Reggie, you do a lot of pretty absent-minded things. For instance, you pinched all our matches almost as soon as you came aboard. Not that I grudge you them in the least; but I mean. . . ."

"How do you know? Did you see me pick up so much as a single box?"

"No, I can't honestly say I did. But I was wildly looking for a light and saw your raincoat hanging up and tapped the pockets, and they positively rattled. . . ."

"I brought a lot of matches with me. Useful contribution, I thought. . . ."

She let that go with a warning grimace. But the corkscrew mystery remained unsolved. I sincerely hoped that I hadn't suddenly become a major thief, as Borley had wished I would. It might land me in a police court—and eventually in a home for kleptomaniacs. I picked up the corkscrew, which I'd have recognized in a million. It was a stout eighteen-eightyish affair, with an ivory handle and a brush at one end, I suppose for whisking away the cobwebs from the necks of 1847 port bottles.

"Who were the people who chartered *Psyche* last week?" I asked.

"The Greenyer-Thoms; friends of Dick's brother in-law George. He's an estate agent; she paints. They live near Banbury."

"Aha!" I said, "that explains it. They must have been at the sale of Borley's effects. The principal legatee is his Air Force cousin, who lives there."

"Violent T.T. types, the Grennyer-Thoms, both of them," Alice objected.

"Secret drinkers," I countered, replacing the corkscrew on the rack. "That's why they wanted the yacht. It's easy to dispose of the empties; just drop them into the water under cover of night."

After supper Murdoch asked me jocosely whether he might be allowed to smell the cork of one of my famous brandies. I roused myself from a dark-brown study, fetched a bottle, and reached for the corkscrew. It was not on the rack. I glanced sharply from face to face and asked: "Who's hidden it?"

They all looked up in surprise, but nobody spoke.

"I put it back on the rack and now it's gone. Hand it over, Bunny! You're playing a dangerous game. I'm foolishly sensitive about that corkscrew."

"I haven't touched it, Mr. Massie—drop dead, I haven't—I swear!"

"Tap Massie's pockets, Mrs. Semphill," Murdoch invited. "They're positively wriggling with corkscrews."

Dick caught a nose-tweaking glint in my eye. "Gentlemen, gentlemen!" he cried warningly. Then he pulled out his pocket knife. "—This will do, Reggie," he said.

Dick's a decent fellow.

As I silently uncorked the brandy, Bunny went down on his hands and knees and searched among our feet. Then he rummaged among the cushions behind us.

"*Couldn't* it be in one of your pockets, Mr. Massie?" he asked at last.

"Certainly not!" I snapped. "And for God's sake don't fidget so, child! Go on deck if you're bored with adult conversation."

"I was only trying to help."

"Well, don't try so hard."

Alice didn't like the way I pitched into the boy and came to his rescue. "I really think he had a right to ask you that," she said. "Especially as I can see the end of my best drawing pencil peeping out of your breast pocket."

"It's not yours, woman; it's mine!"

"Let me umpire this tug of war," said Murdoch. "I'm the fairest-minded man in all East Anglia."

"Keep out of this, Murdoch!" I warned him.

"Oh, forget it, chaps, for Christ's sake!" said Dick. "If we're

going to squabble about matches and pencils on the very first
night of our sail. ..."

Under the influence of the Domecq, which everyone praised,
we soon recovered our self-possession—but half an hour later,
when we had finished washing up and were going on deck,
Bunny looked at me curiously.

"Who hung the corkscrew on that hook?" he asked. "Did
you?"

"Captain Murdoch has a devious sense of humour," I told him,
"and if you find yourself catching it, lay off!" But a cold shiver
went through me and I stayed below for a supplementary drink.
The blasted thing was dangling from a hook above the galley
door. If I had been sure who the practical joker was, I'd have
heaved him overboard.

For the sake of peace Dick must have asked the others not
to comment on the corkscrew's reappearance, because the next
day there was an eloquent silence, unbroken by myself, when
I borrowed Dick's knife to uncork another bottle of claret. But
for the rest of the holiday I was careful to go through my
pockets, morning, afternoon, and night, to make sure that I had
left enough matches and pencils lying about for general use. I
had a superstitious feeling that, if I did, the corkscrew would
stay on its hook. And I was right.

I am a little vague about where we went, or what weather we
had; but I know that when the time came to say goodbye, Alice
couldn't resist asking: "Haven't you forgotten your trick corkscrew? It's still hanging up in the saloon."

"No," I said. "It isn't mine and never was. The Greenyer-
Thoms left it here. Anyhow, *Psyche* can do with an ivory-
handled corkscrew."

"Thank you," said Alice quizzically. "But I don't think Borley
intended it for us."

That evening, back in my flat, I found that in the hurry of my
departure I had forgotten to frisk myself for matches and pencils.
Among the day's collection I found an outsize box of Swan
Vestas boldly marked in ink *John Murdoch, his property; please
return to the Guards Club*, and Alice's double-B Koh-i-Noor
pencil with her initials burned on it—with a red-hot knitting

needle?—at both ends and in the middle. This made me cross. "Bunny must have planted them on me," I reassured myself. "It couldn't have been Murdoch—he went off yesterday morning —and Alice wouldn't have been so unkind."

"Nice gentlemanly corkscrew you've brought back, sir," my Mrs. Fiddle remarked as she bustled in with the soup.

"Oh, I have, have I?" I almost yelled. "Then throw it out of the window!"

She looked at me with round, reproachful eyes. "Oh, sir, I could never do such a thing, Mr. Massie, sir. You can't buy a corkscrew like that nowadays."

I jumped up. "Then I'll have to throw it away myself. Where is it?"

"On the pantry shelf, next to the egg cups," she answered resignedly, picking up my fallen napkin. "But it seems such wicked waste."

"*Where* did you say it was?" I called from the pantry. "I don't see it."

"Come back, Mr. Massie, and eat your soup while it's hot," she pleaded. "The corkscrew can wait its turn, surely?"

Not wanting to look ridiculous, I came back and restrained myself until dessert, when I asked her curtly to fetch the thing.

She was away some little time and showed annoyance when she returned.

"You're making game of me, sir. You've hid that corkscrew; you know you have."

"I have done nothing of the sort, Mrs. Fiddle."

"There's only the two of us in the flat, sir," she said, pursing her lips.

"Correct, Mrs. Fiddle. And if you want the corkscrew yourself, you're welcome to it, so long as you don't bring it back here. I should, of course, have offered it to Mr. Fiddle before I talked of throwing it out of the window."

"Are you accusing me of hiding it with intent to deceive you, Mr. Massie?"

"Didn't you accuse *me* of that, just now?"

The thrust went home. "I didn't mean anything rude, sir, I'm sure," she said, weakening.

"I should hope not. But, tell me, Mrs. Fiddle, are you certain you saw a corkscrew? What was it like?"

"Ivory-handled, sir, with a sort of shaving brush at one end, and a little round silver plate set in the other with some initials and a date."

This was too much. "That's the one," I muttered, "but, upon my word, I never noticed the initials."

"Well, look again, Mr. Massie, and see if I'm not right," she said. And then, plaintively, as she retired into the kitchen, with her apron to her eyes: "But you oughtn't to pull my leg, sir! I take things so seriously, ever since my little Shirley died."

I poured her a drink, and we made peace.

Next day the corkscrew turned up in the pantry at the back of the napkin drawer. Mrs. Fiddle produced it in triumph. "Here it is, sir. Now see if I wasn't right about the initials."

I took it gingerly from her, and there was the silver plate all right. I couldn't understand how I had missed it. *F.C.C.B. 1928,* the silver slightly tarnished.

"Yes, sir, it could do with a nice rub-up."

I saw no way out of this awkward situation but to earn credit as a practical joker. "The fact is," I blustered, "I bought it at Lowestoft as a present for Mr. Fiddle. I didn't intend you to see it, and that's why I made a bit of a mystery of the whole affair. I meant to keep it for his birthday. First of next month, isn't it?"

"No, sir. Fiddle's birthday was the first of last month. Very kind of you, sir, all the same, I'm sure."

But she still seemed dissatisfied. "Fiddle isn't a wine or spirit-drinker, sir," she explained after a pause, "and bottled beer comes with screw tops these days."

"How very stupid of me! All right, let's chuck it out of the window, after all."

"Oh, no, sir! You might hurt someone passing in the street. Besides, it's a nice article. Keep it for yourself, and give Fiddle a couple of bottles of stout, instead. He'd take that very kindly, though belated. And so would I, if it comes to that, Mr. Massie, sir."

Late that evening, with a neat package in my hand, I walked along the Mall until I came to Hammersmith Bridge. When no one was about, I hurled it into midstream. What a load off my mind! But that night I dreamed that a nasty looking corpse floating in the water had grabbed the parcel just as it sank and shouted to me to come back and collect my property. He rose dripping

from the Thames; it was F. C. C. Borley himself. I turned and
fled screaming towards the Broadway, but he came after me. "It's
yours, you damned thief!" he bawled. "Wait! I've brought it!"
And then, as a parting shot, heard indistinctly through the rumble
of traffic: "And the Worser Part (Bins K to T) for Mr. Reginald
Massie." That was the operative phrase in his will.

I awoke with chattering teeth, jumped out of bed, switched on
all the lights in the flat, poured myself a stiff drink, and went
along to see whether the corkscrew were back again on the
pantry hook. Thank God, it wasn't!

I repacked my suitcase and read myself to sleep again.

In the morning when Mrs. Fiddle brought my tea I told her
that I had been rung up by another set of yachting friends in
South Devon, and was catching the morning train there. I'd send
her a wire to let her know when I was returning, and what to do
with my letters. This was nothing unusual; I frequently leave
home on a sudden impulse.

I booked for Brixham, where I knew that a regatta was in
progress. Also, a bachelor uncle of mine lived on the hill overlooking the harbour: an ex-Marine colonel whom I had not seen
for years and whose chief interest was British fresh water molluscs. We exchanged cards at Christmas and his were always
superscribed: "Come and visit a lonely old man." I thought:
"Here's my chance to show a little family feeling; besides, all the
pubs are sure to be full because of the regatta."

Uncle Tim was delighted to see me and discuss his molluscs
and his rheumatism. That evening he took me in a taxi to the
Yacht Club for an early supper. "You look depressed, my boy,"
he said, "and not too well in spite of your holiday. You ought to
get married. Man isn't meant to live by himself. Marriage would
tone you up and give you a motive in life." He added sadly: "I
put it off too long. Molluscs and marriage don't go together. Children would have played the deuce with my aquarium and cabi-
nets."

"Oh, they grow up," I said airily. "Seven years' patience, and
your collection would have been safe enough."

"You may be right; but the poor little blighters couldn't
wait."

"Who? The children?"

"No, no, stupid! The molluscs!"

"I beg your pardon. But why ever not?"

"River pollution: those confounded chemical manures washed off the soil, you know. A regular massacre of the innocents: whole species destroyed every year."

I shook my head in sympathy.

"But there's nothing to prevent *you* from marrying, is there?" he persisted.

"I collect matchboxes," I answered, rattling my pockets gloomily. "Mine is one of the finest collections in Europe. It would hardly be fair to bring up children among so much incendiary material, would it?"

Presently Uncle Tim, reaching for the menu, said that his rheumatism be damned: with our Dover sole and roast chicken we'd have a bottle of the Club's famous hock, tacitly reserved for resident members. "I know that you appreciate a sound wine, Reginald," he said. "Not many young men do, with all these confounded mixed drinks about. Gin and vermouth—gin and tonic —gin and bitters that's what it's come to. Even in the Navy. Pollution, I call it!" He finished enigmatically: "Whole species destroyed every year."

"Did you ever come across a youngster called Borley?" he went on. "Chap I met once, here at the Club. He wore a floppy hat and an absurd tie like a Frenchman; said he was writing a book. A mind like a corkscrew—went round and round, and in and in, and then pop! out would come something wet. But, for all that, he had a remarkable knowledge of wine; and consented to approve of our hock."

A waiter tiptoed in, cradling the bottle, and ceremoniously dusted its neck with the brush at the end of an ivory-handled corkscrew. "I've brought it, fellow drinker," he whispered with a confidential leer.

"Good heavens, boy!" cried Uncle Tim. "What's amiss? Are you taken ill?"

I had dashed out of the Club, and was half running, half flying, down the slope to the Fish Market. The evening crowds in Fore Street blocked my way, but I swerved and zigzagged through them like an international wing three-quarter.

"Hey, Reggie, stop!" a woman shouted almost in my ear.

I handed her off and darted across the narrow street, where I found myself firmly tackled around the waist.

"For God's sake, Reggie, what's the hurry? Have you murdered someone?"

It was Dick Semphill! I stopped struggling and gaped at him. "Come into this café and tell Alice and me what's happened."

I followed him in, still gaping, and sat down. "What on earth are you doing in Brixham?" I asked, when I found my voice.

"The regatta, of course," Alice answered.

"But why aren't you up in Lowestoft?"

"That's not till next month. We've been here since Friday. *Psyche's* not distinguished herself yet, but there's still hope."

"*Psyche?* But she can't possibly have sailed from Suffolk in the time!"

"I don't know what you're driving at. She's not been in the Broads since last year. You're coming up there next month—at least we hope you are—and we're going to have a wonderful time. By the way, you haven't yet told us whether Oulton Broad on the fifteenth suits you."

"Where's Bunny?"

"At school in Somerset. Murdoch will collect him when he breaks up."

"Dick—Alice, I believe I'm going off my head." I told them the whole story from the beginning, even making a clean breast of the matchbox business. They both looked thoroughly uncomfortable when I had finished.

Alice said: "Obviously, it was a dream, but I can't make out exactly at what point it began and ended. Listen: I'll ring up the Yacht Club and find out if your Uncle Tim's there."

The phone was close to our table. Presently I heard her say: "You're sure! Not since last Tuesday? Laid up with rheumatism? Oh, I'm so sorry. No, no message. Thanks very much."

She put back the receiver. "It's not so bad, Reggie," she said. "You haven't let your uncle down. As a matter of fact, they don't serve meals at the Yacht Club; and the only cellar there is the commodore's personal bottle they keep under the counter. So your dream didn't end until Dick woke you up a moment ago. It was a bit more than a dream, of course; a sort of sleep walk, probably due to worrying about that chap Borley. Lucky we met you. Do you mind turning out your pockets, Reggie, dear? That may give us a clue to how long you've been away from your flat."

I obeyed dazedly. Out came eight matchboxes of different sorts, seven pencils and, among other odds and ends, the return half of a railway ticket from Paddington, and an unposted letter to Alice herself, written from my flat and confirming the Oulton Broad rendezvous.

"You came down here only this afternoon," she said, showing me the date on the ticket.

There was also a bulky envelope containing all the documents concerned with my winding-up of Borley's affairs. Alice ran through them. "I see you duly delivered the wine to the Warden and Fellows of Wadham College," she said. "And here's the itemized bill for the funeral at Kirtlington Parish Church. Oh, and a note from Squadron Leader Borley of Banbury, saying that if you'd like any souvenir from his cousin's effect before the auctioneer disposes of them, you're very welcome, but will you please let him know as soon as possible. He wrote on Thursday; I don't suppose you've answered him yet. Hullo, here's a photostat of the will itself! What beastly wriggly writing! Yes, it's witnessed by—"

Dick had kept quiet all this time. Now he grabbed the will and read it. "It's all right, Reggie," he said. "You've not gone nuts, and we won't even have to get you psychoanalyzed. You've merely been haunted—by a ghost which it ought to be easy enough to lay." Then he burst out: "You dolt, why didn't you take the trouble to find out whether your friend Borley was a Protestant or a Catholic?"

"I did take a great deal of trouble, but nobody knew. Even the College couldn't tell me, so I followed the line of least resistance and had him buried C. of E."

"Exactly. That's what all the trouble's been about! You see now why in your dream he called you a damned thief?"

"I don't understand."

"Read the will again. Read it aloud!"

I read:

"I appoint Reginald Massie to be my executor . . . the Better Part of my Cellar (Bins A to J) are for the Warden and Fellows of Wadham College, Oxford. The Worser Part (Bins K to T) are for Mr. Reginald Massie. . . ."

"Not '*for Mr. Reginald Massie*,' idiot; if he'd meant you he'd have written 'the said Reginald Massie.' It's '*for the Requisite Masses*'! Masses for his soul's repose, don't you see?"

The exhumation was not easy to wangle, but I got it fixed up in the end. Then I handed over the wine to the St. Aloysius people at Oxford and they agreed to do the rest. And on Alice's insistence, I wrote to Squadron Leader Borley, asking for the corkscrew as a keepsake. Since he sent it I haven't pocketed a single matchbox or pencil—so far as I know, that is. . . .

The Wine Beyond the World

ALFRED NOYES

Alfred Noyes (1880–1958) was an English narrative and epic poet, a critic and a Catholic convert (1925). He will survive by virtue of several anthology pieces, notably "The High-wayman." At the moment his pleasant but traditional verse is out of favor. This pretty piece of fluff, "The Wine Beyond the World," will of course remind the reader of a more re-nowned tale by Hans Christian Andersen.

H AVE you supped at the Inn of Apollo,
*   While the last light fades from the West?*
Has the Lord of the Sun at the World's End
*   Poured you his ripest and best?*
O, there's wine in that Inn of Apollo;

Wine, mellow and deep as the sunset
*   With mirth in it, singing aloud*
As the skylark sings in a high wind,
*   High over a crisp, white cloud.*
Have you laughed in that Inn of Apollo?

At the ancient German village of Rosenheim, in those incredible years before 1914—for this is not a tale of war—there was an old, half-timbered inn, as beautiful as a fairy-tale and almost as true. It had gabled roofs, a host who resembled Han Sachs, and it was famous for a wine so unimaginably mellow that it could only be described as a bottled sunset. It was unimaginably mellow in more ways than one, for it was the most costly wine in the world. For many years it had been reserved for the private use of the Emperor. Even the Emperor could only afford to drink one glass

183

of it annually, and a very small glass at that—a mere thimbleful, hardly enough to spice the palate of a Black Forest gnome. It was known as the "Emperor's Wine," and the sacramental fame of it was rolled upon the tongues of all the connoisseurs of the Rhineland. It was the unattainable dream; the vintage of the purple distance; the wine beyond the world.

If the Emperor drank only one glass a year, the twelve cobwebbed bottles of this nectar that still remained in the cellars of the ancient inn at Rosenheim, at the date when my story commences, might very well last him for a life-time; but it was necessary to prevent mad poets and rich merchants and jolly bishops and other golden-banded bees of Bacchus from sipping, so a fancy price had been set upon it, very much as they set a fantastic figure upon a prize-winner at a dog show, and the price was fixed at three thousand marks a bottle.

It was rumoured in Rosenheim, the tiny, clustering village whose elfin beehives and gardens and thatched roofs and rambling outside staircases all climbed and pointed to the inn as the centre of their being, that the Emperor had desired to buy the entire stock of the precious vintage outright; but his annual visit to drink his single glass of wine was so glorious a rubric in the local calendar, that all Rosenheim viewed the suggestion with dismay. The inhabitants drew up a petition, the resident artist illuminated it, the Burgomaster himself presented it to His Majesty, and His Majesty graciously agreed to continue the ceremonial tradition *in sæcula sæculorum*. After all, it should be the pride and privilege of Emperors to give the common people as much innocent pleasure as His Majesty found convenient; and he knew that when he drank his annual glass of that divine beverage, his people tasted it vicariously, and the mellow fire that flowed through the imperial veins rejoiced them all by proxy.

It was also rumoured among the beehives and the thatched roofs, that the artist who had illuminated the successful petition to the Emperor had been allowed to smell the next cork that was drawn, and that, taking advantage of his position, as these lawless fellows often will, he had thrust the cork into his mouth and sucked it. This is not regarded, among connoisseurs, as the best way of forming an opinion upon either the body or the bouquet of a wine; but the effect upon the artist, the ecstatic expression of his countenance, was almost as great a tribute to the excellence of the wine as the punctual return of the Emperor. Indeed, the artist had become almost a legendary figure in Rosenheim. It was told by villagers who remembered him that for nearly a week after his misbehaviour he had acted like a man intoxicated with joy, and that, on being questioned regarding the flavour of the crimson driblets that he had so nefariously secured, he quivered with renewed ecstasy from head to foot, flung up his arms and murmured "*Nunc Dimittis.*" At the end of a week, in fact, he did actually depart, and he had never been seen in Rosenheim again, either because he preferred to dwell with his memories, or because, among some envious spirits, there had been some talk of punishing him for *Majestäts-Beleidigung*. After his departure, however, it was agreed that even if he had sucked an entire ruby drop from the cork it had not been wasted upon him; for the delight of the Emperor in his annual glass was necessarily expressed with a certain ceremonial dignity and restraint; and, if it had not been for the emotion of a low-born artist, nobody else could ever have imagined the wonder of that wine.

Now, on a certain summer's day there arrived at that famous hostelry, in a large touring car, a Mr. and Mrs. Roland Gayley, of Newport, Rhode Island. They were a young bride and bridegroom, who were leaving the hours of their honeymoon behind them like a winding golden road through Europe. Mr. Roland Gayley was one of those tall young sons of the New World, who have the outward appearance of a Greek god, the wealth of a Crœsus, and the happy-go-lucky temperament of a d'Artagnan. His bride was one of those daughters of the New World who have beaten the Frenchwoman with her own weapons. She was a consummate artist in the tilt of a hat, and in what—one regrets to say—she described as the "slinkiness" of a gown. Physically, too, she was a goddess: Diana at breakfast, Hebe at lunch, and Aphrodite in the evening. There was just the happy difference between their tastes that makes for harmony. Mr. Gayley liked Europe because it was old, and like all true Americans he was very indignant whenever he discovered the slightest attempts at progress in the customs of the Old World. Mrs. Gayley also liked Europe for the purposes of a honeymoon; but she liked it somewhat as a lover of musical comedy will turn to a Chinese fantasia for an hour's amusement. She had no desire to live permanently among the mandarins. They often argued the matter during their lovers' pilgrimage to the shrines of the great poets and musicians of the "dark ages," as Mrs. Gayley called them. But she threw herself enthusiastically into Mr. Gayley's romantic scheme of paying tribute, sometimes with gifts of flowers, and sometimes in a more substantial way, to their memory. Mr. Gayley's chief argument, in fact, was from old books, old wine, old violins, and old friends; and in all these matters Mrs. Gayley agreed with him, though she affirmed that the merit was not entirely in their age, even in the case of the wine.

She declared moreover, that for practical purposes she preferred the comforts of her house at Newport to the most romantic ruins of the Middle Ages; and, knowing full well that her husband only enjoyed ruins because he was not obliged to live in them, she was greatly amused at his distress over what he called "the putting of new wine into old bottles." "In England," he said, "you have the modern spirit with a mediæval equipment; in Germany you have the modern equipment with a mediæval spirit. Surely there must be some inn beyond the pinewoods, some unsuspected valley beyond the world, where we can find the old wine in the old bottles? I have an idea. We will end our wedding-tour with a visit to the famous inn at Rosenheim, where, I am told, they have a very marvellous wine; and you will forgive me for saying so, honey"—this term of endearment was a regrettable lapse into modernism; but, after all, the bees that swarmed upon the lips of the Greek poet might have liked it; Mr. Gayley certainly used it, and truth requires it—"you will forgive me for saying so, honey, but I believe it's the oldest wine in existence."

And so—with that enchanted gleam before them—they had rambled through the Middle Ages, reconciling two forms of happiness that are usually, and falsely, held to be incompatible— the joy of life and the beauty of the past. Mr. Gayley, indeed, was something of a poet, and he expressed himself in two ways. In the morning he sometimes amused himself by putting into light verse his opinions and impressions of persons and places. Once or twice recently an editor had sent him a cheque almost large enough to buy him a box of cigars. As a general rule, however, he wrote for private circulation, and indulged occasionally in the luxury of a sumptuous little edition, printed on hand-made paper, at his own expense, and distributed on feast-days among his friends.

In the afternoon he would compose a poem of an entirely different kind while he was smoking the post-luncheon cigar that he had earned so pleasantly. He was very much of a poet indeed at this time, and there was nothing trivial about his mood as he composed the menu for the evening dinner. Every detail had to be considered, down to the colour-harmonies of the flowers, the wines, and the sauces.

Both of these forms of happiness were considered in the scheme of their ramble through Europe. To one little village on a river of Elfland, whose name shall never be torn from me, they had journeyed for the purpose of eating lampreys. But they were divine lampreys, fattened in a stream whose banks were knotty with the roots of vines, and their very mud an essence of vine-leaves. The flavour of those lampreys— But no apology is necessary for those joyous wanderers. Keats at least would have wished them well; and, as for those who love in cottages, there is surely a happiness in the thought that, once in the history of the world, two lovers were entirely free from care and could obtain everything that they desired.

Once or twice they had followed a mere will-o'-the wisp of humour. They went to Rüdesheim for the sole purpose of seeing the castle of Boosenburg, where a descendant of Count Johann Boos had once won an entire village in a wager by emptying a jack-boot full of wine at a single draught. Mr. Gayley maintained, however, in the poem that he wrote upon this memorable feat, that it could hardly have been accomplished by a mere descendant, and that it must be attributed to the noble founder of the line, Count Johann Boos himself.

After this frivolous excursion, they had visited Weimar and left a magnificent bunch of roses at number twelve, Schiller Street. They went to Ilmenau and walked through the woods to the little wooden shooting-box on the site where Goethe had sung and slept, and they scattered violets wherever they thought he had trodden.

They had visited the Black Forest and picnicked in the woods. Mr. Gayley had sent a chef with a specially constructed table ahead of them in another motor-car, without the knowledge of Mrs. Gayley. He had then led her through the woods by various romantic ways, until in a deep glen they had come by surprise upon the table decked with the red lights of fairyland and saw

the white-capped chef and his waiter peering like gnomes through
the tall ferns behind it.

  And now, finally, they had arrived at Rosenheim, the goal of
their quest, and the home of the wine beyond the world. On the
morning of their arrival Mr. Gayley's poem had been more severe
than usual, for he had noticed several distressingly modern suggestions in the local newspaper. He composed his poem while he
was refreshing himself in a pine-cone bath after his journey; but
he was unable to eliminate what might be called the local colour
of his own country. He entitled it *The Reformers*, and it ran
thus:

" 'If I were the blue-bird that fashioned the sky,'
    Said the little blue wizard to me,
  With a flirt of his wings and a flash of his eye,
    As he perched in the crab-apple tree,
  'If I were the Master-Magician, I'd make
  The universe over again for our sake.

" 'The world should be all under blue-bird control,
    And boys should be just of a size
  For me and my missus to swallow 'em whole
    Like spiders or honey-fed flies;
  While earth should have nothing but trees on her breast,
  Where blue-birds like me and my missus could nest.'

" 'If I were the web-footed Wizard you mean,'
    Croaked a fat little bullfrog below,
  'I should bubble and squeak in an oozier green
    Than aught in the world that we know;
  While your saccharine song would grow vital and harsh,
  For I'd turn the whole universe into a marsh.'

"Oh, crimson as wine were the beautiful beads
    Of his eyes, as he stared at the west,
  And croaked, 'I'd have nothing but puddles and reeds!
    I don't see the use of a nest!
  I'd have myriads of gnats' (his eyes blackened like blood),
  'And legions of wives all asprawl in the mud.—'

" 'If I were the Mouse that created us all,'
    A squeak in the wainscot began,
'I am sure I could mould this terrestrial ball
    On a more economical plan;
It's a matter, I think, for ironical mirth,
That the moon should be cheese while the mice are on earth.'

" 'If I were the Queen of the Universe,' purred
    The little black witch with the claws,
'How the mouse and the frog and the mesmerised bird
    Would love the red yawn of my jaws!
How the redolent houses would rustle with rats
If the world were arranged for the comfort of cats!

" 'How men, at one twitch of my whiskers would fly
    To fetch me my milk in a bowl;
And how, at one wink of my wicked green eye,
    They would feed me on salmon and sole;
How sweetly my kittens would sleep overhead,
In the very best sheets of the very best bed.'

" 'If I could remodel Cosmopolis,' cried
    The man on the tub to the crowd.
'We've heard the suggestion before,' they replied,
    And they melted away like a cloud.
For they thought it might lead to some dreadful mistakes
If he made the world over again for their sakes.

" 'It is better,' they growled, 'that to each should be given
    His own bit of bliss, if you please,
Than that earth should be turned into somebody's heaven,
    Which might be a marsh or a cheese;
For the child of the sun must endure for a night
Lest, abolishing shadows, he lose the world's light.

" 'There are myriads of bitter, black wrongs to redeem,
    But the very best way to begin,
Is for each to go home with a definite scheme
    For scotching his own little sin;
It's a pretty grim task, for we're mostly beginners,
But a world without sin isn't fashioned by sinners!' "

The menu for the evening, too, was a very charming lyric; but it did not strike either Mr. or Mrs. Gayley as a masterpiece until it was presented to the head-waiter, when they presumed that it must be something unusual by the extraordinary confusion of that gentleman's features.

"The Emperor's Wine!" he gasped, as if he had felt the foundations of his house moving. Then, recovering himself, he smiled condescendingly and murmured a mild reproof into Roland Gayley's ear. "This wine, sir, is the famous vintage that only the Emperor can afford to drink. I am afraid it is not for ordinary mortals, and that you will not care to pay the price."

Now this was the first time in his life that Roland Gayley had been treated, even by a Herr Ober, with that kind of benevolence; and, though he was the most amiable of beings and had never lost his temper in his life, all the pugnacity of his father, the Steel King, gleamed for a moment in his eyes.

"I did not ask the price," he replied. "I ordered the wine."

"But the wine is t'ree t'ousand marks a bottle, sir. It is the Emperor's Wine."

Mrs. Gayley stiffened slightly. Her eyes were fixed on her husband's face, and this, of course, determined him. It must be remembered that, young as they were, they could hardly rid themselves of their possessions if they lived to be a thousand.

"I am afraid my German is not good," said Roland Gayley, looking at the head-waiter's agitated face with the calm of the Steel King during a Wall Street panic. "I have already told you that I did not inquire about the price. I ordered the wine."

The head-waiter turned away dumbly and held a kind of international conference in the corner of the room with a Swiss and an Italian waiter. Again he approached the strange visitors.

"I wish to understand quite correctly," he said. "You have ordered a bottle of the Emperor's Wine."

"Certainly."

"At t'ree t'ousand marks a bottle?"

Mr. Gayley chuckled happily. He was never angry. What was the use, when you had sixty millions to play with, and a sense of humour? "At three thousand marks a bottle," he repeated. "Is this a debating society?"

For the second time the head-waiter retired in dumb distress. If this were a genuine offer, of course, an entirely new problem was raised. The price had not been put upon the wine in order to tempt lunatics. It was a precaution, not a bait. On the other hand, three thousand marks was a great deal of money. The proprietor might desire to sell a bottle at that price, if he could do so se- cretly, and without destroying the tradition of his inn. The visi- tors were evidently persons of consequence. They had ordered a dinner that commanded his respectful attention. There was a second international conference in the corner; then the Herr Ober resolved that this was too great a matter for his own judg- ment, and that it must be referred to the landlord himself. The Swiss waiter was dispatched to find him, and, in a few minutes the potentate of the inn appeared, wiping his mouth and marching forward like a Major-General, with the entire staff at a respectful distance behind him.

He ran his imperial eye over the visitors and smiled.

"You have made a mistake," he said. "This wine that you have ordered is very costly. The Emperor himself drinks less than a thimbleful once a year."

"I quite understand," said Mr. Gayley. "Madame here is a little tired, and a glass of this good wine is just what she would like as a restorative with her dinner."

"But you do not understand. Even if it were sold by the glass it would cost you a t'ousand marks, and it is only sold by the bottle. The price is t'ree t'ousand marks."

"I have ordered a bottle," said Mr. Gayley, still chuckling, but with the dangerous glint in his eyes again. It was the first time that Mrs. Gayley had become aware of the re-incarnation of the Steel King in her husband, and she watched him with awe.

"The only thing I don't understand," he continued, "is why everybody in this confounded inn wants to come and talk to me about the dinner I've ordered. Do you usually argue with your guests about the price of things?"

"But I fear you do not understand. Are you aware that this wine—"

"Look here, my friend, don't wave that napkin in my face! I don't object to your having Emperors and cathedrals and things, so why should you object to my spending my pocket-money just as I please? Now if this is really an inn, where things can be bought to eat and drink, will Your Majesty please tell my waiter to bring me what I ordered from your own wine-list."

The landlord bowed, and retired in confusion, followed by his entire staff. A dramatic hush brooded over the inn. It was nearly ten minutes before he or any of his satellites re-appeared. Part of the time had been used—as was disclosed later—in cross-examining the chauffeur about the strange visitor's ability to pay his bills. The chauffeur had spoken quite frankly and had talked in very large figures. He had explained that three thousand marks meant about as much to Mr. Gayley as a *pfennig* to the local baron. He had even produced newspapers and certain documentary evidence to prove that Mr. Gayley was the son of the Steel King. The results were admirable.

The hush of the dining-room was broken at last by the footsteps of the landlord and the staff returning. There was a whisper of "Amerika" and "Kolossal" somewhere outside. Then they all entered in stately procession, and with not a little of the pomp that they had hitherto reserved for the visits of the Emperor.

The landlord came first, carrying the sacramental bottle, as if it were the most precious baby in the world; as if, in fact, it were a little Crown Prince; as if the cobwebs that clothed it were more costly than all the silks of the Empress; and as if every grain of dust that clung to it were more radiantly beautiful than the most priceless jewel of the imperial diadem. Behind him came the Herr Ober, carrying a voluminous white napkin, as if it were destined for some sublime hieratical function; and behind him again all the other Obers, in order of precedence, and distinctly awe-stricken, followed at a discreet distance as if they were expecting an explosion.

Even the vivacious Mrs. Gayley was a little awed by the solemnity of the proceedings.

"Do you think we really ought, Roland?" she murmured. "It seems to mean so very much to the poor dears."

But it was too late to draw back. The precious red blood of the sun, of which even the Emperor drank only one thimbleful in a year, was already winking in the glasses of those two visitants from the New World. The costly bubbles, the least of which must have been worth a week's pay to any of the officiating hierophants, were bursting and evaporating with a heart-breaking carelessness. Mr. and Mrs. Gayley raised their glasses. They touched them together. They smiled at the landlord.

"Prosit," said Roland.

"Prosit," said Madame.

Then came the tragedy. The wine had no sooner touched the lips of Mr. and Mrs. Gayley than they rose to their feet, spluttering.

"Ugh! How disgusting!" said Madame.

"Ugh! Bilge!" gasped Roland.

"Um Gottes Himmels Willen!" cried the landlord.

The Herr Ober rushed forward with his napkin to wipe the spilled wine from the dress of Madame, while the Ober, who came next in precedence, performed the same office for the trousers of Roland.

The two visitors recovered themselves more quickly than the staff of the inn, who stood trembling around them, looking from one to the other in a chaos of interrogation.

"Now I understand," said Roland, "why the Emperor only calls for one thimbleful in the year."

"And spits it into his handkerchief," said Madame, shuddering again.

"Landlord," said Roland calmly, "this wine is too glorious for me. It is worse than high treason—it is blasphemy for ordinary mortals to drink it. Bring us very quickly a bottle of this Rhine wine"—he indicated a number on the wine list—"this, you understand at four marks a bottle. Be quite sure that you understand. We shouldn't like to drink the Emperor's Wine again by mistake."

"But vot shall I do with this bottle of the Emperor's Wine?" said the landlord, in a voice husky with emotion.

"I have bought it," said Roland, "and, of course, it must be put down upon the bill. I understand that it is your birthday tomorrow. I give it to you for a birthday present."

The landlord retired, overwhelmed with his good fortune, and the dinner eventually proved to be quite worthy of its composer.

"How fortunate it is," said Roland, as he lighted his cigar, "that even when one has a great deal of money it is always possible to procure the wine that is drunk by those who have little."

"But you know, Roland, this proves everything that I have said about the Old World. I am sure it is all just like that, if the poor dears would only understand," said Madame.

Roland lighted her cigarette. "I wonder," he said thoughtfully, "I wonder what became of that artist."

INTERLUDE:

CORDIAL AND SPIRITUAL

Another Temple Gone

C. E. MONTAGUE

Charles Edward Montague (1867–1928), novelist, essayist, dramatic critic, short-story writer and political journalist, merits, if not revival, at least the most vivid and grateful remembrance. A war hero (dyeing his hair at the age of forty-seven, he enlisted in 1914 and distinguished himself for his superb physical courage), he was also a noted Alpinist and star writer for the Manchester Guardian *during its finest period (1890–1925). As a satirical anti-war novelist of quality and short-story writer (see* Fiery Particles, *1923) he is undeservedly neglected. Perhaps his Irish parental heritage (though he was born in London) lies back of this funny, touching and slightly over-styled story about a spiritual distillation from County Clare. When they have read it, I am sure my readers will forgive me for including in this assemblage of wine stories a tale about whiskey.*

THEY say that there may be a speck of quiet lodged at the central point of a cyclone. Round it everything goes whirling. It alone sits at its ease, as still as the end of an axle that lets the wheel, all about it, whirl any wild way it likes.

That was the way at Gartumna in those distant years when the "land war" was blowing great guns all over the rest of the County Clare. Gartumna lay just at the midst of that tempest. But not a leaf stirred in the place. You paid your rent if you could, for the coat that the old colonel had on his back—and he never out of the township—was that worn you'd be sorry. Suppose you hadn't the cash, still you were not "put out of it." All that you'd have to suffer was that good man buzzing about your holding, wanting to help; he would be all in a fidget trying to call to mind the way

197

that some heathen Dane, that he had known when a boy, used to be-devil salt butter back into fresh—that or how Montenegrins would fatten a pig on any wisp of old trash that would come blowing down the high road. A kind man, though he never got quit of the queer dream he had that he knew how to farm.

Another practising Christian we had was Father O'Reilly. None of the sort that would charge you half the girl's fortune before they'd let the young people set foot in the church. And, when it was done, he'd come to the party and sing the best song of anyone there. However, at practical goodness Tom Farrell left the entire field at the post. Tom had good means: a farm in fee simple—the land, he would often tell us, the finest in Ireland, "every pitaty the weight of the world if you'd take it up in your hand"; turf coming all but in at the door to be cut; besides, the full of a creel of fish in no more than the time you'd take dropping a fly on the stream: the keeper had married Tom's sister. People would say, "Ach, the match Tom would be for a girl!" and gossips liked counting the "terrible sum" that he might leave when he'd die, if only he knew how to set any sort of value on money. But this he did not. The widow Burke, who knew more about the great world than a body might think, despaired of the man because, she said, "no one could come and ask for a thing but he'd give it them." Then, as she warmed to the grateful labour of letting you know what was what, the widow might add: "I question will Tom ever make a threepenny piece, or a penny itself, out of that old construction he has away there in the bog."

At these words a hearer would give a slight start and glance cannily round, knowing that it would be no sort of manners to give a decent body like Sergeant Maguire the botheration and torment of hearing the like of that said out aloud. But the Sergeant would never be there. For he, too, had his fine social instincts. He would be half a mile off, intent on his duty, commanding the two decent lads that were smoking their pipes, one on each of his flanks, in the tin police hut away down the road. Gartumna did not doubt that this tactful officer knew more than he ever let on. A man of his parts must surely have seen, if not smelt, that no unclean or common whisky, out of a shop, had emitted the mellow sunshine transfiguring recent christenings and wakes. But who so coarse as to bring a functionary so right-minded up against the brute choice between falling openly short in professional zeal and wounding the gentle bosom of Gartumna's peace?

And yet the widow's sonorous soprano, or somebody else's, may have been raised once too often on this precarious theme. For, on one of the warmest June mornings that ever came out of the sky, Sergeant Maguire paraded his whole army of two, in line, on a front of one mile, with himself as centre file and file of direction, and marched out in this extremely open order into the fawn-coloured wilderness of the bog. "You'll understand, the two of yous," he had said to his right flank, Constable Boam, and to Constable Duffy, his left, "that this is a sweeping or dhragging movement that we're making."

The sun was high already; your feverish early starts were no craze of the Sergeant's. The air over the bog had tuned up for the day to its loudest and most multitudinous hum and hot click of grasshoppers and bees; all the fawn surface swam in a water-coloured quiver of glare; the coarse, juiceless grass and old roots, leathery and slippery, tripped up the three beaters' feet. Hour by hour the long morning greased and begrimed the three clean-shaven good-soldier faces that had set out on the quest; noon came blazingly on; its savage vertical pressure seemed to quell and mute with an excess of heat the tropical buzz of all the basking bog life that the morning's sunshine had inspirited; another hour and the bog was swooning, as old poets say, under the embraces of the sun, her friend, when a thin column of more intensely quivering air, a hundred yards off to the Sergeant's half-left, betrayed some source of an ardour still more fiery than the sun's. Just for the next five or ten minutes, no more, the Sergeant had some good stalking. Then it was all over. The hunting was done: nothing left but to whistle in his flank men and go over the haul.

The tub and worm of the illicit still had not been really hidden; they were just formally screened with a few blocks of turf as though in silent appeal to the delicacy of mankind to accept as adequate this symbolic tribute to the convention of a seemly reticence. Farrell, a little, neatly-made, fine-featured man with a set, contained face, but with all the nervousness of him quivering out into the restless tips of his small, pointed fingers, gazed at the three stolid uniformed bulks, so much grosser than he, while they disrobed his beloved machinery of that decent light vesture and rummaged with large coarse hands among the mysteries of his craft. He wore the Quakerish black suit and the broad and low-crowned soft black hat in which a respectable farmer makes his soul on a Sunday morning. Silent and seemingly not ashamed, nor yet enraged, neither the misdemeanant caught in the act nor the parent incensed by a menace to its one child, he looked on, grave and almost compassionate. So might the high priestess of Vesta have looked on when the Gaulish heathen came butting into the shrine and messed about with the poker and tongs of the goddess's eternal flame. How could the poor benighted wretches know the mischief that they might be doing the world?

Sergeant Maguire, too, may have had his own sense of our kind's tragic blindness quickened just then—that a man, a poor passionate man, should so rush upon his own undoing! "Ach, it's a pity of you, Farrell," he presently said. "A pity—you with the grand means that you have of your own! An' you to be out here, distillin' pocheen!"

"Pocheen!" The little, precise, nervous voice of Farrell ran up into a treble of melancholy scorn. With an austere quality in his movements he drew a brown stoneware jar from among some heaped cubes of turf that the barbarians had not yet disarranged. From another recess he took a squat tumbler. Into this he poured from the jar enough to fill a liqueur glass rather smaller than most. "Tell me," he bade almost sternly, holding the tumbler out to Maguire, "d'ye call that pocheen?"

"Ye can take a sup first," was the canny reply. Maguire had heard how Eastern kings always make cooks and premiers taste first.

Farrell absorbed the tot, drop by drop. He did not cross himself first, but there was something about his way of addressing himself to the draught that would make you think of a man crossing himself before some devout exercise or taking the shoes from off his feet before stepping on some holy ground. As the potion irrigated his soul he seemed to draw off from the touch of this clamorous world into some cloistral retreat. From these contemplative shades he emerged, controlling a sigh, a little time after the last drop had done its good office. He poured out for Maguire.

"Well, here's luck," said the Sergeant, raising the glass, "and a light sentence beyond." The good fellow's tone conveyed what the etiquette of the service would not allow him to say—that in the day of judgment every mitigating circumstance would be freshly remembered.

Up to this his fortieth year Maguire, conversing with the baser liquors of this world and not with philtres of transfiguration, had counted it sin to drink his whisky as if it would burn him. So the whole of the tot was now about to descend his large-bore throat in close order, as charges of shot proceed through the barrel of a gun. But the needful peristaltic action of the gullet had scarcely commenced when certain tidings of great joy were taken in at the palate and forwarded express to an astonished brain. "Mother of God!" the Sergeant exclaimed. "What sort of a hivven's delight is this you've invented for all souls in glory?"

A sombre satisfaction gleamed out of Farrell's monkish face. Truth was coming into its own, if only too late. The heathen was seeing the light. "It's the stuff," he said gravely, "that made the old gods of the Greeks and Romans feel sure they were gods."

"Be cripes they were right," asseverated Maguire. He was imbibing drop by drop now, as the wise poets of all times have done, and not as the topers, the swillers of cocktails, punch and cup and any old filth only fit to fill up the beasts that perish. Not hoggishness only, but infinite loss would it have seemed to let any one drop go about its good work as a mere jostled atom, lost in a mob of others. If ever the bounty of Heaven should raise a bumper crop of Garricks on earth, you would not use them as so many supers, would you?

Farrell, after a short pause to collect his thoughts, was stating another instalment of the facts. "There's a soul and a body," he said, "to everything else, the same as ourselves. Any malt you'll have drunk, to this day, was the body of whisky only—the match of these old lumps of flesh that we're all of us draggin' about till we die. The soul of the stuff's what you've got in your hand."

"It is that," said the Sergeant, and chewed the last drop like a lozenge. He now perceived that the use of large, bold, noble figures of speech, like this of Farrell's, was really the only way to express the wonderful thoughts filling a man's mind when he is at his best. That was the characteristic virtue of Farrell's handiwork. Its merely material parts were, it is true, pleasant enough. They seemed, while you sipped, to be honey, warm sunshine embedded in amber and topaz, the animating essence of lustrous brown velvet, and some solution of all the mellowest varnish that ever ripened for eye or ear the glow of Dutch landscape or Cremona fiddle. No sooner, however, did this potable sum of all the higher physical embodiments of geniality and ardour enter your frame than a major miracle happened in the domain of the spirit: you suddenly saw that the most freely soaring poetry, all wild graces and quick turns and abrupt calls on your wits, was just the most exact, business-like way of treating the urgent practical concerns of mankind.

So the Sergeant's receivers were well tuned to take in great truths when Farrell, first measuring out the due dram for Constable Duffy, resumed, "You'll remember the priest that died on us last year?"

"I do that, rest his soul," said each of the other two Catholics. Constable Boam was only a lad out of London, jumped by some favour into the force. But a good lad.

"Ye'll remember," Farrell continued, "the state he was in at the end? Perished with thinness, and he filled with the spirit of God the way you'd see the soul of him shining out through the little worn webbin' of flesh he had on, the match for a flame that's in one of the Chinese lanterns you'd see made of paper. Using up the whole of his body, that's what the soul of him was—convertin' the flesh of it bit by bit into soul till hardly a tittle of body was left to put in the ground. You could lift the whole with a finger."

"Now aren't ye the gifted man?" The words seemed to break, of themselves, out of Constable Duffy. Rapt with the view of entire new worlds of thought, and the feel of new powers for tackling them, Duffy gazed open-lipped and wide-eyed at Farrell the giver.

Farrell's face acknowledged, with no touch of wicked pride, this homage to truth. *Non nobis, Domine.* Austere, sacerdotal, Farrell inspected the second enraptured proselyte. Then he went on, his eyes well fixed on some object or other far out on the great bog's murmurous waste—the wilfully self-mesmerising stare of the mystic far gone. "The body's the real old curse. Not a thing in the world but it's kept out of being the grand thing it's got the means in it to be if it hadn't a hunk of a body always holding it back. You can't even have all the good there is in a song without some old blether of words would go wrong on your tongue as likely as not. And in Ireland the glory an' wonder that's sent by the will of God to gladden the heart of a man has never got shut till this day of sour old mashes of barley and malt and God alone knows what sort of dishwashin's fit to make a cow vomit, or poisons would blister half of the lining off the inside of an ass."

Constable Duffy was no man of words. But just at this moment he gained his first distinct view of philosophy's fundamental distinction between matter and form, and the prospect so ravished his whole being that as he handed in the drained tumbler to Farrell he murmured in a kind of pensive ecstasy, "Hurroosh to your soul!" and for a long time afterwards was utterly lost in the joys of contemplation.

Constable Boam's reversionary interest in paradise had now matured. While Farrell ministered to Boam, the grapes of the new wine of thought began abruptly to stammer through the lips of the Sergeant. "Aye! Every man has a pack of old trash discommodin' his soul. Pitaties and meal and the like—worked up into flesh on the man. An' the whole of it made of the dirt in the fields a month or two back! The way it's a full barrow-load of the land will be walking on every two legs that you'd see shankin' past! It's what he's come out of. And what he goes back into being. Aye and what he can't do without having, as long as he lasts. An' yet it's not he. An' yet he must keep a fast hold on it always, or else he'll be dead. An' yet I'll engage he'll have to be fighting it always—it and the sloth it would put on the grand venomous life he has in him. God help us, it's difficult." Along the mazy path that has ever followed in the wake of Socrates the Sergeant's mind slowly tottered, clinging at each turn to some reminiscence of Farrell's golden words, as a child makes its first adventurous journey on foot across the wide nursery floor, working from chair to chair for occasional support.

"Sorra a scrap of difficulty about it," Farrell assured him, "once you've got it firm set in your mind that it's all an everlasting turnin' of body into soul that's required. All of a man's body that's nothing at all but body is nothing but divvil. The job is to cut a good share of it right out of you, clever and clean, an' then to fill up the whole of the bit you have left with all the will and force of your soul till it's soul itself that the whole has become, or the next thing to the whole, the way the persons that lay you

out after you die, and the soul has quitted, would wonder to see
the weeny scrap that was left for anybody to wake. You could
take anything that there is in the world and go on scourin' an'
scourin' away at the dross it has all about it and so releasin' the
workin's of good till you'd have the thing that was nine parts
body and one part soul at the start changed to the other way
round, aye and more. By the grace of God that's the work I've
been at in this place. Half-way am I now, as you can see for yourselves, to transformin' the body of anny slushy old drink you'd
get in a town into the soul of all kindness and joy that our blessed
Lord put into the water the good people had at the wedding.
Nothing at all to do but walk straight on, the way I was going,
to work the stuff up to the pitch that you'd not feel it wetting
your throat, but only the love of God and of man, and the true
wisdom of life, and comprehension of this and of that, flowing
softly into your mind. Divvil a thing stood in me way, save
only"—here the mild-hearted fanatic stooped for a moment from
those heights where his spirit abode, to note with a wan smile of
indulgence a little infirmity of mankind's—"a few of the boys do
be lying around in the bog, the way they have me worn with the
fear they'd lap the stuff hot out of the tub an' be killed if I'd turn
me back for one instiant."

"They'll quit, from this out," the Sergeant said, with immense
decision. "I'll not have anny mischievous trash of the sort mo-
lestin' a man at his work."

"Ow! it's a wonderful country," Constable Boam breathed to
himself. The words had been rising to Boam's Cockney lips at
almost every turn of affairs since his landfall at Kingstown. Now
they came soft and low, soft and low. A peace passing all understanding had just invaded the wandering South-East Briton's
mind.

Let not the English be tempted to think that by no other race
can a law be dodged for a long time without overt scandal.
Neither the Sergeant nor either man of his force was ever a shade
the worse for liquor that summer. To Tom's priestly passion for
purging more and yet more of the baser alloys out of the true
cult there responded a loftly impulse, among the faithful, to
keep undeflowered by any beastlike excess the magical garden of
which he had given them the key.

For it was none of your common tavern practice to look in at Tom's when the loud afternoon hum of the bees was declining reposefully towards the cool velvety play-time of bats and fat moths. All that plays and the opera, lift of romance and the high, vibrant pitch of great verse are to you lucky persons of culture; travel, adventure, the throwing wide open of sudden new windows for pent minds to stare out, the brave stir of mystical gifts in the heart, gleams of enchanting light cast on places unthought of, annunciatary visits of that exalting sense of approach to some fiery core of all life, watch-tower and power-house both, whence he who attains might see all manner of things run radiantly clear in their courses and passionately right. The local police did not offer this account of their spiritual sensations at Tom's, any more than the rest of Gartumna did. But all this, or a vision of this, was for mankind to enjoy as it took its ease on the crumbling heaps of dry turf by the still, what time the inquisitive owls were just beginning to float in soundless circles overhead. From some dull and chilly outer rim of existence each little group of Tom's friends would draw in together towards a glowing focus at which the nagging "No," "No," "No," of life's common hardness was sure to give place to the benedictive "Yes," "Yes," "O, yes," of a benignly penetrative understanding of earth, heaven, and everything else. Who such a beast as to attempt to debauch the delicate fairy conducting these mysteries? Too good to imperil, they seemed, besides, too wonderful to end. Dust, all the same, hath dimmed Helen's eyes, which seemed to so many people as if their light could not go out.

All revolutions, some pundits say, are, at bottom, affairs of finance. And Mrs. Burke had diagnosed truly. Tom bore within him the germ of that mortal illness of giving away all before him. His reign in all hearts at Gartumna resembled that of the *Roi Soleil* over France both in the measureless glory of its meridian and in the fundamental insolvency of its afternoon. He had always given the work of his hands to the worthy, free and without price. The fitness to receive was all: something sacramental about the consumption of his latest masterpiece by small, close-drawn parties of beautiful souls made the passing of coin at such seasons abhorrent to Tom. "Would you have me keep a shebeen?" he had indignantly asked, when the Sergeant made a stout, shame-faced effort to pay. So, from day to day, they kept up an urbane routine month after month. Tom would always proffer the squat glass with a shy, tentative gesture; this made it clear that in the sight of God, so to speak, no such freedom had ever been taken, or thought of, before. The Sergeant would always accept in the jocose, casual tone of a martinet making one playful and really quite absurd exception to his rules, the case being one which, anyhow, cannot recur, so that there need be no uneasiness about setting up a precedent now. But all summers end, and urbanity butters no parsnips.

The brownness of later August was deepening round Tom's place of research before he saw that the thing couldn't go on as it was. He suddenly saw it, about ten o'clock one morning. That evening, when the day's tide of civilian beneficiaries had tactfully receded from the still, and the police, their normal successors, had laid rifle and helmet aside, Tom held up his dreadful secret from minute to minute while the grey moth of twilight darkened on into brown-moth-coloured night. He tried to begin telling, but found he could not trust both his voice and his face at the same time. As soon as his face could no longer be clearly seen he worked up a prodigious assumption of calm and said to the three monumental silhouettes, planted black on their three plinths of turf, "I'm ruined. Apt you'll be to find me quit out of the place if you come back in two days or three."

The Sergeant leapt off his plinth, levered up by the shock. "God help us!" he said. "What wild trash are you just after gabbing?"

"Me fortune's destroyed," Tom pursued. His face had crumpled up with distress as soon as he began; but the kind darkness hid that; his voice was in fairly good preservation. "I borrad the full of the worth of me holding to get"—and no doubt he was going on, "get along with the work I'm at, here," but felt, perhaps, that this would not be quite the thing, considering. He broke off and said only, "The back of me hand to the Jew mortgagee that's foreclosing."

"God help us," again said the Sergeant. "And we drinking the creature out of house and home a good while back! Men—!" He abruptly stiffened all the muscles of Duffy and Boam with the cogent parade voice that braces standing-easy into standing-at-ease. Then he thought for a moment. O, there was plenty to think of. Tom, the decent body, put out of his farm by the sheriff. Police aid, no doubt, requisitioned. The whole district, perhaps, in a hullabaloo, like all those around it. The Garden of Eden going straight back to prairie. He must be firm. "Men," he resumed, "are we standing by to see a man ruined that's done the right thing by ourselves? I engage it's a mod'rate share only of cash he'll require to get on in peace with his work. An' the three of us unmarried men, with full pay and allowances."

The heart of the ancient and good-natured people of England aligned itself instantly with the chivalrous spirit of the Gael. "Thet's right, Sawgeant," said Constable Boam.

Constable Duffy's range of expression had not the width to cover fully the whole diversity of life. He ejaculated, "Hurroosh to your souls! Five shillin's a week."

"Sime 'ere," subjoined Boam.

"Mine's ten," said Maguire. "I've got me rank to remember."

So swiftly and smoothly may any man's business pass, with seeming success, into a small limited company. Farrell, the innocent Farrell, took heart afresh and toiled on at the disengagement of Bacchus, the actual godhead, from out his too, too solid coatings of flesh. The force stilled the first wild fears of its heart and felt it was getting good value for its money—a quiet beat for the body, and for the soul an ever-open line of communication with the Infinite. Through all Gartumna a warning shudder had run at the first crisis. Now the world seemed safe again; the civilian lamb lay down once more beside the three large lions of the law, dreaming it to be enough that these were no man-eaters. Children all, chasing a butterfly further and further into the wilds, under a blackening sky. While they chased, the good old Resident Magistrate, Ponting, was dying of some sudden internal queerness he had, he that had never done harm to a soul if looking the other way could prevent it. And into Old Ponto's seat was climbing a raging dragon of what a blind world calls efficiency.

Major Coburn came, in fact, of that redoubtable breed of super-dragons, the virtuous, masterful, hundred-eyed cavalry sergeants who carve their way to commissions somewhat late in their careers. Precise as some old maids of exemplary life, as fully posted up in the tricks of the crowd that they have left as a schoolboy turned by magic into a master, they burn with a fierce, clear flame of desire to make up the enjoyable arrears of discipline that they might, under luckier stars, have exercised in their youth. Being the thing he was, how could the man Coburn fail to do harm, with all the harm that there was crying out to be done?

He sent for Sergeant Maguire. Quin, the District Inspector— quite enough of an Argus himself without any extra prompting —was there when the Sergeant marched into the Major's room. To outward view at this terrible moment Maguire was fashioned out of first-rate wood. Within he was but a tingling system of apprehension. First, with gimlet eyes the two superiors perfo- rated his outer timbers in numerous places, gravely demoralising the nerve centers within. When these exploratory borings had gone pretty far, the crimelessness of Gartumna was touched upon, in a spirit of coarse curiosity, far, far from felicitation.

Maguire faintly propounded the notion that keeping the law was just a hobby rife among the wayward natives. "They're queer bodies," he said in conclusion.

No fantasy like that could be expected to weigh with a new broom possessed with its first fine passion for sweeping.

"Don't tell me," the Major snapped. His voice vibrated abom- inably with menace. "You know as well as I do, Sergeant, the sort of a squadron it is where a man's never crimed." He paused, to let this baleful thrust tell its tale in the agonised Sergeant's vitals. Then he went on—"and you know what it means," and again he paused and the four gimlet eyes resumed their kindly task of puncturing him at assorted points.

To Maguire's previous distresses was now added the choice mortification which always attends the discovery that you have been firing off an abstract and friarly morality at heavily armour- plated men of the world. With no loss of penetrative power the Major continued: "Screening—that's what it means. Sergeants who need the stripes taking off them—that's what it means. Go back to your duty and see to it."

Sergeant Maguire withdrew.

"He'd not comprehend. He'd not comprehend," the Sergeant despairingly told himself, over and over again, as he legged back the four miles to Gartumna under the early falling September dew. If only the darkened mind of Major Coburn could gain understanding! Anybody on earth, you might think, if he had any wit at all to know good from bad, must see that this was a case in a thousand—that here, if ever in man's history, the spirit which giveth life was being borne down by the letter that killeth. But that body Coburn—! Maguire had been a soldier, he knew those middle-aged rankers. "Shut-headed cattle!" he groaned to himself. "No doin' anything with them." The dew was quite heavy. Sundown, autumn, and all that was best in the world going the way of honeysuckle and wild rose. Before he reached the tin hut one of the longest in human use among Melancholy's standard dyes had suffused pretty deeply the tissues of the Sergeant's mind.

It seemed next morning as if that summer's glowing pomp of lustrous months were taking its leave with a grand gesture of self-revival on the eve of extinction, as famous actors will bend up every nerve in order to be most greatly their old selves on the night of farewell. Midsummer heat was burning again, and the quicksilvery haze shimmered over the bog when Maguire went out alone to see Farrell, just as the Sergeant remembered it on the day when the scorched air from the furnace first showed him the still. Farrell, a little leaner now, a little less natty in his clothes, a little more absent-eyed with the intensity of a single absorption, raised from his work the patiently welcoming face of genius called away by affairs of this world from its heavenly traffic with miracles.

"All destroyed, Tom," the Sergeant said quickly. The longer he waited to bash in the unsuspecting upturned face of Farrell's child-like happiness, the more impracticable would it have grown. "The glory," he added by way of detail, "is departed entirely."

Farrell stared. He did not yet take it in well enough to be broken.

"It's this devastatin' divvil," the Sergeant went on, "that they've sent us in lieu of Old Ponto, God rest his kind soul."

Farrell did not seem to have even heard of that sinister accession. They say there were Paris fiddlers who fiddled right through the French Revolution and did not hear about the Bastille or the Terror. Live with the gods and deal with the Absolute Good, and Amurath's succession to Amurath may not excite you.

"God help the man, can't he see he's destroyed?" Fretful and raw from a night of wakeful distress, the Sergeant spoke almost crossly, although it was for Tom that he felt most sorely in all that overshadowed world.

The worker in the deep mine whence perfection is hewn

peered, as it were, half-abstractedly up the shaft. Not otherwise might some world-leading thinker in Moscow have looked partly up from his desk to hear, with semi-interested ears, that a Bolshevik mob was burning the house.

The disorganised Sergeant veered abruptly all the way round from pettishness to compunction. "Dear knows," he said, "that it's sorry I am for ye, Tom." He collected himself to give particulars of the catastrophe. "A hustlin' kind of a body," he ended; "et up with zeal till he'd turn the grand world that we have into a parcel of old rags and bones and scrap iron before you could hold him at all. An' what divvil's work would he have me be at, for a start, but clap somebody into the jug, good, bad, or indifferent? Now do ye see? There isn't a soul in the place but yourself that does the least taste of a thing that anny court in the wide world could convict for. What with you and the old priest and the new, and the old Colonel below, you've made the whole of the people a very fair match for the innocent saints of God. An' this a flea of a creature you couldn't ever trust to be quiet an' not stravadin' out over the bog by himself like a spy, the way he'd soon have the whole set of us supping tribulation with a spoon of sorrow!"

Farrell subsided on one of the seat-like piles of sunned peat. The fearful truth had begun to sink in. He sat for a while silent, tasting the bitter cup.

The heat that day was a wonder. Has anyone reading this ever been in the Crown court at Assizes when three o'clock on a torrid dog-day comes in the dead vast and middle of some commonplace murder case, of poignant interest to no one except the accused? Like breeze and bird and flower in the song, judge and usher, counsel and witnesses, all the unimperilled parties alike "confess the hour." Questions are slowly thought of by the Bar and languidly put; the lifeless answers are listlessly heard; motes of dust lazily stirring in shafts of glare thrown from side windows help to drowse you as though they were poppy-seeds to inhale; all eyes but one pair are beginning to glaze; the whole majestic machine of justice seems to flag and slow down as if it might soon subside into utter siesta, just where it is, like a sun-drugged Neapolitan pavior asleep on his unfinished pavement. Only the shabby party penned in the dock is proof against all the pharma-copœia of opiates. Ceaselessly shifting his feet, resetting his neck-

cloth, hunting from each sleepy face to the next for some gleam
of hope for himself, he would show, were anyone there not too
deeply lulled to observe, how far the proper quality and quantity
of torment is capable of resisting the action of Nature's own
anodynes.

Out in the bog a rude likeness of that vigil of pain, set amidst
the creeping peace of the lotus, was now being staged. Under
the rising heat of the tropical day the whole murmurous pulse
of the bog, its flies and old bees, all its audible infestation with
life seemed to be sinking right down into torpor while Sergeant
Maguire's woe-begone narrative dribbled off into silence and
Tom came to the last of his hopeless questions. Questions? No;
nothing so open: mere ineffectual sniffings among the bars of the
closed cage of their fate. Then both lay back on the warm turf,
some ten feet apart, Tom staring blankly straight up into the
unpitying blue while the Sergeant stuck it out numbly within
the darkened dome of his helmet, held over his face, striving
within the rosy gloom of that tabernacle to gather up all his
strength for the horrible plunge.

The plunge had to come. The Sergeant rose on one elbow. He
marshalled his voice. "There's the one way of it, Tom," he got
out at last. "Will you quit out of this and away to the States
before I lose all me power to keep a hand off you?"

Farrell partly rose, too. His mind had not yet journeyed so far
as the Sergeant's along the hard road.

"I'll make up the fare from me savings," the Sergeant said
humbly.

Farrell turned upon him a void, desolate face. The Sergeant
hurried on: "The three of us down below will clear up when
you're gone. An' we'll sling the still for you into the bog-hole.
Aye, be sections, will we. An' everything."

Farrell seemed to be eyeing at every part of its bald surface
the dead wall of necessity. That scrutiny ended, he quietly said,
"Me heart's broke," and lay back again flat on the peat. So did
the Sergeant. Nothing stirred for awhile except the agonised
quiver and quake of the burnt air over the homely drain-pipe
chimney of Tom's moribund furnace.

The Sergeant wangled a day's leave of absence to go down
to Queenstown the day Farrell sailed for New York. Farrell

absently waving a hand from some crowded lower deck of the departing ship was a figure of high tragic value. Happy the mole astray above ground, or the owl routed out into the sun by bad boys, compared with the perfect specialist cast out upon a bewilderingly general world. The Sergeant came away from the quay with his whole spirit laid waste—altruistic provinces and egoistic alike; his very soul sown with salt. He had been near the centre of life all the summer and felt the beat of its heart! now he was somewhere far out on its chill, charmless periphery. "As the earth when leaves are dead." He had not read Shelley. Still, just the same thing.

"I've done me duty," he said, in an almost God-cursing tone, as the three of them sat in the tin hut that night, among ashes, and heard the hard, perpetual knock of the rain on the roof, "an' I've done down meself."

"Aye, and the whole of us," Constable Duffy lamented, not meaning reproach, but sympathy only; just his part in the common threnody, antiphone answering unto phone.

Constable Boam had a part in it, too. " 'Eaven an' 'Ell, 'Eaven an' 'Ell!'" He almost chanted his dreary conspectus of their vicissitudes. "Ow! A proper mix-up! Gord! it's a wonderful country!"

Nothing more was heard of Farrell. He may have died before he could bring back into use, beside the waters of Babylon, that one talent which 'twas death to hide. Or the talent itself may have died out in his bosom. Abrupt terminations have ere now been put to the infinite; did not Shakespeare dry up, for no visible cause, when he moved back to Stratford? All that we know is that Tom's genius can never have got into its full swing in the States. For, if it had, the States could never have gone to the desperate lengths that they afterwards did against the god of his worship.

The Elixir of the Rev. Father Gaucher

ALPHONSE DAUDET

Alphonse Daudet (1840–1897) is remembered for his Lettres de Mon Moulin *(1869),* Tartarin de Tarascon *(1872) and* Sapho *(1884)—and perhaps also for having fathered the intransigent* Action Française *journalist and Royalist politician Léon Daudet. This mildly irreverent story of Father Gaucher's profitable elixir surely cannot offend the most orthodox. However, it may move even the enthusiastic lover of liqueurs to ask himself whether the human stomach is so constituted as to permit the ingestion of "three flasks an evening" of a cordial apparently similar to Benedictine or Chartreuse. The good Father Gaucher must have been graced by God with a cast-iron intestinal system.*

DRINK this, neighbour, and tell me what you think of it."
And drop by drop, with the painstaking care of a lapidary counting pearls, the curé of Graveson poured out for me two fingers of a golden-green, warm, sparkling, exquisite liqueur. My stomach was as if bathed in sunlight.

"This is Father Gaucher's elixir, the joy and health of our Provence," said the worthy man, with a triumphant air; "it is made at the convent of Prémontrés, two leagues from your mill. Isn't it better than all the chartreuses on earth? And if you knew how interesting the story of this elixir is! Listen."

Thereupon, as artlessly as possible, without the slightest tinge of irony, in that parsonage dining-room, so placid and calm, with its *Road to the Cross* in tiny pictures, and its pretty light curtains ironed like surplices, the abbé began a somewhat skeptical and irreverent anecdote, after the fashion of a tale of Erasmus or d'Assoucy.

"Twenty years ago, the Prémontrés, or the White Fathers, as we Provençals call them, had fallen into utter destitution. If you had seen their convent in those days, it would have made your heart ache.

"The high wall, the Pacôme Tower, were falling in pieces. All around the grass-grown cloisters, the pillars were cracked, the stone saints crumbling in their recesses. Not a stained-glass window whole, not a door that would close. In the courtyards, in the chapels, the wind from the Rhône blew as it blows in Camargue, extinguishing the candles, breaking the leaden sashes of the windows, spilling the water from the holy-water vessels. But the saddest of all was the convent belfry, silent as an empty dove-cote; and the fathers, in default of money to buy a bell, were obliged to ring for matins with clappers of almond-wood!

"Poor White Fathers! I can see them now, in the procession on Corpus Christi, pacing sadly along in their patched hoods, pale and thin, fed on pumpkins and watermelons; and behind them monseigneur the abbé, marching with downcast head, ashamed to exhibit in the sunlight his tarnished crook and his worm-eaten mitre of white wool. The ladies of the fraternity wept with compassion in the ranks, and the stout banner-bearers whispered sneeringly to one another as they pointed to the poor monks:

" 'The starlings grow thin when they fly in flocks.'

"The fact is, the unfortunate White Fathers had reached the point where they asked themselves if they would not do better to fly out into the world and to seek pasturage each for himself.

"Now, one day when this grave question was being discussed in the chapter, the prior was informed that Brother Gaucher desired to be heard in the council. I must say for your information that this Brother Gaucher was the drover of the convent; that is to say, he passed his days waddling from arch to arch through the cloister, driving before him two consumptive cows, which tried to find grass between the cracks of the flagstones. Supported until he was twelve years old by an old madwoman of the Baux country, called Aunt Bégon, then taken in by the monks, the wretched drover had never been able to learn anything except to drive his beasts and to repeat his paternoster; and even that he said in Provençal, for his brain was thick and his mind as dull as a leaden dagger. A fervent Christian, however, although somewhat visionary, comfortable in his haircloth shirt, and inflicting discipline upon himself, with sturdy conviction, and such arms!

"When they saw him come into the chapter-hall, simple and stupid of aspect, saluting the assemblage with a leg thrown back, prior, canons, steward, and everybody began to laugh. That was always the effect produced by that good-natured face with its grizzly, goatlike beard and its slightly erratic eyes, whenever it appeared anywhere; so that Brother Gaucher was not disturbed thereby.

" 'Reverend fathers,' he said in a wheedling voice, playing with his chaplet of olive-stones, 'it is quite true that empty casks make the best music. Just imagine that, by dint of cudgelling my poor brain, which was already so hollow, I believe that I have thought out a way to help us out of our poverty.

" 'This is how. You know Aunt Bégon, that worthy woman who took care of me when I was small—God rest her soul, the old hag! she used to sing some very vile songs after drinking— I must tell you then, reverend fathers, that Aunt Bégon, in her lifetime, knew as much about the mountain herbs as an old Corsican blackbird, and more. In fact, toward the end of her life, she compounded an incomparable elixir by mixing five or six kinds of simples that we picked together in the mountains. That was a good many years ago; but I believe that with the aid of St. Augustine and the permission of our worshipful abbé, I might, by careful search, discover the composition of that mysterious elixir. Then we should only have to bottle it and sell it at a rather high price, to enable the community to get rich as nicely as you please, like our brothers of La Trappe and La Grande—'

"He was not allowed to finish. The prior sprang to his feet and fell upon his neck. The canons seized his hands. The steward, even more deeply moved than all the rest, kissed respectfully the ragged edge of his cowl. Then they all returned to their chairs to deliberate; and the chapter decided on the spot that the cows should be intrusted to Brother Thrasybule, so that Brother Gaucher might devote himself exclusively to the compounding of his elixir.

"How did the excellent monk succeed in discovering Aunt Bégon's recipe! At the price of what efforts, or what vigils? History does not say. But this much is sure, that after six months, the elixir of the White Fathers was very popular. Throughout the Comtat, in all the Arles country, there was not a farmhouse, not a granary, which had not in the depths of its buttery, amid the bottles of mulled wine and the jars of olives *à la picholine*, a little jug of brown earthenware, sealed with the arms of Provence, and with a monk in a trance on a silver label. Thanks to the popularity of its elixir, the convent of the Prémontrés grew rich very rapidly. The Pacôme Tower was rebuilt. The prior had a new mitre, the church some pretty stained windows; and in the fine openwork of the belfry, a whole legion of bells, large and small, burst forth one fine Easter morning, jingling and chiming with all their might.

"As for Brother Gaucher, that unfortunate lay brother, whose rustic manners amused the chapter so much, was never spoken of in the convent. Henceforth they only knew the Reverend Father Gaucher, a man of brains and of great learning, who lived completely apart from the trivial and multifarious occupations of the cloister, and was shut up all day in his distillery, while thirty monks hunted the mountain for him, seeking fragrant herbs. That distillery which no one, not even the prior, had the right to enter, was an old abandoned chapel, at the end of the canons' garden. The simplicity of the worthy fathers had transformed it into something mysterious and redoubtable; and if by chance some audacious and inquisitive young monk happened to get as far as the rosework of the doorway, he retreated very quickly, terrified by the aspect of Father Gaucher, with his sorcerer's beard, leaning over his furnaces, scales in hand; and all about him retorts of red sandstone, huge alembics, serpentine glasses, a whole strange outfit, flaming as if bewitched, in the red gleam of the stained-glass.

"At nightfall, when the last Angelus rang, the door of that abode of mystery would open softly, and the father would betake himself to the church for the evening service. You should have seen the welcome that he received when he passed through the monastery! The brethren drew up in two lines for him to pass. They said to one another:

" 'Hush! he knows the secret!'

"The steward followed him and spoke to him with down-cast eyes. Amid all this adulation, the father walked along, mopping his forehead, his broad-brimmed, three-cornered hat placed on the back of his head like a halo, glancing with an air of condescension at the great courtyards full of orange-trees, the blue roofs surmounted by new weathervanes; and, in the cloister, glaringly white between the gracefully carved pillars, the monks, newly dressed, marching two by two with placid faces.

" 'They owe all this to me!' the father would say to himself; and every time that thought caused his bosom to swell with pride.

"The poor man was well punished for it, as you will see.

"Imagine that one evening, during the service, he arrived in the church in a state of extraordinary excitement: red-faced, breathless, his hood awry, and so perturbed that when he took his holy-water he wet his sleeves to the elbow. They thought at first that his excitement was due to being late; but when they saw him make profound reverences to the organ and the galleries instead of saluting the main altar, when they saw him rush through the church like a gust of wind, wander about the choir for five minutes looking for his stall, and, when once seated, bow to the right and left with a beatific smile, a murmur of amazement ran through the three naves. From breviary to breviary the monks whispered:

" 'What can be the matter with our Father Gaucher? What can be the matter with our Father Gaucher?'

"Twice the prior, in his annoyance, struck his crook on the flagstones to enjoin silence. In the choir the psalms continued; but the responses lacked vigour.

"Suddenly, in the very middle of the *Ave verum*, lo and behold Father Gaucher fell backward in his stall and chanted in a voice of thunder:

" *'In Paris there is a White Father—*
Patatin, patatan, tarabin, taraban.' "

"General consternation. Everybody rose.

" 'Carry him away! he is possessed!' they cried.

"The canons crossed themselves. Monseigneur's crook waved frantically. But Father Gaucher neither saw nor heard anything; and two sturdy monks were obliged to drag him away through the small door of the choir, struggling like one bewitched and continuing his *patatans* and his *tarabans* louder than ever.

"The next morning, at daybreak, the poor wretch was on his knees in the prior's oratory, confessing his sin with a flood of tears.

" 'It was the elixir, monseigneur, it was the elixir that took me by surprise,' he said, beating his breast. And seeing him so heart-broken, so penitent, the good prior was deeply moved himself.

" 'Come, come, Father Gaucher, calm yourself; all this will dry up like the dew in the sunshine. After all, the scandal was not so great as you think. To be sure there was a song which was a little—however, we must hope that the novices did not hear it. Now, tell me just how the thing happened to you. It was while you were trying the elixir, was it not? Your hand was a little too heavy. Yes, yes, I understand. It was like Brother Schwartz, the inventor of powder; you were the victim of your invention. And tell me, my dear friend, is it really necessary that you should try this terrible elixir upon yourself?'

" 'Unluckily, yes, monseigneur. The test-tube, to be sure, gives me the strength and degree of heat of the alcohol; but for the finishing touch, the velvety smoothness, I can trust nothing but my tongue.'

" 'Ah! very good. But listen to what I ask. When you taste the elixir thus as a duty, does it taste good to you? Do you enjoy it?'

" 'Alas! yes, monseigneur,' said the unhappy father, turning as red as a beet; 'for two evenings now I have found such a bouquet, such an aroma in it! It is certainly the devil who has played me this vile trick. So I have determined only to use the test-tube henceforth. If the liqueur is not as fine, if it is not as smooth as before, so much the worse!'

" 'Do nothing of the sort,' interrupted the prior, earnestly. 'We must not take the risk of displeasing our customers. All that you have to do now that you are warned is to be on your guard. Tell me, how much do you need to drink, for your test? Fifteen or twenty drops, is it not? Let us say twenty drops. The devil will be very smart if he can catch you with twenty drops. Moreover, to avert all chance of accident, I excuse you from coming to church henceforth. You will repeat the evening service in the distillery. And now, go in peace, my father, and above all things count your drops carefully.'

"Alas! the poor father counted his drops to no purpose; the demon had him in his clutch, and he did not let him go.

"The distillery heard some strange services!

"In the daytime everything went well. The father was tranquil enough; he prepared his retorts, his alembics, carefully assorted his herbs—all Provençal herbs, fine and gray, and burned with perfume and sunlight. But at night, when the simples were steeped and the elixir was cooling in great basins of red copper, the poor man's martyrdom began.

" 'Seventeen, eighteen, nineteen, twenty.'

"The drops fell from the tube into the silver goblet. Those twenty, the father swallowed at one draught, almost without enjoyment. It was only the twenty-first that aroused his longing. Oh! that twenty-first drop! To avoid temptation, he would go and kneel at the end of the laboratory and bury himself in his paternosters. But from the still warm liqueur there ascended a wreath of smoke heavily laden with aromatic odours, which came prowling about him, and drew him back towards the basins, whether he would or no. The liqueur was a beautiful golden-green. Leaning over it, with distended nostrils, the father stirred it gently with his tube, and it seemed to him that he saw, in the sparkling little spangles on the surface of the emerald lake, Aunt Bégon's eyes laughing and snapping as they looked at him.

" 'Nonsense! just one more drop!'

"And from drop to drop the poor wretch ended by filling his goblet to the brim. Then, at the end of his strength, he would sink down in an easy-chair; and his body relaxed, his eyes half closed, he would enjoy his sin by little sips, murmuring to himself with ecstatic remorse:

" 'Ah! I am damning myself! I am damning myself!'

"The most terrible part of it was, that in the depths of diabolical elixir, he remembered, by some witchery or other, all Aunt Bégon's naughty songs: 'There were three little gossips, who talked of giving a feast'; or, 'Master André's shepherdess goes to the woods alone'; and always the famous one of the White Fathers: 'Patatin, patatan!'

"Imagine his confusion the next day when his old neighbours said to him with a sly expression:

" 'Ha! ha! Father Gaucher, you had grasshoppers in your head when you went to bed last night.'

"Then there were tears, despair, fasting, haircloth, and penance. But nothing could prevail against the demon of the elixir; and every evening, at the same hour, the possession began anew.

"Meanwhile, orders rained upon the abbey like a blessing from Heaven. They came from Nîmes, from Aix, from Avignon, from Marseille. From day to day the convent assumed the aspect of a factory. There were packing brothers, labelling brothers, brothers to attend to the correspondence, draymen brothers; the service of God lost a few strokes of the bell now and then, to be sure, but the poor people of the neighbourhood lost nothing, I assure you.

"But one fine Sunday morning, while the steward was reading to the chapter his annual inventory, and the good canons were listening with sparkling eyes and smiling lips, behold Father Gaucher rushed into the midst of the conference, exclaiming:

" 'It is all over! I can't stand it any longer! give me back my cows.'

" 'What is the matter, pray, Father Gaucher?' asked the prior, who had a shrewd idea what the matter might be.

" 'The matter, monseigneur? The matter is that I am laying up for myself an eternity of hell-fire and blows with the pitchfork. The matter is that I am drinking, drinking like a miserable wretch.'

" 'But I told you to count your drops.'

" 'Count my drops! Oh, yes! I should have to count them by goblets now. Yes, my fathers, I have reached that point. Three flasks an evening. You must see that that cannot last. So let whomsoever you choose make the elixir. May God's fire consume me if I touch it again!'

"The chapter laughed no longer.

" 'But you are ruining us, unhappy man!' cried the steward, waving his ledger.

" 'Do you prefer that I should damn myself forever?'

"Thereupon the prior rose.

" 'My fathers,' he said, putting forth his beautiful white hand, upon which the pastoral ring glistened, 'there is a way to arrange everything. It is at night, is it not, my dear son, that the demon tempts you?'

" 'Yes, monsieur prior, regularly every evening. So now, when night comes, a cold sweat takes me, saving your presence, like Capitou's donkey when he saw the saddle coming.'

" ' 'Tis well! be comforted. Henceforth, every evening, at the service, we will repeat in your favour the prayer of St. Augustine, to which plenary indulgence is attached. With that, whatever happens, you are safe. It affords absolution during sin.'

" 'Oh well! in that case, thanks, monsieur prior!'

"And, without asking anything more, Father Gaucher returned to his laboratory, as light-hearted as a lark.

"And in truth, from that day forward, every evening at the end of the complines, the officiating father never failed to say:

" 'Let us pray for our poor Father Gaucher, who is sacrificing his soul in the interest of the community. *Oremus, Dominie—*'

"And while the prayer ran quivering over those white hoods, prostrate in the shadow of the nave, as a light breeze rushes over the snow, yonder at the other end of the convent, behind the flaming stained-glass of the distillery, Father Gaucher could be heard singing at the top of his lungs:

> *"In Paris there is a White Father,*
> *Patatin, patatan, tarabin, taraban;*
> *In Paris there is a White Father*
> *Who dances with the nuns,*
> *Trin, trin, trin, in a garden,*
> *Who dances with the—"*

Here the good curé stopped, in dismay.

"Merciful Heaven!" he exclaimed, "suppose my parishioners should hear me!"

A Miser of Armagnac

H. WARNER ALLEN

The name of H. Warner Allen needs no introduction to wine-lovers. He is the author of at least a dozen standard works on wine. Among his best books: The Wines of France, Through the Wine Glass, A Contemplation of Wine, The Romance of Wine. *He even wrote a thriller called* Mr. Clerihew, Wine Merchant. *His latest volume,* A History of Wine, *crowns his long career as authority and connoisseur.*

"IF you had sold your armagnac, you would no longer have it." My inane remark set the wrinkles of Joseph's weather-beaten face expanding in a radiant smile. His little blue eyes twinkled, and the corners of his thin lips twitched. His expression combined a bland childlike simplicity with more than a touch of that sly cunning which the peasant shares with the wild animals he knows so well. My words for him were full of meaning, and he repeated them to himself chuckling with satisfaction: "If I had sold my *eau-de-vie*, I should no longer have it."

A sturdy, thickset Gascon of 76, Joseph was standing in the vineyard of his property, 20 or 30 rich acres of vines, pasture and wood, in the heart of that Bas-Armagnac which is to armagnac what Grande Champagne is to cognac, the very apple of the eye. The sun was scorching with the menace of a storm, and as he worked in the strange mixture of clay and sand, known as *boulbène* and beloved by the vine, with two of his tenants who shared both his labours and his profits, his head was protected by an immense straw hat with the *béret* from which he was never parted neatly fitted over its crown. On his feet he wore boatlike sabots enclosing carpet-slippers—a favourite foot-gear in these parts even for motor-cyclists—and pale blue socks.

He had been complaining that no one would buy his armagnac. My friend Castarède, who was initiating me into the mysteries of armagnac, had warned me that Joseph was as miserly over his famous brandy as Harpagon over his gold, and scared off intending purchasers by asking preposterous prices, preferring to part only with wines and spirits by which he set no great store and live, not, indeed, meanly—he would have given us a splendid lunch, if we had been able to accept his invitation—but thriftily and very simply, consuming only what his estate provided.

The rarely visited and sparsely populated region of Armagnac lies inland between Bordeaux and the Pyrenees. It is a great mistake to think that armagnac brandy is only an inferior kind of cognac. Distilled on a different principle, with a much lower alcoholic strength, it has an individuality of its own. It does not attain the heights of ethereal transcendence to which the finest cognacs aspire, but it boasts modest charms of its own which are hardly less attractive. Armagnac represents in volume one-fifth of the wine employed for its distillation, cognac one-eighth, and, consequently, armagnac retains a higher percentage of wine constituents other than alcohol. It smacks more of the soil, and is altogether less commercialised, pleasing by its unsophisticated freshness and a variety of such scents as a country lane offers on a summer day.

Castarède wanted to taste Joseph's 1950 *eau-de-vie* as a matter of business; Joseph was all agog to show off the masterpieces he had grown and distilled to a foreigner who had come specially from England to study armagnac. So we strolled through the wood to the farm and the *chai*, the lofty massive building propped with huge oak beams, where the brandies were stored. On the way Joseph grumbled at old age which prevented him from working as hard as he used. Rheumatism had driven him to seek relief at a Pyrenean spa, and so forced him to leave his native Armagnac for the first time in his life.

We plunged from the Midi glare into the freshness and dim light of the great *chai*. "O, the dark translucence of the deep-eyed cool!" Never did the lord of a great house do the honours of his collections, never did a painter display the works of his art, with greater zest than that with which Joseph submitted to our appreciation examples of his wine-growing and wine-distilling skill; but Castarède's requests for a taste of last year's spirit were quietly ignored as if they had not been made. Was the 1950 brandy below par? Or was it too good to sell?

Joseph might be a miser when it came to selling his treasure; he was positively extravagant in the precautions he took to set off its beauties to the best possible advantage. A test tube at the end of a string served to bring up the spirit from the cask, and there followed a ritual of purification worthy of the Orphic mysteries. The glass held lengthwise was revolved, and brandy poured liberally over its outer surface to remove any speck of exterior contamination; and then its inside was rinsed and swilled with even greater care. In the end almost as much spirit was used to cleanse the glass as eventually went into it for the taster, and this process was repeated as we passed from cask to cask, so that each sample might stand or fall by its own isolated qualities. With tears in his eyes Joseph implored us to heat the glass thoroughly in our hands before we attempted to savour the bouquet of its contents or submit their aroma to our palates. Were we not dealing with the subtlest of perfumes and the most delicate shades of taste?

Two vast *foudres*, or vats, perched high on scaffolding, held the gem of Joseph's collection, *eau-de-vie* of the renowned 1904 vintage, on which the leading armagnac firms had been casting covetous eyes for years and years. Sixty years ago he had helped to make these giant casks out of the home-grown black oak in which alone armagnac can be matured. Mature brandy both in cognac and armagnac owes nearly as much to the wood as it does to the wine from which it is distilled: for the colourless spirit takes from the oak staves all its colour and half its taste and bouquet.

"Yes," said my friend in my ear, "but Joseph's *eaux-de-vie* have long ago drained the wood of all its virtues. They ought to have been bottled years ago. Now they can only go downhill. He knows it, but he will never sell."

Joseph was leading the way to the house for the tasting of the 1904, which could not be conveniently drawn from the *foudres*, and I asked Castarède what value he would put on Joseph's stock of fine brandies. "At present rates I should reckon about fifty million francs." Fifty million francs is worth a good deal more than its exchange value of £50,000 to the average Frenchman, and enormously more to such an Armagnac peasant as Joseph. Yet who can doubt that he has been wise in his generation?

The furniture of our host's room consisted of a cupboard and a table, well garnished with bottles and glasses, some rush-bottomed chairs, and on a peg a top hat which must need a deal of attention before Joseph can don it for solemn occasions. No doubt my expert friend was right when he said that the 1904 was going downhill: but I found it remarkable with an agreeable tang of its own, still beautifully fresh, and particularly enjoyed that mellowness of age known as *rancio,* so-called because in excess it becomes rancidity.

We tasted and talked. In 1914 Joseph's two brothers were called up, and he, the eldest, left in charge at home. During their absence he sold a cask of his 1904 brandy for what seemed to him the fabulous price of 5,000 francs. A year later, when his brothers came home on leave, they were furious with him for having wasted their common patrimony: he could now have got 10,000 francs for the same cask. He was not to be caught twice. Now his brothers are dead, he has not married, and what will happen to his armagnac when he dies no one knows.

This hoarding of armagnac has made him a potentially rich man, and he has had great pleasure from it. It has been fun watching would-be buyers' faces when they have heard his selling-price. It has been real enjoyment to demonstrate to his neighbours the greater virtue of his soil, his mastery of viticulture and the superiority of his own distilling. Better amass what can be drunk or eaten than paper, or even gold; and, better still, Joseph feels that he has done what all Frenchmen love to do—cheated the tax-collector.

A MIXED
CASE

Taste

ROALD DAHL

Roald Dahl (1916–   ) is the author of three books of stories, of which the latter two (Someone Like You *and* Kiss Kiss) *contain several miniature masterpieces of the macabre. Married to the actress Patricia Neal, he has two daughters, and divides his time between England and New York. Several of his hobbies (which include collecting eighteenth-century English furniture, betting on horses, and growing roses) are reflected in his stories. The tale that follows, an outgrowth of his interest in wine-drinking, made its first stunning appearance in* The New Yorker.

THERE were six of us to dinner that night at Mike Schofield's house in London: Mike and his wife and daughter, my wife and I, and a man called Richard Pratt.

Richard Pratt was a famous gourmet. He was president of a small society known as the Epicures, and each month he circulated privately to its members a pamphlet on food and wines. He organized dinners where sumptuous dishes and rare wines were served. He refused to smoke for fear of harming his palate, and when discussing a wine, he had a curious, rather droll habit of referring to it as though it were a living being. "A prudent wine," he would say, "rather diffident and evasive, but quite prudent." Or, "a good-humored wine, benevolent and cheerful —slightly obscene, perhaps, but nonetheless good-humored."

I had been to dinner at Mike's twice before when Richard Pratt was there, and on each occasion Mike and his wife had gone out of their way to produce a special meal for the famous gourmet. And this one, clearly, was to be no exception. The moment we entered the dining room, I could see that the table was laid for a feast. The tall candles, the yellow roses, the quantity of shining silver, the three wineglasses to each person, and above all, the faint scent of roasting meat from the kitchen brought the first warm oozings of saliva to my mouth.

As we sat down, I remembered that on both Richard Pratt's previous visits Mike had played a little betting game with him over the claret, challenging him to name its breed and its vintage. Pratt had replied that that should not be too difficult provided it was one of the great years. Mike had then bet him a case of the wine in question that he could not do it. Pratt had accepted, and had won both times. Tonight I felt sure that the little game would be played over again, for Mike was quite willing to lose the bet in order to prove that his wine was good enough to be recognized, and Pratt, for his part, seemed to take a grave, restrained pleasure in displaying his knowledge.

The meal began with a plate of whitebait, fried very crisp in butter, and to go with it there was a Moselle. Mike got up and poured the wine himself, and when he sat down again, I could see that he was watching Richard Pratt. He had set the bottle in front of me so that I could read the label. It said, "Geierslay Ohligsberg, 1945." He leaned over and whispered to me that Geierslay was a tiny village in the Moselle, almost unknown outside Germany. He said that this wine we were drinking was something unusual, that the output of the vineyard was so small that it was almost impossible for a stranger to get any of it. He had visited Geierslay personally the previous summer in order to obtain the few dozen bottles that they had finally allowed him to have.

"I doubt anyone else in the country has any of it at the moment," he said. I saw him glance again at Richard Pratt. "Great thing about Moselle," he continued, raising his voice, "it's the perfect wine to serve before a claret. A lot of people serve a Rhine wine instead, but that's because they don't know any better. A Rhine wine will kill a delicate claret, you know that? It's barbaric to serve a Rhine before a claret. But a Moselle —ah!—a Moselle is exactly right."

Mike Schofield was an amiable, middle-aged man. But he was a stock-broker. To be precise, he was a jobber in the stock market, and like a number of his kind, he seemed to be somewhat embarrassed, almost ashamed to find that he had made so much money with so slight a talent. In his heart he knew that he was not really much more than a bookmaker—an unctuous, infinitely respectable, secretly unscrupulous bookmaker—and he knew that his friends knew it, too. So he was seeking now to become a man of culture, to cultivate a literary and aesthetic taste, to collect paintings, music, books, and all the rest of it. His little sermon about Rhine wine and Moselle was a part of this thing, this culture that he sought.

"A charming little wine, don't you think?" he said. He was still watching Richard Pratt. I could see him give a rapid furtive glance down the table each time he dropped his head to take a mouthful of whitebait. I could almost *feel* him waiting for the moment when Pratt would take his first sip, and look up from his glass with a smile of pleasure, of astonishment, perhaps even of wonder, and then there would be a discussion and Mike would tell him about the village of Geierslay.

But Richard Pratt did not taste his wine. He was completely engrossed in conversation with Mike's eighteen-year-old daughter, Louise. He was half turned toward her, smiling at her, telling her, so far as I could gather, some story about a chef in a Paris restaurant. As he spoke, he leaned closer and closer to her, seeming in his eagerness almost to impinge upon her, and the poor girl leaned as far as she could away from him, nodding politely, rather desperately, and looking not at his face but at the top-most button of his dinner jacket.

We finished our fish, and the maid came around removing the plates. When she came to Pratt, she saw that he had not yet touched his food, so she hesitated, and Pratt noticed her. He waved her away, broke off his conversation, and quickly began to eat, popping the little crisp brown fish quickly into his mouth with rapid jabbing movements of his fork. Then, when he had finished, he reached for his glass, and in two short swallows he tipped the wine down his throat and turned immediately to resume his conversation with Louise Schofield.

Mike saw it all. I was conscious of him sitting there, very still, containing himself, looking at his guest. His round jovial face seemed to loosen slightly and to sag, but he contained himself and was still and said nothing.

Soon the maid came forward with the second course. This was a large roast of beef. She placed it on the table in front of Mike who stood up and carved it, cutting the slices very thin, laying them gently on the plates for the maid to take around. When he had served everyone, including himself, he put down the carving knife and leaned forward with both hands on the edge of the table.

"Now," he said, speaking to all of us but looking at Richard Pratt. "Now for the claret. I must go and fetch the claret, if you'll excuse me."

"You go and fetch it, Mike?" I said. "Where is it?"

"In my study, with the cork out—breathing."

"Why the study?"

"Acquiring room temperature, of course. It's been there twenty-four hours."

"But why the study?"

"It's the best place in the house. Richard helped me choose it last time he was here."

At the sound of his name, Pratt looked around.

"That's right, isn't it?" Mike said.

"Yes," Pratt answered, nodding gravely. "That's right."

"On top of the green filing cabinet in my study," Mike said. "That's the place we chose. A good draft-free spot in a room with an even temperature. Excuse me now, will you, while I fetch it."

The thought of another wine to play with had restored his humor, and he hurried out the door, to return a minute later more slowly, walking softly, holding in both hands a wine basket in which a dark bottle lay. The label was out of sight, facing downward. "Now!" he cried as he came toward the table. "What about this one, Richard? You'll never name this one!"

Richard Pratt turned slowly and looked up at Mike; then his eyes travelled down to the bottle nestling in its small wicker basket, and he raised his eyebrows, a slight, supercilious arching of the brows, and with it a pushing outward of the wet lower lip, suddenly imperious and ugly.

"You'll never get it," Mike said. "Not in a hundred years."

"A claret?" Richard Pratt asked, condescending.

"Of course."

"I assume, then, that it's from one of the smaller vineyards?"

"Maybe it is, Richard. And then again, maybe it isn't."

"But it's a good year? One of the great years?"

"Yes, I guarantee that."

"Then it shouldn't be too difficult," Richard Pratt said, drawling his words, looking exceedingly bored. Except that, to me, there was something strange about his drawling and his boredom: between the eyes a shadow of something evil, and in his bearing an intentness, that gave me a faint sense of uneasiness as I watched him.

"This one is really rather difficult," Mike said, "I won't force you to bet on this one."

"Indeed. And why not?" Again the slow arching of the brows, the cool, intent look.

"Because it's difficult."

"That's not very complimentary to me, you know."

"My dear man," Mike said, "I'll bet you with pleasure, if that's what you wish."

"It shouldn't be too hard to name it."

"You mean you want to bet?"

"I'm perfectly willing to bet," Richard Pratt said.

"All right, then, we'll have the usual. A case of the wine itself."

"You don't think I'll be able to name it, do you?"

"As a matter of fact, and with all due respect, I don't," Mike said. He was making some effort to remain polite, but Pratt was not bothering overmuch to conceal his contempt for the whole proceeding. And yet, curiously, his next question seemed to betray a certain interest.

"You like to increase the bet?"

"No, Richard. A case is plenty."

"Would you like to bet fifty cases?"

"That would be silly."

Mike stood very still behind his chair at the head of the table, carefully holding the bottle in its ridiculous wicker basket. There was a trace of whiteness around his nostrils now, and his mouth was shut very tight.

Pratt was lolling back in his chair, looking up at him, the eyebrows raised, the eyes half closed, a little smile touching the corners of his lips. And again I saw, or thought I saw, something distinctly disturbing about the man's face, that shadow of intentness between the eyes, and in the eyes themselves, right in their centers where it was black, a small slow spark of shrewdness, hiding.

"So you don't want to increase the bet?"

"As far as I'm concerned, old man, I don't give a damn," Mike said. "I'll bet you anything you like."

The three women and I sat quietly, watching the two men. Mike's wife was becoming annoyed; her mouth had gone sour and I felt that at any moment she was going to interrupt. Our roast beef lay before us on our plates, slowly steaming.

"So you'll bet me anything I like?"

"That's what I told you. I'll bet you anything you damn well please, if you want to make an issue out of it."

"Even ten thousand pounds?"

"Certainly I will, if that's the way you want it." Mike was more confident now. He knew quite well that he could call any sum Pratt cared to mention.

"So you say I can name the bet?" Pratt asked again.

"That's what I said."

There was a pause while Pratt looked slowly around the table, first at me, then at the three women, each in turn. He appeared to be reminding us that we were witness to the offer.

"Mike!" Mrs. Schofield said. "Mike, why don't we stop this nonsense and eat our food. It's getting cold."

"But it isn't nonsense," Pratt told her evenly. "We're making a little bet."

I noticed the maid standing in the background holding a dish of vegetables, wondering whether to come forward with them or not.

"All right, then," Pratt said. "I'll tell you what I want you to bet."

"Come on, then," Mike said, rather reckless. "I don't give a damn what it is—you're on."

Pratt nodded, and again the little smile moved the corners of his lips, and then, quite slowly, looking at Mike all the time, he said, "I want you to bet me the hand of your daughter in marriage."

Louise Schofield gave a jump. "Hey!" she cried. "No! That's not funny! Look here, Daddy, that's not funny at all."

"No, dear," her mother said. "They're only joking."

"I'm not joking," Richard Pratt said.

"It's ridiculous," Mike said. He was off balance again now.

"You said you'd bet anything I liked."

"I meant money."

"You didn't *say* money."

"That's what I meant."

"Then it's a pity you didn't say it. But anyway, if you wish to go back on your offer, that's quite all right with me."

"It's not a question of going back on my offer, old man. It's a no-bet anyway, because you can't match the stake. You yourself don't happen to have a daughter to put up against mine in case you lose. And if you had, I wouldn't want to marry her."

"I'm glad of that, dear," his wife said.

"I'll put up anything you like," Pratt announced. "My house, for example. How about my house?"

"Which one?" Mike asked, joking now.

"The country one."

"Why not the other one as well?"

"All right then, if you wish it. Both my houses."

At that point I saw Mike pause. He took a step forward and placed the bottle in its basket gently down on the table. He moved the saltcellar to one side, then the pepper, and then he picked up his knife, studied the blade thoughtfully for a moment, and put it down again. His daughter, too, had seen him pause.

"Now, Daddy!" she cried. "Don't be *absurd!* It's *too* silly for words. I refuse to be betted on like this."

"Quite right, dear," her mother said. "Stop it at once, Mike, and sit down and eat your food."

Mike ignored her. He looked over at his daughter and he smiled, a slow, fatherly, protective smile. But in his eyes, suddenly, there glimmered a little triumph. "You know," he said, smiling as he spoke. "You know, Louise, we ought to think about this a bit."

"Now, stop it, Daddy! I refuse even to listen to you! Why, I've never heard anything so ridiculous in my life!"

"No, seriously, my dear. Just wait a moment and hear what I have to say."

"But I don't *want* to hear it."

"Louise! Please! It's like this. Richard, here, has offered us a serious bet. He is the one who wants to make it, not me. And if he loses, he will have to hand over a considerable amount of property. Now, wait a minute, my dear, don't interrupt. The point is this. *He cannot possibly win.*"

"He seems to think he can."

"Now listen to me, because I know what I'm talking about. The expert, when tasting a claret—so long as it is not one of the famous great wines like Lafite or Latour—can only get a certain way toward naming the vineyard. He can, of course, tell you the Bordeaux district from which the wine comes, whether it is from St. Emilion, Pomerol, Graves, or Médoc. But then each district has several communes, little counties, and each county has many, many small vineyards. It is impossible for a man to differentiate between them all by taste and smell alone. I don't mind telling you that this one I've got here is a wine from a small vineyard that is surrounded by many other small vineyards, and he'll never get it. It's impossible."

"You can't be sure of that," his daughter said.

"I'm telling you I can. Though I say it myself, I understand quite a bit about this wine business, you know. And anyway, heavens alive, girl, I'm your father and you don't think I'd let you in for—for something you didn't want, do you? I'm trying to make you some money."

"Mike!" his wife said sharply. "Stop it now, Mike, please!"

Again he ignored her. "If you will take this bet," he said to his daughter, "in ten minutes you will be the owner of two large houses."

"But I don't want two large houses, Daddy."

"Then sell them. Sell them back to him on the spot. I'll arrange all that for you. And then, just think of it, my dear, you'll be rich! You'll be independent for the rest of your life!"

"Oh, Daddy, I don't like it. I think it's silly."

"So do I," the mother said. She jerked her head briskly up and down as she spoke, like a hen. "You ought to be ashamed of yourself, Michael, ever suggesting such a thing! Your own daughter, too!"

Mike didn't even look at her. "Take it!" he said eagerly, staring hard at the girl. "Take it, quick! I'll guarantee you won't lose."

"But I don't like it, Daddy."

"Come on, girl. Take it!"

Mike was pushing her hard. He was leaning toward her, fixing her with two hard bright eyes, and it was not easy for the daughter to resist him.

"But what if I lose?"

"I keep telling you, you can't lose. I'll guarantee it."

"Oh, Daddy, must I?"

"I'm making you a fortune. So come on now. What do you say, Louise? All right?"

For the last time, she hesitated. Then she gave a helpless little shrug of the shoulders and said, "Oh, all right, then. Just so long as you swear there's no danger of losing."

"Good!" Mike cried. "That's fine! Then it's a bet!"

"Yes," Richard Pratt said, looking at the girl. "It's a bet."

Immediately, Mike picked up the wine, tipped the first thimbleful into his own glass, then skipped excitedly around the table filling up the others. Now everyone was watching Richard Pratt, watching his face as he reached slowly for his glass with his right hand and lifted it to his nose. The man was about fifty years old and he did not have a pleasant face. Somehow, it was all mouth —mouth and lips—the full, wet lips of the professional gourmet, the lower lip hanging downward in the center, a pendulous, permanently open taster's lip, shaped open to receive the rim of a glass or a morsel of food. Like a keyhole, I thought, watching it; his mouth is like a large wet keyhole.

Slowly he lifted the glass to his nose. The point of the nose entered the glass and moved over the surface of the wine, delicately sniffing. He swirled the wine gently around in the glass to receive the bouquet. His concentration was intense. He had closed his eyes, and now the whole top half of his body, the head and neck and chest, seemed to become a kind of huge sensitive smelling-machine, receiving, filtering, analyzing the message from the sniffing nose.

Mike, I noticed, was lounging in his chair, apparently unconcerned, but he was watching every move. Mrs. Schofield, the wife, sat prim and upright at the other end of the table, looking straight ahead, her face tight with disapproval. The daughter, Louise, had shifted her chair away a little, and sidewise, facing the gourmet, and she, like her father, was watching closely.

For at least a minute, the smelling process continued; then, without opening his eyes or moving his head, Pratt lowered the glass to his mouth and tipped in almost half the contents. He paused, his mouth full of wine, getting the first taste; then he permitted some of it to trickle down his throat and I saw his Adam's apple move as it passed by. But most of it he retained in his mouth. And now, without swallowing again, he drew in through his lips a thin breath of air which mingled with the fumes of the wine in the mouth and passed on down into his lungs. He held the breath, blew it out through his nose, and finally began to roll the wine around under the tongue, and chewed it, actually chewed it with his teeth as though it were bread.

It was a solemn, impressive performance and I must say he did it well.

"Um," he said, putting down the glass, running a pink tongue over his lips. "Um—yes. A very interesting little wine—gentle and gracious, almost feminine in the aftertaste."

There was an excess of saliva in his mouth, and as he spoke he spat an occasional bright speck of it onto the table.

"Now we can start to eliminate," he said. "You will pardon me for doing this carefully, but there is much at stake. Normally I would perhaps take a bit of a chance, leaping forward quickly and landing right in the middle of the vineyard of my choice. But I must move cautiously this time, must I not?" He looked up at Mike and he smiled, a thick-lipped, wet-lipped smile. Mike did not smile back.

"First, then, which district in Bordeaux does this wine come from? That is not too difficult to guess. It is far too light in the body to be from either St. Emilion or Graves. It is obviously a Médoc. There's no doubt about *that*.

"Now—from which commune in Médoc does it come? That also, by elimination, should not be too difficult to decide. Margaux? No. It cannot be Margaux. It has not the violent bouquet of a Margaux. Pauillac? It cannot be Pauillac, either. It is too tender, too gentle and wistful for a Pauillac. The wine of Pauillac has a character that is almost imperious in its taste. And also to me, a Pauillac contains just a little pith, a curious dusty, pithy flavor that the grape acquires from the soil of the district. No, no. This—this is a very gentle wine, demure and bashful in the first taste, emerging shyly but quite graciously in the second. A little arch, perhaps, in the second taste, and a little naughty also, teasing the tongue with a trace, just a trace, of tannin. Then, in the aftertaste, delightful—consoling and feminine, with a certain blithely generous quality that one associates only with the wines of the commune of St. Julien. Unmistakably this is a St. Julien."

He leaned back in his chair, held his hands up level with his chest, and placed the fingertips carefully together. He was becoming ridiculously pompous, but I thought that some of it was deliberate, simply to mock his host. I found myself waiting rather tensely for him to go on. The girl Louise was lighting a cigarette. Pratt heard the match strike and he turned on her, flaring suddenly with real anger. "Please!" he said. "Please don't do that! It's a disgusting habit, to smoke at table!"

She looked up at him, still holding the burning match in one hand, the big slow eyes settling on his face, resting there a moment, moving away again, slow and contemptuous. She bent her head and blew out the match, but continued to hold the unlighted cigarette in her fingers.

"I'm sorry, my dear," Pratt said, "but I simply cannot have smoking at table."

She didn't look at him again.

"Now, let me see—where were we?" he said. "Ah, yes. This wine is from Bordeaux, from the commune of St. Julien, in the district of Médoc. So far, so good. But now we come to the more difficult part—the name of the vineyard itself. For in St. Julien there are many vineyards, and as our host so rightly remarked earlier on, there is often not much difference between the wine of one and the wine of another. But we shall see."

He paused again, closing his eyes. "I am trying to establish the 'growth,'" he said. "If I can do that, it will be half the battle. Now, let me see. This wine is obviously not from a first-growth vineyard—nor even a second. It is not a great wine. The quality, the—the—what do you call it?—the radiance, the power, is lacking. But a third growth—that it could be. And yet I doubt it. We know it is a good year—our host has said so—and this is probably flattering it a little bit. I must be careful. I must be very careful here."

He picked up his glass and took another small sip.

"Yes," he said, sucking his lips, "I was right. It is a fourth growth. Now I am sure of it. A fourth growth from a very good year—from a great year, in fact. And that's what made it taste for a moment like a third—or even a second-growth wine. Good! That's better! Now we are closing in! What are the fourth-growth vineyards in the commune of St. Julien?"

Again he paused, took up his glass, and held the rim against that sagging, pendulous lower lip of his. Then I saw the tongue shoot out, pink and narrow, the tip of it dipping into the wine, withdrawing swiftly again—a repulsive sight. When he lowered the glass, his eyes remained closed, the face concentrated, only the lips moving, sliding over each other like two pieces of wet, spongy rubber.

"There it is again!" he cried. "Tannin in the middle taste, and the quick astringent squeeze upon the tongue. Yes, yes, of course! Now I have it! This wine comes from one of those small vineyards around Beychevelle. I remember now. The Beychevelle district, and the river and the little harbor that has silted up so the wine ships can no longer use it. Beychevelle . . . could it actually be a Beychevelle itself? No, I don't think so. Not quite. But it is somewhere very close. Château Talbot? Could it be Talbot? Yes, it could. Wait one moment."

He sipped the wine again, and out of the side of my eye I noticed Mike Schofield and how he was leaning farther and farther forward over the table, his mouth slightly open, his small eyes fixed upon Richard Pratt.

"No. I was wrong. It was not a Talbot. A Talbot comes forward to you just a little quicker than this one; the fruit is nearer to the surface. If it is a '34, which I believe it is, then it couldn't be Talbot. Well, well. Let me think. It is not a Beychevelle and it is not a Talbot, and yet—yet it is so close to both of them, so close, that the vineyard must be almost in between. Now, which could that be?"

He hesitated, and we waited, watching his face. Everyone, even Mike's wife, was watching him now. I heard the maid put down the dish of vegetables on the sideboard behind me, gently, so as not to disturb the silence.

"Ah!" he cried. "I have it! Yes, I think I have it!"

For the last time, he sipped the wine. Then, still holding the glass up near his mouth, he turned to Mike and he smiled, a slow, silky smile, and he said, "You know what this is? This is the little Château Branaire-Ducru."

Mike sat tight, not moving.

"And the year, 1934."

We all looked at Mike, waiting for him to turn the bottle around in its basket and show the label.

"Is that your final answer?" Mike said.

"Yes, I think so."

"Well, is it or isn't it?"

"Yes, it is."

"What was the name again?"

"Château Branaire-Ducru. Pretty little vineyard. Lovely old château. Know it quite well. Can't think why I didn't recognize it at once."

"Come on, Daddy," the girl said. "Turn it round and let's have a peek. I want my two houses."

"Just a minute," Mike said. "Wait just a minute." He was sitting very quiet, bewildered-looking, and his face was becoming puffy and pale, as though all the force was draining slowly out of him.

"Michael!" his wife called sharply from the other end of the table. "What's the matter?"

"Keep out of this, Margaret, will you please."

Richard Pratt was looking at Mike, smiling with his mouth, his eyes small and bright. Mike was not looking at anyone.

"Daddy!" the daughter cried, agonized. "But, Daddy, you don't mean to say he's guessed it right!"

"Now, stop worrying, my dear," Mike said. "There's nothing to worry about."

I think it was more to get away from his family than anything else that Mike then turned to Richard Pratt and said, "I'll tell you what, Richard. I think you and I better slip off into the next room and have a little chat?"

"I don't want a little chat," Pratt said. "All I want is to see the label on that bottle." He knew he was a winner now; he had the bearing, the quiet arrogance of a winner, and I could see that he was prepared to become thoroughly nasty if there was any trouble. "What are you waiting for?" he said to Mike. "Go on and turn it round."

Then this happened: The maid, the tiny, erect figure of the maid in her white-and-black uniform, was standing beside Richard Pratt, holding something out in her hand. "I believe these are yours, sir," she said.

Pratt glanced around, saw the pair of thin horn-rimmed spectacles that she held out to him, and for a moment he hesitated. "Are they? Perhaps they are. I don't know."

"Yes sir, they're yours." The maid was an elderly woman— nearer seventy than sixty—a faithful family retainer of many years standing. She put the spectacles down on the table beside him.

Without thanking her, Pratt took them up and slipped them into his top pocket, behind the white handkerchief.

But the maid didn't go away. She remained standing beside and slightly behind Richard Pratt, and there was something so unusual in her manner and in the way she stood there, small, motionless, and erect, that I for one found myself watching her with a sudden apprehension. Her old gray face had a frosty, determined look, the lips were compressed, the little chin was out, and the hands were clasped together tight before her. The curious cap on her head and the flash of white down the front of her uniform made her seem like some tiny, ruffled, white-breasted bird.

"You left them in Mr. Schofield's study," she said. Her voice was unnaturally, deliberately polite. "On top of the green filing cabinet in his study, sir, when you happened to go in there by yourself before dinner."

It took a few moments for the full meaning of her words to penetrate, and in the silence that followed I became aware of Mike and how he was slowly drawing himself up in his chair, and the color coming to his face, and the eyes opening wide, and the curl of the mouth, and the dangerous little patch of whiteness beginning to spread around the area of the nostrils.

"Now, Michael!" his wife said. "Keep calm now, Michael, dear! Keep calm!"

The Cask of Amontillado

EDGAR ALLAN POE

The short, unhappy life of Edgar Allan Poe (1809–1849) is too well known to call for summary. Notable as was his erudition in a dozen other subjects, from conchology to cryptography, there is little evidence in the famous old chestnut that follows that he knew much about wine. He is taken apart, not too tenderly, by H. Warner Allen, whose amusing commentary I have appended to Poe's chiller.

THE thousand injuries of Fortunato I had borne as I best could; but when he ventured upon insult, I vowed revenge. You, who so well know the nature of my soul, will not suppose, however, that I gave utterance to a threat. *At length* I would be avenged; this was a point definitively settled—but the very definitiveness with which it was resolved, precluded the idea of risk. I must not only punish, but punish with impunity. A wrong is unredressed when retribution overtakes its redresser. It is equally unredressed when the avenger fails to make himself felt as such to him who has done the wrong.

It must be understood, that neither by word nor deed had I given Fortunato cause to doubt my good-will. I continued, as was my wont, to smile in his face, and he did not perceive that my smile *now* was at the thought of his immolation.

He had a weak point—this Fortunato—although in other regards he was a man to be respected and even feared. He prided himself on his connoisseurship in wine. Few Italians have the true virtuoso spirit. For the most part their enthusiasm is adopted to suit the time and opportunity—to practise imposture upon the British and Austrian *millionnaires*. In painting and gemmary Fortunato, like his countrymen, was a quack—but in the matter of old

243

wines he was sincere. In this respect I did not differ from him materially: I was skilful in the Italian vintages myself, and bought largely whenever I could.

It was about dusk, one evening during the supreme madness of the carnival season, that I encountered my friend. He accosted me with excessive warmth, for he had been drinking much. The man wore motley. He had on a tight-fitting parti-striped dress, and his head was surmounted by the conical cap and bells. I was so pleased to see him, that I thought I should never have done wringing his hand.

I said to him: "My dear Fortunato, you are luckily met. How remarkably well you are looking to-day! But I have received a pipe of what passes for Amontillado, and I have my doubts."

"How?" said he. "Amontillado? A pipe? Impossible! And in the middle of the carnival!"

"I have my doubts," I replied; "and I was silly enough to pay the full Amontillado price without consulting you in the matter. You were not to be found, and I was fearful of losing a bargain."

"Amontillado!"

"I have my doubts."

"Amontillado!"

"And I must satisfy them."

"Amontillado!"

"As you are engaged, I am on my way to Luchesi. If any one has a critical turn, it is he. He will tell me—"

"Luchesi cannot tell Amontillado from Sherry."

"And yet some fools will have it that his taste is a match for your own."

"Come, let us go."

"Whither?"

"To your vaults."

"My friend, no; I will not impose upon your good nature. I perceive you have an engagement. Luchesi—"

"I have no engagement;—come."

"My friend, no. It is not the engagement, but the severe cold with which I perceive you are afflicted. The vaults are insufferably damp. They are encrusted with nitre."

"Let us go, nevertheless. The cold is merely nothing. Amontillado! You have been imposed upon. And as for Luchesi, he cannot distinguish Sherry from Amontillado."

Thus speaking, Fortunato possessed himself of my arm. Putting on a mask of black silk, and drawing a *roquelaure* closely about my person, I suffered him to hurry me to my palazzo.

There were no attendants at home; they had absconded to make merry in honour of the time. I had told them that I should not return until the morning, and had given them explicit orders not to stir from the house. These orders were sufficient, I well knew, to insure their immediate disappearance, one and all, as soon as my back was turned.

I took from their sconces two flambeaux, and giving one to Fortunato, bowed him through several suites of rooms to the archway that led into the vaults. I passed down a long and winding staircase, requesting him to be cautious as he followed. We came at length to the foot of the descent, and stood together on the damp ground of the catacombs of the Montresors.

The gait of my friend was unsteady, and the bells upon his cap jingled as he strode.

"The pipe?" said he.

"It is farther on," said I; "but observe the white web-work which gleams from these cavern walls."

He turned toward me, and looked into my eyes with two filmy orbs that distilled the rheum of intoxication.

"Nitre?" he asked, at length.

"Nitre," I replied. "How long have you had that cough?"

"Ugh! ugh! ugh!—ugh! ugh! ugh!—ugh! ugh! ugh!—ugh! ugh! ugh!—ugh! ugh! ugh!"

My poor friend found it impossible to reply for many minutes.

"It is nothing," he said, at last.

"Come," I said, with decision, "we will go back; your health is precious. You are rich, respected, admired, beloved; you are happy, as once I was. You are a man to be missed. For me it is no matter. We will go back; you will be ill, and I cannot be responsible. Besides, there is Luchesi—"

"Enough," he said; "the cough is a mere nothing; it will not kill me. I shall not die of a cough."

"True—true," I replied; "and, indeed, I had no intention of alarming you unnecessarily; but you should use all proper caution. A draught of this Médoc will defend us from the damps."

Here I knocked off the neck of a bottle which I drew from a long row of its fellows that lay upon the mould.

"Drink," I said, presenting him the wine.

He raised it to his lips with a leer. He paused and nodded to me familiarly, while his bells jingled.

"I drink," he said, "to the buried that repose around us."

"And I to your long life."

He again took my arm, and we proceeded.

"These vaults," he said, "are extensive."

"The Montresors," I replied, "were a great and numerous family."

"I forget your arms."

"A huge human foot d'or, in a field azure; the foot crushes a serpent rampant whose fangs are imbedded in the heel."

"And the motto?"

"*Nemo me impune lacessit.*"

"Good!" he said.

The wine sparkled in his eyes and the bells jingled. My own fancy grew warm with the Médoc. We had passed through walls of piled bones, with casks and puncheons intermingling, into the inmost recesses of the catacombs. I paused again, and this time I made bold to seize Fortunato by an arm above the elbow.

"The nitre!" I said; "see, it increases. It hangs like moss upon the vaults. We are below the river's bed. The drops of moisture trickle among the bones. Come, we will go back ere it is too late. Your cough—"

"It is nothing," he said; "let us go on. But first, another draught of the Médoc."

I broke and reached him a flagon of De Grâve. He emptied it at a breath. His eyes flashed with a fierce light. He laughed and threw the bottle upward with a gesticulation I did not understand.

I looked at him in surprise. He repeated the movement—a grotesque one.

"You do not comprehend?" he said.

"Not I," I replied.

"Then you are not of the brotherhood."

"How?"

"You are not of the masons."

"Yes, yes," I said, "yes, yes."

"You? Impossible! A mason?"

"A mason," I replied.

"A sign," he said.

"It is this," I answered, producing a trowel from beneath the folds of my *roquelaure.*

"You jest," he exclaimed, recoiling a few paces. "But let us proceed to the Amontillado."

"Be it so," I said, replacing the tool beneath the cloak, and again offering him my arm. He leaned upon it heavily. We continued our route in search of the Amontillado. We passed through a range of low arches, descended, passed on, and descending again, arrived at a deep crypt, in which the foulness of the air caused our flambeaux rather to glow than flame.

At the most remote end of the crypt there appeared another less spacious. Its walls had been lined with human remains, piled to the vault overhead, in the fashion of the great catacombs of Paris. Three sides of this interior crypt were still ornamented in this manner. From the fourth the bones had been thrown down, and lay promiscuously upon the earth, forming at one point a mound of some size. Within the wall thus exposed by the displacing of the bones, we perceived a still interior recess, in depth about four feet, in width three, in height six or seven. It seemed to have been constructed for no especial use within itself, but formed merely the interval between two of the colossal supports of the roof of the catacombs, and was backed by one of their circumscribing walls of solid granite.

It was in vain that Fortunato, uplifting his dull torch, endeavoured to pry into the depth of the recess. Its termination the feeble light did not enable us to see.

"Proceed," I said; "herein is the Amontillado. As for Luchesi—"

"He is an ignoramus," interrupted my friend, as he stepped unsteadily forward, while I followed immediately at his heels. In an instant he had reached the extremity of the niche, and finding his progress arrested by the rock, stood stupidly bewildered. A moment more and I had fettered him to the granite. In its surface were two iron staples, distant from each other about two feet, horizontally. From one of these depended a short chain, from the other a padlock. Throwing the links about his waist, it was but the work of a few seconds to secure it. He was too much astounded to resist. Withdrawing the key I stepped back from the recess.

"Pass your hand," I said, "over the wall; you cannot help feeling the nitre. Indeed it is *very* damp. Once more let me *implore* you to return. No? Then I must positively leave you. But I must first render you all the little attentions in my power."

"The Amontillado!" ejaculated my friend, not yet recovered from his astonishment.

"True," I replied; "the Amontillado."

As I said these words I busied myself among the pile of bones of which I have before spoken. Throwing them aside, I soon uncovered a quantity of building stone and mortar. With these materials and with the aid of my trowel, I began vigorously to wall up the entrance of the niche.

I had scarcely laid the first tier of the masonary when I discovered that the intoxication of Fortunato had in a great measure worn off. The earliest indication I had of this was a low moaning cry from the depth of the recess. It was *not* the cry of a drunken man. There was then a long and obstinate silence. I laid the second tier, and the third, and the fourth; and then I heard the furious vibrations of the chain. The noise lasted for several minutes, during which, that I might hearken to it with the more satisfaction, I ceased my labours and sat down upon the bones. When at last the clanking subsided, I resumed the trowel, and finished without interruption the fifth, the sixth, and the seventh tier. The wall was now nearly upon a level with my breast. I again paused, and holding the flambeaux over the mason-work, threw a few feeble rays upon the figure within.

A succession of loud and shrill screams, bursting suddenly from the throat of the chained form, seemed to thrust me violently back. For a brief moment I hesitated—I trembled. Unsheathing my rapier, I began to grope with it about the recess; but the thought of an instant reassured me. I placed my hand upon the solid fabric of the catacombs, and felt satisfied. I reapproached the wall. I replied to the yells of him who clamoured. I re-echoed—I aided—I surpassed them in volume and in strength. I did this, and the clamourer grew still.

It was now midnight, and my task was drawing to a close. I had completed the eight, the ninth, and the tenth tier. I had finished a portion of the last and the eleventh; there remained but a single stone to be fitted and plastered in. I struggled with its weight; I placed it partially in its destined position. But now there came from out the niche a low laugh that erected the hairs

upon my head. It was succeeded by a sad voice, which I had difficulty in recognizing as that of the noble Fortunato. The voice
said—

"Ha! ha! ha!—he! he!—a very good joke indeed—an excellent
jest. We will have many a rich laugh about it at the palazzo—he!
he! he!—over our wine—he! he he!"

"The Amontillado!" I said.

"He! he! he!—he! he! he!—yes, the Amontillado. But is it not
getting late? Will not they be awaiting us at the palazzo, the Lady
Fortunato and the rest? Let us be gone."

"Yes," I said, "let us be gone."

"For the love of God, Montresor!"

"Yes," I said, "for the love of God!"

But to these words I hearkened in vain for a reply. I grew impatient. I called aloud:

"Fortunato!"

No answer. I called again:

"Fortunato!"

No answer still: I thrust a torch through the remaining aper-
ture and let it fall within. There came forth in return only a
jingling of the bells. My heart grew sick—on account of the
dampness of the catacombs. I hastened to make an end of my
labour. I forced the last stone into its position; I plastered it up.
Against the new masonry I re-erected the old rampart of bones.
For the half of a century no mortal has disturbed them. *In pace
requiescat!*

A NOTE ON POE'S WINEMANSHIP

*The horror story has undergone so much development and
so many mutations since Poe's time that this fine old chestnut has lost much of its power to shock. To experience the
true* frisson *of horror one must concentrate not on the story
but on Poe's weird wine howlers. "I was skilful in the Italian
vintages myself, and bought largely whenever I could." From
this sentence one may draw the conclusion that Poe, perhaps
influenced by what may have seemed to him the Italianate
ending of the word, thought Amontillado was an Italian wine.
What he thought "a flagon of De Grâve" could be is almost
beyond conjecture.*

In H. Warner Allen's A Contemplation of Wine *there
are a few delightful paragraphs about* The Cask of Amontillado *which I herewith transcribe.*

*My good friend E. C. Bentley, the sole begetter of that rival
to the Limerick, the Clerihew, and the author of* Trent's Last
Case, *appended to the notes on Sherry I had derived from
Pasteur the following notions about that wine which he owed
to Edgar Allan Poe. He had been reading* The Cask of
Amontillado, *which happens not to be in my collection of
Poe's tales, and what he read there about wine had tickled his
fancy. The scene is laid in Rome* during the supreme madness
of the carnival season *in a period when people wore* roque-
laures *and popped on silk masks from time to time. Fortunato, with whose cruel fate the story deals,* prided himself
on his connoisseurship in wine, *and the teller of the story,
Montresor, claims to be equally gifted in this respect. "I was
skilful in the Italian vintages myself, and bought largely
whenever I could."*

*One day Montresor, plotting murder against Fortunato, con-
fides in his future victim the startling news: "I have received
a pipe of what passes for Amontillado, and I have my doubts."
"How!" exclaims Fortunato. "Amontillado? A pipe? Impossible!" On first thoughts I credited Poe with the elementary
technical knowledge that the pipe is the home of Port and the
butt, the home of Sherry, but the solecism passes unnoticed
even by Fortunato's connoisseurship. What was agitating him
was the idea that Amontillado was a rarity of rarities and as
unlikely to be found in bulk as Tokay Essence. Montresor
says that he is on his way to find his friend Luchesi and ask
him what he thinks of the wine.*

*"Luchesi," replies Fortunato crushingly, "is quite incapable
of telling Amontillado from Sherry."*

*And later tells Montresor what he thinks about Amontillado.
"Amontillado! You have been imposed upon; and as for Luchesi, he cannot distinguish Sherry from Amontillado."*

*One wonders whether he could have distinguished Saint
Emilion or Médoc from Claret. It is sad Poe could not have
referred to André Simon's wine* Encyclopaedia, *where he
would have read: "Amontillado, one of the most popular
types of Sherry, neither too dry nor too sweet. It may be a*

Fino *or merely a* Vino de Pasto *wine in quality, but it is meant to possess a fairly dry finish, somewhat similar to the finish of the wines of Montilla near Cordoba." Poe might try to excuse himself with the plea that he was confusing Amontillado with Montilla, which is not a Jerez wine at all, though within it under another name there flourishes the austerely generous spirit of Sherry, but Montresor does nothing to restore his creator's reputation for connoisseurship. Taking Fortunato to view this remarkable pipe, he draws a bottle from a mouldering pile, knocks off its neck and announces that "a draught of this Médoc will defend us from the damps." This summary method of decanting, when apparently there was no trouble with the cork, and the denial of Sherry-hood to Amontillado, reduce Poe as a connoisseur of wine to the level of the lady novelist who opined that Cheval Blanc must be a white wine, though she probably did not expect Black and White Whisky to be striped. At any rate, Fortunato is left, walled up alive in the cellar to reflect, till death releases him, on the distinction between Sherry and Amontillado.*

The 1865

G. B. STERN

Gladys Bronwyn Stern (1890———), English novelist, short-story writer and memoirist, is perhaps best known for her Matriarch *series, a roman fleuve of Anglo-Jewish life. She herself was "never very keen" on her saga of the Rakonitzes, setting a higher value on her studies of Stevenson and Jane Austen. She avers "a profound interest" in wolf-dogs, talking, ping-pong and collecting walking sticks. Her interesting autobiography* All in Good Time *records her conversion to Catholicism (1947). As far back as 1927 she published an account* (Bouquet), *which I remember with pleasure, of a wine tour in France. Thus she comes naturally by the theme of* The 1865.

I AM aware," said Sir Elwin Strickland, half-closing his eyes, the better to draw up the aroma from the cognac which lay in a fiery pool at the bottom of his enormous tulip-shaped glass, "I am aware that when a man of fifty-nine asks a young woman of—twenty-four, is it? Ah, yes—of twenty-four to be his wife, I am aware that he ought to talk profusely and sentimentally about May and December. Need I, however?"

Pamela laughed, and shook her pretty head. "No, I'll let you off."

He looked relieved. "Just so. You must have heard it all so often. You're the type that has always attracted December; probably because you take more trouble with a rich old man than you do with a poor young one."

Pamela's apple-blossom complexion deepened slightly. "I'm not sure if I like that."

He watched her, coolly amused at having drawn her fire. "Because it's true."

"Perhaps."

252

"Well, let's be truthful. It will save trouble later on when we are husband and wife. I may as well tell you that I don't dream for a single moment of babbling about my years as an impediment to our match; wondering whether I dare ask you to immure yourself with a man old enough to be your grandfather. In fact, I consider on the whole, my child, that you're lucky, and that all the benefits are showered from my side; material benefits, that goes without saying, but the other kind as well. I have wisdom, experience, subtlety, and if I may say so, a sort of white-haired distinction. Why in heaven's name should I wax maudlin over this young girl's fresh youth, when she peddles it for all these advantages? Why should I bow humbly before a hobbledehoy alternative whose trespassing would be as a crowd of picnickers trampling and tearing through a wood of bluebells? *Why?*" ... Yet his sad light eyes wistfully challenged his own bluff. He would have liked to be young again, for Pamela.

"A wood of bluebells?" she mocked him. "Do I really remind you of a wood of bluebells? Do go on, Sir Elwin. This is refreshingly like sentiment, after all."

Although his tone was caustic, his eyes twinkled appreciation. Then: "Will you marry me, Pamela? As you see, I'm not in the least humble, and if you behave like a minx, I shall shut you up and beat you. On the other hand, having taken all that I can richly provide, if you attempt to enlist sympathy by standing huddled with your back to the wall, your eyes like the eyes of a shot pheasant, moaning: 'I am so young, so young, so *young!*' —then I'll do worse than lock you up and beat you; I'll put you in a glass case and exhibit you in the Natural History Museum, in the parasite section!"

And again Pamela's laugh rippled through the small and surpassingly expensive restaurant which was the scene of this original courtship. The sound drew the attention of a good-looking but austere dark boy of about fifteen, who had just taken his seat with an elderly man at the next table. The boy stared at Pamela, but absently, as though, while her laugh existed, she had no presence to back the impression. Pamela was not used to such lack of compliment, even from a boy's gaze. Her own eyes flashed stormily; then she twisted herself round in her chair, and devoted all her attention to Sir Elwin.

Meanwhile, Vernon Barracott's father was looking in a worried fashion at his son, while his hand fingered the wine-list and the *à la carte*.

"Will you have—ah—plum duff or spotted dog?"

The boy smiled faintly. "Neither, thank you, Father. They're the same thing. And certainly pudding is out of place before the caviare!"

The connoisseur's knitted brows relaxed slightly at the word "caviare." "You will drink, I presume," he went on, "ginger-pop?" His tongue fingered the word fastidiously, as though it were unfamiliar, and he hoped it would remain so. "Or, as this is a—ah—grand bust up, let's go the whole hog and make it fizz, shall we?"

"Father," replied Vernon, "both your language and your suggestions are revolting to me. I prefer a white Burgundy to a white Bordeaux with the fish, but we must not ignore the claims of a Palatinate vintage; for instance, a Ruppertsberger. After that, I leave the choice to you. I'm only an ignorant, uncouth school-boy!"

And then Guy Barracott knew that this was indeed his son, with his very own tastes and his own reticences. Their evening together was a happy one.

"On the night you are twenty-one, Vernon, we will open my last bottle of the 1865 Hermitage. My boy, you won't know what love and passion can be till you have drunk that wine and of that year! By Saint Dionysius—" He became lyrical and a little absurd.

And then he died. Not that same evening, but a few months later. In his will he made the superlative mistake of his life. He named for his son's trustees two shrewd, worthy, honourable solicitors, both connoisseurs in wine.

When Vernon Barracott came into his inheritance, including one of the best cellars in the kingdom, there was no 1865 red Hermitage.

"Where," he cried wrathfully to his worthy, shrewd and honourable trustees, "where is that one priceless, peerless bottle from the hill on which Saint Christopher built his shrine?"

There was a faint quiver in the atmospheric reaction of the two elderly solicitors. A clairvoyant might have said that they licked their chops. But sadly they shook their heads, and spoke of dishonest butlers.

Vernon Barracott went out into the world, feeling that destiny had robbed him. One day, he vowed, he would drink a glass of the '65 Hermitage. Often his father had described to him the quality and perfection of its colour, its aroma and bouquet; its deep glowing wallflower browns and purples; and that elusive flavour, more maddening than a woman's charm, which men, crude sportsmen, have named "gun-flint"; his father had started him down a trail of the dreams, now wild and dark, now soft, caressing and velvety, which are flung in the wake of this divine gift from Bacchus; dreams of ecstasy yearning, and ecstasy satisfied.

Being a sensible young man, he began his pilgrimage by going to Tain-Tournon, the very source of Hermitage, and speaking with the few owners who divided the quiet slopes of the hill. To his surprise, though they murmured courteous responses when he mentioned the 1865, he could only rouse them to real enthusiasm on the subject of *very* weak whisky and water as a beverage.

"Well, but the 1865—may I have some? May I have twelve dozen bottles?" asked Vernon shyly.

In chorus they laughed, wagging their beards. Each one just dimly remembered what each one's father had said, when drinking the last remaining bottle of all the '65 that had remained in cellar with them. As for the rest of the yield, it had been casked, bottled, and sold out into the great world. Finally, one charming old vintner was able to trace in his books a fairly recent sale, not more than thirty-nine years ago, to a well-known London wine merchant.

The ardent lover hastened back to London, flushed with the prospect of an easy end to his quest. The well-known London wine merchant, a man echoing in his pleasant mellow personality most of the adjectives that appeared in his own catalogues, smiled reminiscently at mention of the 1865 Hermitage, and said: "Oh yes. Yes. A glorious wine. My father had some in his private cellars. I remember how he told me that on drinking the last bottle—"

"A murrain on all your fathers!" cried the impatient pilgrim. "A pest and a murrain and a plague!"

Mr. Manfred looked mildly astonished. He had been fond of his father. His visitor was obviously not sane. Look at the way he was flinging himself round the room, now and then picking up a specimen jeroboam of Imperial Tokay as if he would smash it against the wall, and then reluctantly returning it to its niche.

"Fathers!" he raved; "Wherever I go I hear nothing but this prattle of fathers and last bottles! Did none of your fathers die *before* they had had the last bottle? Were they all so damned healthy that their besotted cringing doctors allowed them to go on drinking wine, and a heavy wine at that, long after they should have been put on a diet of barley-water and milk-and-soda? Fathers, indeed! Father me no fathers!"

"I won't, I won't," Mr. Manfred soothed him. "As it happens, I seem to remember that we didn't keep and drink quite all that purchase of the '65. Wait a minute. . . . It comes back to me now! Sir Elwin Strickland—no, it would have been *his* father; it was before I came into the firm, of course—yes, surely he was promised half of it. Old Sir Reginald Strickland and my father were great cronies. The whole yield is very small, as, of course, you know, and very difficult to acquire, but I think—"

Vernon stood muted, trembling, expectant, while bells were rung, and respectful young men were sent in search of ancient ledgers.

"Here we are," cried Mr. Manfred at last. "Yes, a dozen bottles only, and a great favour at that. I have heard connoisseurs swear that there was no vintage like this in the whole history of wine. Well now, *that's* all right!" He beamed encouragingly on young Vernon Barracott. "Now, all you have to do is to get to know Sir Elwin Strickland. He's quite a well-known connoisseur; eccentric old fellow; lives in Chester Square. Perhaps by degrees he might grow to like you; if you pamper him a bit: flowers to his wife, and so on. And then, one day, if you are tactful—but I'd go slow if I were you; very, very slow; however, as I was saying, perhaps one day, with a bit of luck—"

"Oh yes," bitterly Vernon interrupted him, "perhaps one day, after wasting my youth, I may have the pleasure of hearing him tell me how, fifty years ago, his father had broken the seal of the last bottle of the 1865. Thank you, I'd rather buy a bottle of three-and-sixpenny Barsac, instead, at the grocer's."

"No, don't do that. That's taking a desperate view," quoth Mr. Manfred, smiling. "I shall be seeing Sir Elwin in a day or two, and I'll find out from him, without saying why, of course, if any of the '65 still remains; and I'll let you know. And after that, it's up to you!"

In spite of his optimistic declaration that Pamela had derived a fuller sum of benefits than he from their union, Sir Elwin was nevertheless surprised that for the first few years of this marriage there were no suitors in the courtyard; then, quite suddenly, the courtyard, figuratively speaking, seemed to be thronged with them. With his usual affectation of cynical detachment, but inwardly very badly frightened, Sir Elwin counted them: Donald Liddell, Edward Gulliver, George Leyton, Alistair Wynne, Ronnie Marsh, Tommy Curtis, Gaspard Le Marchant. Finally, young Vernon Barracott, whom the husband feared most; for he had youth, slim, dark, passionate youth, youth with its adorable shyness, its white fires, without, alas, any of the trampling hobbledehoy clumsiness which, the elderly connoisseur had often and soothingly reassured himself, must necessarily be youth's accompaniment.

Barracott was decorative, undeniably decorative; and he added the final burnished grace of mystery to his attractions. For though he was for ever wooing his lady, yet he never, by word, nor by touch, nor, indeed, by look, claimed a reward. He was, in fact, that ideal swain who is for ever pursuing. Flowers and flowers and many flowers he sent to Pamela, and— Ah! the wily fellow!—an occasional curio or etching or some such suitable toy to Sir Elwin himself, to divert suspicion from the very meadows and hot-houses of adoration with which he filled their house. Books, too, in strange and beautiful bindings, were part of this stubborn siege for Pamela's favour; and royal boxes for the theatre and opera. He was a queer, freakish boy, this Vernon Barracott; for, having got the measure of her hand (some glove carelessly left behind, perhaps, in the big cinnamon-coloured Rolls-Royce in which his fortune enabled him to drive her, sometimes) he suddenly conceived the idea of sending her gloves; no ordinary gloves, but such as Marie Antoinette or Queen Elizabeth might have worn; a fantasy, a saraband of gloves; gloves broidered or slashed or pearled, gloves of the finest and softest skins, gloves gauntleted and furred. And after each fresh arrival of delicate five-fingered compliment, Pamela would say with a shrug—as though, careless rogue, she did not care— "We had better ask him to dinner," or "Perhaps he will lunch with us," or "Do you mind, Elwin, if we ask Vernon to come on to supper after the show to-night?" Once, even, she asked him to breakfast, and this, thought her jealous protector, was carrying things a little too far; for about breakfast there is a warmth, a bacon-and-kidney intimacy. . . .

Then, all in a minute, she stopped asking him, as though she were tired of him.

"This," reflected Sir Elwin, "is the dangerous time. From now onward I must watch."

So, from now onward, genial invitations radiated from him instead of from Pamela; for obviously it involved least effort for Sir Elwin to watch his young wife and her suitor at his own table. Besides, he was a not disagreeable guest, this Vernon Barracott. He had travelled; knew much about food; more, even, about wine. But while they were at the very height of discussion over some rivalry, for instance, between Château Yquem as opposed to Montrachet to be drunk with *filets de sole Ravigotte*, the young man would unexpectedly check, stammer, blush scarlet, and forget to go on . . . as though some longing had profoundly moved him to declare his passion.

Then Sir Elwin would glance at Pamela. And she, more often than not, would be lost as in a dream, chin propped on her hand, lips half smiling.

"In love," decided Sir Elwin grimly.

The symptoms increased. Pamela started when she was spoken to, spent infinite pains over her toilet, murmured in her sleep, sighed at her meals, sang in her bath, sobbed at her looking-glass; she declared a wish to live in the country instead of in town, because sunsets were so beautiful; she gave way to inexplicable fits of rage with her maid; she left vast gaps of time unaccounted for in recital of her day's doings to her husband, and then, confused, tried to cover them with a tightly stretched tissue of falsehood, not even acceptable to the most credulous of marines.

And Sir Elwin was not a marine. Far from it. "She's irrevocably in love," he decided. "What, then, is to be done?"

"Let it be at once stated that there was one terror at which this elderly patrician was wont to blink, and that was the terror of being made to look a fool. And now, despite his good looks,

his wealth, his breeding, his taste in wine, and his rejection of all
that was obvious, coarse or silly; in spite of his wit, his discern-
ment, his generosity, and the crisp way in which his grey hair
curled back from his temples; in spite of his brave record as a
soldier, earned in the days when war was still a dashing pastime;
in spite of having snubbed to death one wife, a timid creature;
of having been divorced by a second, a moral creature (and a
very jolly and impudent divorce, redounding entirely to the
glory of Sir Elwin) in spite of all this, was he still to live and
look a fool, and not be able to avert it? When he married
Pamela, he exposed himself to this peril, certainly; every man is
an Achilles who wantonly pulls off his boot to lay bare his
vulnerable heel. It is a perversity in his nature that tempts him to
do so. But then, Pamela was so very lovely. And then, and yet
again, he had dreamed of making himself secure beforehand by
his caustic acceptance of the May and December situation; he
had challenged laughter with his own laughter; he had called
the situation a cliché; he had boasted of his indifference towards
a possible hobbledehoy lover in the future: May-time to May-
time. Mating time.

Thus, after seven years' immunity, his vigilance relaxed. May
became June. Pamela was thirty-one. And enter April, twenty-
one, and no hobbledehoy at that, but slim, supple, and burning
with a dark and silent ardour.

This loitering about, anticipating cuckoldry, was unbearable
to Sir Elwin Strickland. Nor could the doom be averted now.
Anyone watching Pamela and young Barracott could see that
they loved. They were both rapt and silent, awaiting consum-
mation; awaiting some glorious swing upward into the very
dazzle of fulfilment. Lovers, indeed, when you watched and
studied them apart, as Sir Elwin perpetually did. Less lovers, and
more an enigma, when you watched and studied their behaviour
together. But was that surprising in the presence of the lady's
husband? The lady's husband had no doubts. It was a question
of any moment.

So then his lordliness rose to the occasion. He would not be
cuckolded. No, he would give them to each other, April and
June. He himself, with magnificent bounty, would make the way
easy for their love, for their ultimate wedding. He would have

to divorce her, a very quiet and discreet divorce, as quiet and discreet as money could make it. *His* money, mind you, and *his* power— Oh, generous Sir Elwin! If he were himself the man to move around the hands of the clock, who could then laugh at him if the hands of the clock went round? Sir Elwin was proud; he adored Pamela, but he would give her to Vernon Barracott, and he would compel their respect by the gesture with which he did it: a certain stately formality; or perhaps, alternatively, in the spirit of cynical but kindly humour. He could not decide beforehand which way the mood would take him to act his part; but he had some good lines to deliver, and the stage should be set, again by himself, for their delivery— "And their deliverance!" —mocking at the vision of the elderly husband's sanction, nay, suggestion of such an elopement.

Never mind that. Not cuckolded, at least; not cuckolded. "Pity the poor blind"— No friend or acquaintance, gossiping hereafter, would have cause to say that of him. They would marvel, perhaps, at his gesture; disapprove, perhaps; or more violently be angered by it; but not deride.

"On Friday week, the eighteenth of this month, is my birthday," said Sir Elwin Strickland to Vernon Barracott. "I shall be sixty-five. I hope you will do us the pleasure of dining with us that night. Pamela hopes so, too."

Pamela, her indifference slightly overdone—thus Sir Elwin, in rather finicky criticism!—echoed the invitation; said that she would be delighted.

Barracott bowed. They were a little like figures of a past generation, pacing a formal minuet. A very handsome trio of figures.

Sir Elwin went on: "I mean to celebrate it with pomp and ceremony. You may have noticed, Barracott, that I am a very pompous old man. Pamela shall wear the most expensive new frock she can devise between now and then; and I will bring up the last of my '65 Hermitage." And to himself he added, relishing his pose: "An appropriate wine, for renunciation!"

Sir Elwin Strickland was decanting the 1865. Naturally, the butler had just given notice; for if a butler be not on the premises to decant the super-wines of his cellar, for what then had his master engaged him fourteen years ago? Mason lingered in the

dining-room, casting malevolent glances at Sir Elwin's proceedings.

Sir Elwin was feeling both cheerful and uplifted. Why not?
It was his birthday. Here at his own table, in his own home,
he was going to drink one of the finest vintages of the world.
And thereafter he was going to surprise two people out of
their very skins, and with a superb gesture, save his own face.
Afterwards, of course, he would be a broken man, but that, too,
would have its attractions: "He's taking it splendidly!" in a hushed,
a reverent whisper from the compassionate mob. And he, one
hand shielding his eyes, that their slight moisture might not
betray him to those who looked on—

Not bad. Not bad at all.

"It is right that the young should be happy. It is inevitable
that the old should be lonely," murmured Sir Elwin, wiping the
neck of the bottle.

"H'indeed, sir," said the butler frigidly, glaring at the usurper.

Sir Elwin had not been aware that his subconscious was already rehearsing his speech aloud; for his conscious mind was
preoccupied in watching the melted garnet of the '65 slowly run
through its appointed funnel into the heavy Waterford decanter.

"Liable to throw an unusually heavy sediment, this wine,"
remarked Sir Elwin airily.

"H'indeed, sir," again from the displeased, dispossessed butler.

His employer felt compelled to go on chatting amiably, showing that he did not care a damn for Mason's chagrin: "Lady
Strickland not down yet? You know, Mason, positively she
forgot to give me a birthday present."

"H'indeed, sir." No sympathy there.

Sir Elwin cadged for it: "One might have thought . . . but
perhaps she has one in reserve, to give me at a supreme moment
to-night. Your mistress, Mason, has a most excellent touch with
supreme moments."

"H'indeed, sir."

"And I myself," continued Sir Elwin, desperately attacking the
ramparts of dignity, "I myself intend to bestow a gift on my wife
this very evening."

"H'indeed, sir; and what—" Mason had broken down—"and
what might that be?"

—And at that supreme moment, when baronet and servitor

were on the very brink of sweet communion, the footman brought in a note, gracefully, even jauntily folded into a cocked hat.

"What's this? What's this?"

"Her ladyship, sir. Asked me to give it to you at 7.35 precisely, sir. Just before you had your sherry, sir."

"And why the devil," enquired his lordship, but without the slightest shadow of apprehension, "why the devil didn't she have it put into an envelope?"

Naturally, Herbert had no idea of the odd little breezes and kinks of the mysterious reversion to a great-grandmother who positively thrived on intrigue; of the tendency towards mischief and badinage, which had impelled Pamela to fold her note into the form of a cocked hat, instead of more decorously putting it into an envelope stamped with the Strickland crest and motto. For the crest was: "Sable, on a field vert, an oak tree proper." And the motto: "*Hic sto, hic maneo.*" "Where I am, I remain."

And Pamela had not remained.

My dear Husband,

It is not, alas, possible for me to declare myself less heart-lessly than by saying I have left you for a much younger man. And if I try to modify such heartlessness by adding that even if the man were older, much older than yourself, I would still leave you for him, does that make it better or worse? I'm afraid, worse.

Please don't forgive me. I can at least release you from that weary obligation. Stamp, roar, rage, if you are human enough! I won't even insult you by pretending that I have ever found you human, except once, and that was this morning, when I saw you looking surprised that I had no birthday present for you. Yet a birthday present from me, now and today—wouldn't that have been a joke that was too ironic even to be pleasant?

I am very happy. I've never been happy before. I wonder if you are heroic enough to drink my health to-night in the famous '65, saying as you raise your glass: "She was an impudent minx! I can do without her!"—For you can, you know. But I can't do without myself, and that's one of the reasons why I've run away from you. I wanted to enclose a photograph, to show the other reason, but he won't let me!

Pamela.

Cuckolded, after all.

They had slipped away from his benevolence, Pamela and Vernon, three hours too soon; and left him looking a fool. A rush of dark red blood, darker than the wine of Hermitage, suffused Sir Elwin's neck and face. He glared round at Mason and Herbert, as though wondering where to strike with his fists. And though they had been so deeply interested in the reading of the note that they would gladly have tiptoed up to Sir Elwin, one on each side of him, and read it over his right and his left shoulder, yet they now deemed it prudent to slide and slither away, out of that room where rage was boxed in. In point of fact, Herbert had heard the peal of the front door bell, and his instincts sprang to duty.

Baffled of live prey for his wrath, Strickland's eye was caught and fascinated by the elaborate preparations he had made for that night's ceremonial renunciation. With a curse on Barracott, slim black privateer that slid so silently into other men's harbours, he lifted the decanter filled with the contents of that precious last bottle and dashed it against the marble fireplace. . . .

Ah, the uncontrollable pressure was relieved now! One sacrifice, at least.

Vernon Barracott stood in the doorway, appalled.

He had come to-night, after long seeking, to meet his love . . . and had found her in pools and splashes of dark red on the marble hearth. Apprehension did not leave him a second's solace of doubt. At once he had seen the empty bottle of '65 on the sideboard, beside the properties for decanting. The label told him all.

He lost his temper. "What have you done?" he shouted in an uncontrollable fury. Did ever quest end in so tantalising a disaster?

Sir Elwin swung round and faced his guest. "*You?* What the hell are *you* doing here?"

"You invited me!"

"You ran away with my wife!"

"I didn't!"

"You did! You have!"

"Wife! *Wives!* Good God, man, that was the last bottle!"

"*Bottles!* Good God, that was my last wife! I'm sixty-five. Scoundrel, what have you done with her?"

"It was the 'sixty-five!—Why did you smash it, you fool?"

"You fool!"

"You—you fool!"

"You f-f-fool!!!"

Pamela and Alistair gazed deeply and fondly into each other's eyes. The cliffs of Dover slowly misted and drew away. Presently they would see France.

THE
COMIC SPIRIT

Life among the Winesaps

PETER DE VRIES

Peter De Vries is one of the bright ornaments of The New
Yorker, *a parodist of genius, a comic novelist of original talents (as readers of* The Tunnel of Love *and* Through the
Fields of Clover *are well aware), and a man who has raised
the pun to the level of an art form. A wine man of considerable erudition, he specializes in Rhines. I have read many take-
offs of wine-snob conversation, none as amusing as* Life
among the Winesaps.

B URGUNDY is the king of wines and claret is the queen,"
Almadingen said, bringing a bottle of Médoc to the table
in a wicker cradle. I thought how it would be to close my hands
around his throat, working the fingers well in under the collar,
or to crack him over the scalp with a nice, full-bodied Chambertin. I was not only out of my element but in over my head.
I resented particularly the hopelessness of trying to emerge unex-
posed from the pretense into which I had permitted Almadingen
to lure me.

It had been important that we hit it off, because our wives were
fond of one another. They were old school friends, and had met
again after many years, to find themselves revolving in the same
suburban orbit, with husbands who were strangers to each other.
When we had all got together for the first time, it had been for
dinner at a restaurant in town, and I had been host. "How about
some wine?" I had asked, and Almadingen had said, "Capital!" I'd
got the idea right away that he was a connoisseur, and to conceal
my agitation I had sparred with him across the table, working my
lips warily when I sipped and giving him plenty of time to speak
first. "This is a tidy Chablis," he'd said, putting his glass down.

"Mmm," I had said, nodding assent, thinking that next time it would probably be dinner at the Almadingens' and the strain would be off me.

But would it?

"You should learn to hold your own better when it comes to wines," my wife had said after we'd bade them good night. "Especially with people like the Almadingens. Look, why don't you read up on the subject?"

During the three weeks before we went to the Almadingens', I had dipped into Grossman's *Guide to Wines, Spirits, and Beers* several times, but had always seemed to get hung up in the chapter on brandies. I'd found a good mot there: "Cognac is like a woman —at her best between the ages of twenty-five and forty," which I intended to use after coffee. I didn't see how I could work it in at dinner, for which we were having a roast of beef and this Médoc of which I have spoken.

"You're a wine man," Almadingen said to me, holding his claret up to the light. "You'll be interested to know that I've been laying in a supply of Bordeaux."

I cleared my throat and held my glass up as Almadingen was holding his, sustaining the pose until I could think of something to say. I said the only thing that came into my head. "Speaking of laying in a supply of Bordeaux," I said, "did you ever hear the one about the hen who laid in a supply of coal?"

My wife dissected her roast beef with cold precision, and Marlis—that's Mrs. Almadingen—emitted a tinkle of mechanical laughter. Almadingen, whose first name is Steve, then went into a reminiscence about how he and several companions had once got into a scrape with the London police while "well in their hock." I never got in the aphorism about brandy. We did have brandy after coffee, but mixed with Bénédictine, and I couldn't very well say "B and B is like a woman," etc. So that washed out.

"I must say *that* was a miserable performance!" my wife remarked as we rode home in our car. She drove, and I sat slumped down, with my hands in my pockets. "I hope now you'll really brush up. Not that the Almadingens are ever likely to ask us again. Still, we can invite them once more and maybe pull the fat out of the fire. Hens in a supply of coal! Really!"

We asked the Almadingens to dinner at our house a month later, and I crammed for the occasion with a volume entitled

Notes on a Cellar-Book, by George Saintsbury, as well as with
the Grossman. I was reading in the former when I straightened
in my chair, plucked by something curiously familiar. "If claret
is the queen of natural wines, Burgundy is the king," I read at
the head of a section I was beginning. So! I thought: If that's the
pitch, O.K.!

Learning well in advance what food my wife planned to serve,
I narrowed down my preparations to the three wines indicated.
I cribbed some comments and devised some of my own, and when
the day rolled around, I was letter-perfect. I even solicited a little
co-operation from my wife. "When you hear me speaking of the
king and queen of wines," I said, "ask me, 'And the jack?' Sort of
casually, you know. Have you got that?"

"I guess so," she said. "But it seems pretty shabby."

"This whole thing is shabby, if you only knew," I said. "Now,
have you got that straight?"

The dinner was on a Saturday evening. I drank steadily during
cocktails, watching Almadingen as he sat there draining off Old-
Fashioneds with what I thought was an elaborate relish. "You hate
his guts," I said to myself. I thought of Almadingen, motionless
beside the fire tongs with which I had felled him, down in his
cellar laying in a supply of Bordeaux. "Why did you do it?" the
police asked. "I was in hock," I said. "I needed some money."

The wines were all white. The first was a dry, moderately
chilled bottle to go with the oysters. I sparred with Almadingen
again, waiting for him to open his mouth. "Hmm," he said,
lowering his glass. "This is a tidy Chablis."

I set my own down.

"This Chablis is impeccable," I said. "Neither the long ocean
voyage nor the brutal vehemence of travel by truck seems to
have disheveled our sturdy friend. Give me a good white wine.
I leave to those who need them the flamboyance of the reds; I'll
take this *pierre-à-fusil,* or flinty, taste." I shifted in my chair and
went on. "It is as though one, footsore and cloyed by all the
blowzy hues of Rubens, Titian, and even Gauguin, came at last,
in a gallery, upon the exhilarating understress of the late Piet
Mondrian."

Almadingen muttered something and looked into his plate. The
women stirred uneasily.

"There are conclusions yet to be attained," I said. "Between the dry, wind-chime tinklings of your Graves and the cloying reverberations of Château d'Yquem—not to detain ourselves with that cracked old cowbell, Riesling—lie the clear peals of Montrachet."

I was dilating in this fashion, each glass building on the stimulation left by its predecessor, when the moment came for which I had planned the latter wine—the arrival of the entrée, roast ham. We finished one bottle and I drew another out of the cooler. They all watched uncomfortably as I set my palm critically against the belly of the bottle, opened it, and poured the wine. "As a lover of wines has put it," I said, bringing my eye momentarily to rest on Almadingen, " 'Burgundy is the king of wines and claret the queen.' Meaning, we know from his context, *red* Burgundy." I paused and waited.

"Is everyone finished?" my wife asked, laying her napkin down on the table. "We can have our dessert and coffee in the living room."

"What, then, is the jack?" I said. Almadingen looked restively from his wife to mine. "It is Montrachet," I said, holding my glass aloft in salute to its contents. The others did not lift theirs but looked fixedly into their plates. "Montrachet, that tawny bastard who has come from a vineyard only eighteen and three-quarter acres in extent"—I paused to drink off half of my glass—"striding robust yet fragrant, muscular but unmistakably perfumed—"

My wife rose, and she and the Almadingens filed into the living room. "Don't you agree this is among the few whites that should be gulped?" I asked, following them and spilling wine from my glass, which I was carrying. Almadingen asked for the bathroom and ran upstairs. "As distinguished from those that should be sipped?" I called to him. I heard the door slam at the head of the stairs.

I had planned to chill a Barsac for dessert, but my wife had slipped out and hidden the bottle in a mess of Cokes under the sink. The means I had used to steel myself for the wine ordeal— heavy drinking—had carried me well into the stage where one is under the impression that everything he says is either penetrating or funny, or both. Almadingen eventually emerged, and as we gathered for dessert, I resumed where I had left off, in a way that I never doubted was hilarious. "It came to me like a theorem," I said, "this division of wines on the basis of how they should be drunk. As a matter of fact, I was in the bathtub when it happened. 'Electrolux!' I cried, as distinguished from 'Eureka!,' and ran naked and dripping through the streets of Westport. 'Wines should be gulped to the extent that they are heavy, sipped to the degree that they are light!' "

The Almadingens' faces were as frozen as the sherbets at which they picked. They left at a quarter after ten.

"Well, you've done it again," my wife said.

"I'll work it out right yet," I said.

"I think you can forget about the Almadingens," she said. "We won't hear from them any more."

Weeks passed—a month—and we didn't hear from the Almadingens. Then, one night, we ran into them at a party. "Go over to Steve and apologize," my wife whispered to me. "He's standing there by himself."

I went up to him. He was leaning against the side of a bookcase with a highball in his hand.

"Say, Steve," I said, "I'm sorry I got so noisy at our place that night. I was just racing my motor. You see, I don't really know about wines. I only know what I like."

He laughed through his nose. "I know damn well what *I* like," he said. He finished off his drink and glanced in the direction of the bar. He seemed flushed.

"You *are* a connoisseur, aren't you?" I asked.

He glared into his empty glass. "I suppose I can tell when some things are under par," he said. Then he crossed one foot over the other, lounging against the bookcase. "But after the way you ordered in New York that first night, as though you were daring anybody to follow you—" He broke off, and drew himself erect. "I like a glass of wine at dinner, sure," he said. "And even at lunch. But beyond that the demands sometimes made on a man are too—" He stopped, but I followed his glance to the other end of the room, where Marlis stood, watching him. He frowned into his glass again. "This rye has no character, and it certainly has no age," he said.

"That's for sure!" I said. "Maybe I'm particular, because I'm a rye man myself."

He got a fresh drink and came back. "Look, I've got a bottle of fourteen-year-old Overholt I've been looking for somebody to open with—somebody who'll appreciate it. Why don't you drop over some night and we'll get into it?"

"Swell," I said.

We clinked glasses and drank. An hour later, we were linking our voices in old favorites, among them a chorus of "Song of the Vagabonds."

" 'Sons of France around us, break the chains that bound us, and—to—*hell* with Burgundy!' " we sang.

Our wives scowled at us as we went, arm in arm, once more toward the bar.

Stiff Upper Lip

LAWRENCE DURRELL

Lawrence George Durrell (1912–   ), British poet and novelist of Irish parentage, was born in India and educated at St. Edwards College, Canterbury. His Alexandria Quartet, *a series of four subtly related novels, at once won him his present place among the finest middle-generation fiction writers of our time. An early experimental novel,* The Black Book, *was recently re-published. Mr. Durrell's experiences during and after World War II as a Foreign Service press officer and diplomatic aide may have provided the stimulus for his brace of amusing sketches of old-school-tie British diplomats—*Esprit de Corps *and* Stiff Upper Lip, *whose bibulous title story is ready for your reading.*

AS for the Fair Sex (said Antrobus), I am no expert, old boy. I've always steered clear. Mind you, I've admired through binoculars as one might admire a fine pair of antlers. Nearest I ever came to being enmeshed was in the *Folies Bergères* one night. Fortunately, Sidney Trampelvis was there and got me out into the night air and fanned me with his cape until my head cleared and I realized the Full Enormity of what I'd done. Without realizing it, I had proposed to a delightful little pair of antlers called Fifi and was proposing to take her back to the Embassy and force the Chaplain to gum us up together. Phew! I certainly owe Sidney a debt. We positively galloped away from the place in a horse-drawn contrivance with our opera hats crushed like puff-pastry. Sidney, who was only visiting, and who had also crossed the subliminal threshold and proposed—dear God—to a contortionist; Sidney was even paler than I. That night he dyed his hair green to escape identification and crossed over to Dover on the dusk packet—a bundle of nerves.

But Dovebasket in love was a strange sight. His sighs echoed through the Chancery. There were sonnets and triolets and things all over the backs of the War Office despatches. The little winged youth had certainly pinked him through the spencer. Yes, it was Angela, Polk-Mowbray's niece. I can't think why Polk-Mowbray didn't liquidate one or both of them. But then the Popular Verdict on *him* was that he needed stiffening. Yes, the stiffest thing about him was perhaps his upper lip. As for Dovebasket, I would have described him as an ensanguined poop. A spoon, my dear chap, a mere spoon. Yet love makes no distinctions. Afterwards he published a little book of his poems called *Love Songs of an Assistant Military Attaché* with a preface by Havelock Ellis. A rum book in sooth. I remember one refrain:

> *The moon gleams up there like a cuspidor*
> *Angela, Angela, what are we waiting for?*

You get the sort of stuff? Could lead directly to Nudism. It was clear from all this that he was terribly over-sexed and I for one felt that he would end in Botany Bay or the Conservative Central Office or somewhere. You see, Angela wouldn't respond to the rowel at all. Not her. Press his suit as firmly as he might the wretched chap only got the tip-tilted nose in response. It was clear that she considered him as no more than a worm-powder. And here I must add that we had all been worried about Angela, for she had been showing signs of getting one of her famous crushes on the Russian Military Attaché—Serge, or Tweed, or something by name—a bloater to boot. But of course, the worst aspect of it all was that we weren't officially fraternizing at that time with The Other Bloc. Polk-Mowbray was worried about her security. He had been frightfully alarmed to overhear an idle conversation of hers with a Pole in which she gave away— without a moment's thought—the entire lay-out of Henley Regatta, every disposition, old boy. She even drew a map of the refreshment room. I know that Henley isn't Top Secret, but it might just as easily have been the dispositions of the Home Fleet. Such lightness of speech argued ill for the Mission. One simply did not know what she mightn't reveal in this way.... We were concerned, I might say, Quite Concerned.

Well, it so fell out that during this fruitless romance of Dove-

basket's the Vulgarians invited us all to join them in pushing out
the boat for the Wine Industry. They had always had a Wine
Industry, mind you, but it had never been put on a proper basis
before. So, very wisely, they had imported a trio of French experts and turned them loose among the bins. Within a matter of a
couple of years, the whole thing had been reorganized, new cul-
tures had been sorted out, and Vulgaria was now about to launch
about twenty new wines upon the export market. Advance intelligence from old Baron Hisse la Juppe, the Military Attaché
(who had practically lived down there while experiments were
going on) suggested that something most promising had taken
place. Vulgaria, he said (rather precariously), was on the point
of exporting wines which would equal anything the French and
Italians could do.... We were incredulous, of course, but were
glad to assist in the send-off of the new wines. The whole Corps
accepted the invitation to the *Vin d'Honneur* with alacrity.

The day dawned bright and fair, and it was a merry party of
carefree dips who took the train north to the vineyards. The
whole *vieillesse dorée* of diplomacy, old man. In sparkling trim.
For once, the whole thing was admirably worked out; we were
carried in vine-wreathed carriages to the great main cellars of the
place—more like a railway tunnel than anything, where warm
candle-light glowed upon twinkling glasses and white linen;
where the music of minstrels sounded among the banks of flowers.
... I must say, I was transported by the beauty of the scene.
There lay the banks of labelled bottles, snoozing softly upon the
trestles with the candles shining upon their new names. Our hosts
made speeches. We cheered. Then corks began to pop and the
wine-tasting began. One of the French specialists led us round.
He tried to get us to take the thing rather too professionally—you
know, shuffling it about in the mouth, cocking the chin up to the
ceiling and then spitting out into a kind of stone draining-board.
Well as you know, one is trained to do most things in the F.O.
But not to spit out good wine. No. We simply wouldn't demean
ourselves by this niggardly shuffling and spitting out. We swallowed. I think you would have done the same in our place. What
we were given to taste, we tasted. But we put the stuff away.

And what stuff, my dear boy. Everything that Hisse la Juppe
had said proved true. What wines! Wines to set dimples in the

cheeks of the soul. Some were little demure white wines, skirts lifted just above the knee, as it were. Others just showed an elbow or an ankle. Others were as the flash of a nymph's thigh in the bracken. Wines in sables, wines in mink! What an achievement for the French! Some of the range of reds struck out all the deep bass organ-notes of passions—in cultured souls like ours. It was ripping. We expanded. We beamed. Life seemed awfully jolly all of a sudden. We rained congratulations upon our hosts as we gradually wound along the great cellars, tasting and judging. What wines! I couldn't decide for myself, but after many trials fell upon a red wine with a very good nose. You see, we each had to pick one, as a free crate of it was to be given to each member of the Corps. Sort of Advertisement.

And as we went along the French specialist enchanted us by reading out from his card the descriptions of the wines which we were trying. What poetry! I must hand it to the French, though they tend to make me suspicious in lots of ways. There was one, for example, a sort of hock, which was described as *"au fruité parfait, mais présentant encore une légère pointe de verdeur nullement désagréable."* Another was described as *"séveux et bien charpenté."* And then there was a sort of Vulgarian Meursault which was *"parfait de noblesse et de finesse, une petite splendeur."* I must say, for a moment one almost succumbed to culture, old man. The stuff was damned good. Soon we were all as merry as tom-tits, and I even smiled by mistake at the Bulgarian Chargé. In fact everything would have gone off like a dream if Dovebasket hadn't cut up rough and sat deliberately on the air-conditioning.

Apparently in the middle of all this bonhomie the wretched youth crept up on Angela and breathed a winged word in her ear. It was the old fateful pattern. She turned on her heel and tossing up her little chin went over to the other corner where the crapulous Serge was swigging the least significant of the wines with much smacking of the lips. It was so obvious; Dovebasket was cut as if by a whiplash. A cry of fury broke from his lips to find that she preferred this revolting foreigner who had apparently been named after an inferior British export material; he banged his fist upon the nearest table and cried out, "If I cannot have her, nobody shall!" And all of a sudden made his way to the corner of the tunnel of love and sat down. He took a copy of Palgrave's Golden Brewery from his pocket—one of those anthologies with a monotonous-looking cover—and started to read in a huffy way. Sulks, old man, mortal sulks.

Well, we sighed and went on with our bibbing, unaware that the fellow was sitting upon our life-line, as it were. I have already said that he was mechanically-minded. Apparently he had noticed that the air-supply to the tunnel came through a sort of sprocket with a side-valve cut in a sort of gasket with a remote-control intake—how does one say these things? Anyway. Dovebasket placed his behind firmly on the air-screw, thus cutting off our oxygen supply from the outer world. It was all very well trying to suffocate his rival. But—and such is the power of passion —he was determined to suffocate the entire Corps.

Well, for ages nobody noticed anything. On we went from cask to cask, in ever-growing merriment, getting more and more courtly, with each swig. We thought that Dovebasket was just alone and palely loitering, that he would grow out of it. We didn't know that he was sitting on the very H_2SO_4 or H_2O (I never was much good at chemistry) which nourished human life in these regions. I had never thought much about air before. Apparently there is something quite essential about it. Nutritious as wine is, it cannot apparently sustain life unaided. Well, as I say, there we were unaware of the formaldehyde bubbles which were slowly crawling up the bloodstream, mounting to our brains. Suddenly I noticed that everyone seemed unwontedly hilarious, a rather ghastly sort of hilarity, mind you. Laughter, talk, music—it all seemed to have gone into a new focus.

A grimly bacchanalian note set in. I was vaguely aware that things were not as they should be but I couldn't quite put my finger on it. The first to go was Gool, the British Council man. He lay down quietly in a bed of roses and passed out, only pausing to observe that he could feel the flowers growing over him. We ignored him. The music had got rather ragged at the edges. People were drinking on rather desperately now and talking louder than ever. Somewhere in the heart of it all there was a Marked Discomfort. People seemed suddenly to have aged, bent up. You could begin to see how they would look at ninety if they lived that long. The chiefs of mission had gone an ashen colour. As if they had worn their expressions almost down to the lining. It is hardly believable what a difference air can make to dips, old man.

And now it was that knees began to buckle, stays to creak, guy-ropes to give. Still, in courtly fashion, people began to look around them for something to lean on. Yes, people everywhere began to strap-hang, still talking and laughing, but somehow in a precarious way. Polk-Mowbray had gone a distinctly chalky colour and had difficulty in articulating; the Argentine Minister had quite frankly started to crawl towards the entrance on all fours.

It was Serge, I think, who first noticed the cause of our plight. With a bound he was at Dovebasket's side crying, "Please to remove posterior from the breathing," in quite good Satellite English. Dovebasket declined to do so. Serge pulled him and received a knee in the chest. Dovebasket settled himself firmly once more and showed clearly that he wasn't letting any more air in that week. Serge seized a wicker-covered bottle of the Chianti type and tapped him smartly on the crown. Dovebasket was not going to be treated like a breakfast egg by his hated rival. He dotted him back. This was fatal. One could see at once how wars break out. Poland and Rumania came to the Assistance of Serge, while Canada and Australia answered the call of the Mother Country. It looked like some strange Saturnalia, armed dips circling each other with wicker-covered bottles.

But as the fighting spread, Dovebasket got shifted from his perch and the life-giving H_2SO_4 began to pour once more into the cave. It was only just in time, I should say. The cellar now looked like a series of whimsical details from a Victorian canvas —I'm thinking of the "Kiss Me Hardy" with Nelson down for the count in the Victory's cockpit. Some were kneeling in pleading postures. Some were crawling about in that painstaking way that beetles do when they are drunk on sugar-water. Others had simply keeled over among the flowers. The musicians drooped over their timbrels without enough oxygen between them for a trumpet-call or a groggy drum-tap. Then all of us, suddenly realizing, set up a shout and hurled ourselves towards the life-distributing oxygen pump.

With your permission I will draw a veil over the disgraceful scenes that ensued among the combatants. Dovebasket was knocked out. The Canadian Air Attaché had a collar-bone bruised. The egregious Serge escaped unscathed. A number of bottles were broken. Such language. Life has its ugly side, I suppose. But the main thing was that the Corps lived again, breathed again, could hold up its aching head once more. But one is hardly trained to live dangerously. Nevertheless, I noticed that not one dip failed to make a note of the wine of his choice. It would have been too much to miss that free crate. Some, in default of pencil and paper, had managed to scribble on their dickeys with lipstick. Polk-Mowbray, though beaten to his knees, nevertheless had the presence of mind to write Stella Polaris 1942 on his. Bloody, but relatively unbowed, you see.

And, as a matter of fact, after prayers the next day it was he who summed it all up rather neatly by saying: "And remember that in Peace, in War, in Love and in Diplomacy one thing is needful. I do not, I think, need to tell you what that is."

He didn't. It would have been labouring the point. We knew only too well. The Stiff Upper Lip.

It Puckers Your Mouth

ART BUCHWALD

Mr. Buchwald is the well-known globe-trotting humorous columnist whose doings and sayings are recorded in the New York Herald Tribune *and other fortunate newspapers. Every so often he bundles his funny pieces (and many are funny) together into a little book. From one of them,* Don't Forget to Write, *I have drawn "It Puckers Your Mouth," presenting a lifelike portrait of the one and only great Lichine.*

THERE are not in this world any lords of higher lineage than the great wines of Médoc, which form the first nobility of the vintages of France, whether they be Margaux, Saint-Julien, Saint-Estèphe, Pauillac, or Moulis. They rival each other in their incomparable elegance and in their rich, ruby-red color."

That is what they would have told you if you had gone to Bordeaux for the harvesting of the 1959 grapes. As a guest of Alexis Lichine, proprietor of the Château Prieuré-Lichine and Lascombes, I spent a few days in the Médoc, watching one of the great vintages being brought in. The sight was one to make the heart beat faster. The dry French summer and fall, which had played havoc with vegetables and dairy products, had been a boon to the grapes. Not only was it a great year in quality, but in quantity as well.

In one of those inexplicable French economic explanations we were told that the price of wine would not go down because it had been a successful year. The previous years, 1956, 1957, 1958, were bitter and cold years for the wine growers, and very little wine was made. The shortage sent the price up. This is reasonable. But last year, with wine in quantity, the price still went up.

I made the mistake of asking one of the growers why.

"Because," he said, as if talking to a child, "it is a great year and everybody wants it."

So much for the economics of wine.

M. Lichine promised to take me on a tour of the Médoc and we started, quite naturally, with his own Château Lascombes. He told me that in the course of the tour I would be asked to taste some wines and he didn't want me to disgrace him.

I practiced by tasting some wine from one of his vats. It tasted good, and I swallowed it.

"No, no, no," he said. "Don't swallow it. Swish it around in your mouth."

"Clockwise or counterclockwise?"

"Clockwise. Counterclockwise is for Burgundy. And then spit it on the floor."

I practiced a few times until I got it right.

"Now say something," he said.

"It sure puckers the inside of your mouth."

"No, that's not what you're supposed to say," M. Lichine cried. "You're supposed to say something beautiful like, 'How full and generous. It will fulfill its promise.' "

"Okay, but it still puckers the inside of your mouth."

Our first stop was Château Margaux, one of the four greatest wine châteaux in France. We visited the chai, the long shed where the grapes are put in vats and barrels. The master of the chai asked me if I wanted to taste some. I nodded, and he gave me a glass.

I swished it around and spat it out. Lichine looked pleased at his pupil. "It has a texture all its own," I said. "It tastes like cotton."

Lichine kicked me in the leg. "What he means," he said to the master, "is that it tastes like velvet."

After we were shown around the Château (I discovered that no one in Bordeaux presses wine in their bare feet any more) Lichine took me to the Château Latour, another of the four greatest vineyards in France.

I tasted the Latour wine and said, "A great wine. It has such a rich, soft flavor."

Lichine smiled.

"Could I have some water?" I asked of the owner, Count Hubert de Beaumont.

Lichine's face dropped.

"Water?" The count looked puzzled. "Do you want to wash your hands?"

Before I could say I wanted to drink the water, Lichine dragged me away.

"Never, never, never ask for water in Bordeaux," he admonished me.

"But I tell you my mouth is all puckered up. My cheeks are stuck to my teeth."

Lichine would have none of it. The last château we visited belonged to Philippe de Rothschild, owner of the Mouton-Rothschild vineyards. M. Rothschild, a gracious host, showed us through his caves and invited us to have a glass of champagne with him in his house, one of the most beautiful in France.

We went upstairs and a servant served us each a bubbling glass. Lichine toasted his host and we each sipped some. Then as Lichine looked on in horror, I swished it around in my mouth.

He screamed, "No!"

But it was too late. I spat it on the floor.

My Cellar Book

L. W. DESBROW

This originally appeared in Punch. *The author of the original* My Cellar Book, *crusty old George Saintsbury, would have enjoyed reading these skittish variations on his own lordly pronouncements on rare vintages. Mr. Desbrow is full of valuable information. Which of us, for example, would have known that rhubarb wine does not travel well?*

THE gentle melancholy with which the lover of good wine turns the reminiscent leaves of his cellar book is compounded of regrets for past glories and the memories of great vintages and golden years.

My cellar-book goes back to 1930. I opened it when I laid down a half-dozen of Macgilligoody's Extra Ferruginous Tonic Wine (bottled in Blackfriars Road in 1929). I picked up the half-dozen for a mere song at the local chemist's annual sale, but they gave pleasure far out of proportion to what I paid for them. I had a bottle up when the manager of my department came to dinner, and served it with the Irish stew. Unfortunately the manager had to leave before the bottle was finished, but I could tell from the slow and reverent way in which he consumed it that my judgment had been fundamentally sound. He agreed with me that although it still showed traces of a certain juvenilism, it was pregnant with possibilities. I had the last bottle up only last year when my wife was recovering from a bad cold. It had lived up to its early promise and fully justified the confidence I had placed in it.

Parsnip wine I always regard as generous but rather frolicsome, always ready to play merry little pranks on you, but completely without malice. It is perhaps the best "all purpose" wine of all our native vintages. The best years in the 1930s were 1932, 1936, and of course the glorious 1938. I had a dozen of 1932 (bottled by my mother after six weeks in the copper). Unfortunately three bottles blew their corks in the first six months, but the remainder gave much pleasure to my friends and myself; perhaps, I might almost say, too much pleasure.

We had two magnums of the noble '38 vintage for the committee of the Working Men's Club on the occasion of a recent whist drive and dance. The wine was then "in perfection," friendly on the nose, generous on the palate, but insidious on the gait. A bottle my wife and I shared the night we had a flying bomb at the end of the road led to our removal, somewhat erroneously, as casualties suffering from acute "battle exhaustion." We have just drunk the last bottle, and I was unable to restrain myself from wondering whether we should ever see its like again. These suspicions are partly based on the fact that my mother is beginning to doubt if her wine is strictly non-alcoholic.

Many consider that in rhubarb wine our native vintages have achieved their choicest flowering. The richness of its velvet texture and the full flamboyancy of its bouquet have endeared it to generations of wine-lovers. I had some choice years in my cellar, but unfortunately the wine does not travel well, and we have had to move four times in the last eighteen months.

As all wine-lovers know, the severe attacks on the rhubarb plants by wireworm in the middle twenties had a disastrous effect on the output of rhubarb wine. The wireworm troubles are now largely over, and there have been some very good years in the "post wireworm" period. Memories of the famous "Coronation" vintage are with us yet. There were unfortunately no good years during the war; the labour shortage, coupled with the rationing of sugar, made things very difficult for the *Vignerons*. My sister-in-law, whose wine was adjudged a "first growth" at the Flower Show, 1931, always relied on my brother to turn the mangle by which the fruit was crushed. Naturally, with my brother in the Army, the burden of turning the mangle fell entirely upon my sister-in-law herself. As a result the output for the war years was small in quantity and, owing to the scarcity of sugar, deficient in quality.

At my suggestion we used the whole of the 1944 output as a basis for a fortified wine, produced by blending the native product with two or three bottles of an interesting liquor known, I believe, as "potheen," very graciously presented by some American soldiers as a mark of appreciation for hospitality they had received. The resulting blend, which I named "potbarb," suffered from immaturity, since the donors of the "potheen" insisted on drinking the blend almost before I had entered the bottles in my cellar book. I like to think that this interesting blend strengthened them in their liberating mission, but we have lost touch with them, as we have with so many of our dear friends with whom we have shared a bottle of wine at one time or another.

LAUDAMUS

Romany Stains

CHRISTOPHER MORLEY

Chris Morley (1890–1957) was my friend and professional associate for many years. Some day his extraordinary talents will be properly assessed. He was a fine trencherman and a wine-lover, familiar both with the contents of a bottle and the long, rich history of which it was a part. This little essay, spreading out from a consideration of a brandy-stained flyleaf, is typical of his delightful and discursive mind. It was reprinted, by request, for the Committee of the House of Representatives considering bills for the repeal of the Eighteenth Amendment.

THE LETTERS OF ABELARD AND HELOISE,
now first translated from the Latin by C. K.
SCOTT MONCRIEFF. London, 1925. 4to, buckram,
gilt, uncut. Inside back cover and end fly-leaf
brandy-stained, and label, "Vieux Cognac 1842,"
pasted on former.

THIS I find in the proceedings of a book sale held this week at the Anderson Galleries, and I pay tribute to the delicacy of the cataloguer's discrimination. This is a new refinement of bibliophily, that the connoisseur must not merely describe all the technical points of a rare edition, but be able to identify the nature and provenance of stains and foxings. I was always amused by the wine-spots on a waistcoast of George Washington's preserved in the State House, Philadelphia. Very likely the expert who catalogued "Abelard and Eloise" could tell us the exact vintage of those long-vanished maculations.

And the same day that I found that item in the auction catalogue I met by chance a man who told me that he had foolishly attempted to bring in three bottles of wine when he landed from an Atlantic liner the other day. He is a very honest and unselfish man, he had made no particular attempt to conceal the contraband —which, indeed (he is an author) he intended to give to some publisher friends. But the inspector found it, and they made a public humiliation-scene. My friend was given a severe lecture, before a large grinning crowd of his fellow-passengers; he was heavily fined; and then, like a guilty schoolboy, ordered to carry the bottles to the edge of the pier and hurl them against the side of the ship. Which, in much misery, he did. It must have been a shocking scene, painful even to think about. I only allude to it because it is healthy, some times, to meditate anxious things.

I am not interested to argue whether or not Prohibition is a sagacious political experiment. Quite possibly it is: I cannot pretend to know. At any rate it removes the enjoyment of fine things from those too insensible or uncontriving to ensue them. But the pragmatics of the matter are irrelevant: I look about in my mind for a rationale. I can see many reasons why a government should prohibit. And the maxim *Abusus non tollit usum* may apply in reverse. But you can have no philosophy of the matter until you really know what has been prohibited. The god of pure wine has been crucified between two malefactors, hootch and gin. And much of their discredit has fallen on his divine head. As dear Henry Holt so shrewdly said, "The dinner party has been abolished by those who never saw one."

Wine is under suspicion, as beautiful things so often are. Like religion, love, laughter, any sort of explosive, it is an anxiety to officials. It cannot be tolerated unless under some hygienic pretence. Quite potable vintages are sold, legally and without scathe, because a grain or so of pepsin added makes them, theoretically, a "tonic." Peruna, I have no doubt, rises higher in the alcoholic scale than some of the bottles my friend had to crash against the *Leviathan's* steel plates.

But wine is under suspicion because it is beautiful. It opens the heart, it warms the shy poet hidden in the cage of the ribs. It melts the wax in the ears that music may be heard. It takes the terror from the tongue, that truth can be said, or what rhymes marvellously with truth. The soft warm sting on the cheekbones that a ripe Burgundy gives is only the thin outward pervasion of a fine heat within, when the cruel secret smoulder of the wit leaps into clear flame: flame that consumes the sorry rubbish of precaution and cajolery. The mind is full of answers. And then, presently, if you have dealt justly with the god, not brutishly, he gives you the completest answer of all—sleep.

Wine is under suspicion because it is beautiful, because it is ineradicably woven into the triune mystery, man, woman and god. This is wild palaver, I hear someone say; but it is part of man's folly to have to bear testimony. The goblet, pure color and form, adorably curved as woman herself, is this not fit calix for the miracle within? Or the shallow silver of the Burgundian tasting-cup with its curly snake carved for a handle. The eye of the adder notes you as you tilt the draught: to remind you that we are more than mere botanists. We pay quitrent in Eden yet, and honeysuckle and poison ivy grow gladly in the same clump.

Sage indeed are those who have him under suspicion, the shining god of wine. For his magic treads close to dark giddiness and horror, the sickness of unanswerable things. But there is a moment in his ritual, his clean austere ritual, when the heart is pure as the chemist's adoring the atom, dreaming an easier world. Then, on this warm sandbeach beside the uncounted surf, Bacchus lights his fire. You thought it was a lonely bivouac, yet looking round in the dark there is firelight in other eyes. So if you shudder to have men unburden the packed excess of their souls, you are well-advised to have stoutly drilled squads of inspectors on every pierhead of literature. Governments and good manners, tidy pyramids and proses, are not built of the great blocks of the Unsaid. Leave those to such quarrymen as William Blake and Walt Whitman. Keep Off the Leaves of Grass.

This is a dream, a foolishness, an absurdity. But I don't like to hear people talk of Amendments until they know what they've amended. I am thinking of a cellar I know in Burgundy. There, laid away in rows as carefully ranged as the lines of a poem, are the future gladness of men. There are names that I am selfish enough to enjoy rehearsing. Musigny, rich in bouquet and ether; Romanée-Conti, *d'une délicatesse*. Clos Vougeot, potent and velvety, Richebourg with exquisite power and aroma. Hospice de Beaune, strong but a thought acrid; Pommard that tingles the cheekbone; Pouilly, the perfect luncheon wine. Nuits St. Georges, bright and gracious; Chambertin, which seems to me just faintly metallic, bitterer than the soft Musigny. Meursault, which I rank below Pouilly, and adorable Chablis Moutonne, clear and fine as the lizard's bell-note when he rings, like an elfin anvil, softly under the old stone steps in the mild French dusk.

So I could go on, but I leave it to you to verify my private amateurishness from your own researches. What I want to tell you is this. In the vaulted roof of that cellar, strangely swaying in the hot flicker of the candle you hold, are the crystallized skeletons of spiders. Some moist drip of limestone juices, oozing through long silent dampness of winter, has trickled down the threads of silk, embalmed these fragile creatures in their hammocks, turned them and their webs into gossamers of airy fossil. Perfect, pale, lovely as the most inconceivable daintiness of ivory filigree, they shiver in the tawny gust of candle-heat.

Isn't this just what happens in the darkest of all cellars where purple juice is stored? In the heart of man the wine-god does the same magic. The old spider of doubt, of anguish, of secret despair, is turned to pretty crystal. There, for a while anyhow, he hangs, a tiny brittle charm. An octagonal jewel, an epigram in silk and shell. At least that's part of what I was thinking when I came upon the conjunction of those three ghosts, Abelard, Eloise, and Vieux Cognac.

The Divine Bottle

HILAIRE BELLOC

Hilaire Belloc, considering the copiousness and variety of his output, was one of the most brilliant poets and men-of-letters of his generation. Because he wrote no masterpiece (unless it be The Servile State), *he may be assigned a place in English literature rather below his deserts. Perhaps, when his biographies, histories and polemical works (he was an ardent and persuasive Catholic apologist) are forgotten, he will still be remembered for his verse for children:* The Bad Child's Book of Beasts *and* Cautionary Tales. *As an essayist he ranks among the finest of his generation. His winesmanship, according to report, was truly professional. Belloc's life, particularly toward the end, was not always happy. One is grateful, therefore, that he was vouchsafed at least one ineffably blessed experience, here recorded.*

I TREMBLE as I write that title down! Another has used the phrase before me, but he has been dead these four hundred years, or near, and times have changed. My dread is lest the title and the theme be controversial. I have never quite mastered the meaning of that last word, but I know that it is something abominable and to be shunned. And here let me repeat an old story which was told me by and of a friend of mine. You have heard it often, and it will approach you with the grace of familiar things. In my own poor *corpus* of letters it has cropped up, I fancy, a dozen times. But no matter. Here goes.

This friend of mine was asked to give what is called "an address," not in the sense in which you give such things to the officers of the law, but in the sense in which you give such things to the evening audiences of the suburbs. No subject had been given

out, but just as he got up to speak his chairman whispered to him
that he was requested not to touch upon politics or religion, as
these were controversial. Whereupon did this friend of mine,
standing his full height and speaking out strongly, like Hector
before the trenches round the ships (I hope it was Hector), pronounce these memorable words:

"I have been asked not to speak upon politics or religion; and
since these two subjects comprise all that is of interest to the
human race, I will sit down again."

Such was his address—worthy to be engraved on bronze and
set up in the market place: a speech more true and more inform-
ing than any that have been made since the death of Oratory, in
Florence.

I say, then, that I tremble; but having begun, I must go on. As
Napoleon said, using mixed metaphors, to his Marshal by night
in Moscow, when it was decided to march southward upon
Maloyaroslavets, instead of towards St. Petersburg, "It is the
counsel of the Lion; but now the wine is drawn, we must drink
it"—which brings me back to wine, and to my fear lest I offend.

For it may be that there is an anti-wine religion going about,
and that to praise wine, or even to talk about it, is to inflict a
grievous wound. So that those who may be attached to this religion will not bear anything in praise of wine, and will also, I
suppose, be careful never to say anything against it, for fear of
giving equal pain to others. Yet it would be a pity to leave the
world ignorant of that experience which has moved my pen—the
miracle of Sunday, October 6th, 1929.

You must know, then, that very many years ago, long before
the great war, and I think before Agadir of blessed memory, there
came to my house an odd assortment of wine. It was not more
than half a dozen, and each of a separate kind. I can hardly remember how it came, but I seem to have some sort of idea that it
was what is called "samples." Some wine merchant, generous and
bent on trade, must have sent them to me to choose amongst, that
I might decide from which I should fill what Mr. Pooter called
"my cellar." Anyhow, they lay there through the ages, and all
things passed over them except a draught; for they were covered
thicker and thicker with dust, as the slow years of peace and war
and peace again—or truce—went creeping on; and the donor, I
suppose, has gone to his felicity, and the letter which I presume

he wrote has disappeared, and all record of that antiquity has perished.

It was by accident that I came upon that *cache* of a half-dozen. I was peering with a candle into the corner where they lay, looking for oil with which to make a salad, when I saw that venerable alignment with their earthy cloaks around them—the only things unchanged in a changing world. Through the thick coating which time had very gently laid upon them I could just read the lettering they bore. One was a wine of Anjou, which would to-day be water or vinegar. Another was from the Moselle. Upon a third was a simple label with the word "Larose." There was no year upon that label. No other wording at all: on the cork only brown wax.

I said to myself: "Claret is a doubtful thing. All the wines of the Garonne and of the Dordogne are as diverse as the souls and bodies of men. Some will live it out prodigiously for years, increasing in virtue with time—a process quite against the general order of things. Some die young, and are soured by the wickedness of this world in their first bloom. Some with precocity attain ripeness early like the poets, and hang on like the poets doubtfully, preserving their main quality on into middle age, and then, like the poets, rapidly become intolerably dull, downright bad, and worthy of destruction; sometimes calling for vengeance. Others have so little substance in them that they rot from the first. Some few, some very few, are worthy to be called contemporaries with man himself."

As I said this to myself, I remembered a wine of 1870, born in the same year as myself, a twin brother, a little older than my windmill, a little older than my boat; but we were all much of an age. This wine I had bought in Leadenhall Street; and it was fifty years old before I drank a drop of it; and it remained admirable to the end. So I went on to myself, and I said:

"Let us see what has happened to this Larose."

I took it out very gently, lest I should disturb its sleep and spoil its temper by awaking. I stood it up in a far corner of a warm room, upon a little desk that is there, where it could have a background of sundry writers, a school text-book of the *Iliad, item,* another ditto of the *Odes* of Horace, an *Antigone* from the same days and dates, an *Asmodeus* of Le Sage in French which a friend had given me, and another in English; two Rabelais of the same

sort, two Michelins of the same sort, and a third yellow one for
Spain; Yeats's *Wanderings of Oisin,* and a book called *The Outer
Darkness,* which is all about the Queen of Hell, an old companion
—and many others. There they stood and looked on the wine, and
I sat down opposite and looked on it too, remembering many
things. Then some friends came, and we had our meal, drinking
that kind of wine called Lagune, with a good strong body and of
sufficient development. But when the meal was over, I said to
these friends of mine (they were five in number, all told, making
six with myself, their host), "I have in the next room a bottle of
which I know nothing, except that it is a claret and has slept without so much as turning for nearly twenty years. It may now be
worthless, but I will open it for an experiment." Six is a prodigious
number to share one bottle. It is like turning a squadron of horse
on to one tin trough of water. But two of them I knew would
take but a sip, so the main work would be attacked by only four.
Yet four is a great number.

It was at the coronation of George IV, I think, or possibly of
Queen Victoria, that the public were feasted at tables of four,
with one bottle to a table, so that many sang to the tune of the
National Anthem:

> Happy and glorious,
> One bottle among four of us,
> The devil send no more of us.

Moreover, I may tell you that I was not going to stint myself
as host. It has always seemed to me that such sacrifice was too expensive and worth more than its god. For the God of Hospitality
is hardly worth that abominable feeling of insufficiency in wine.

The cork, then, was drawn with very great care indeed, as one
would deal with some issue concerning the life of a man. The
rim, whence it had come out very sound and dark, was dusted
with the utmost delicacy, and the Unknown was poured out as
gently as the first words of lovers.

Immediately upon tasting it our humanity, there and then,
blessed beyond the limits that are proper to men in this life, knew
that it had come upon something of Paradise.

Are you expecting me to describe that beatitude? Are you
awaiting one of those paragraphs which sundry continentals of
the nineteenth century excelled in—the attempt to put in words

what is not of words but of the glory of the senses of man? Are you eager for just those terms in just that order which might call up some *simulacrum* of such real joy? You will be disappointed. I do not believe the thing can be done, and I at least cannot do it. It transcends my power, of which I cannot boast in such affairs; and what is more, I verily believe and would swear that it transcends the powers of any mortal man that ever was born to breathe and move upon this unhappy earth.

An Aged Wine

GEORGE MEREDITH

George Meredith (1828–1909) is little read today and less admired. Now, however, that the Victorians are all being sympathetically re-examined, the mannered author of The Egoist *and the fine poet of* Modern Love *may soon have his turn. Meredith's interest in wine may have arisen in part from the fascination exerted on him by the drinking habits of the English upper class (he was himself, as he too often remembered, the grandson of a tailor, the "great Mel" of* Evan Harrington*). He also came to it by way of marriage. His father-in-law was Thomas Love Peacock, in whose satirical novels and drinking songs the joys of wine-drinking are avidly evoked. As for this famous passage, drawn from* The Egoist, *one is of two minds about the great Dr. Middleton, father of the book's heroine. Is he cast in the heroic mold of Dr. Johnson—or is he a windy bore?*

S IR WILLOUGHBY advanced, appearing in a cordial mood. "I need not ask you whether you are better," he said to Clara, and raised a key to the level of Dr. Middleton's breast, remarking: "I am going down to my inner cellar."

"An inner cellar!" exclaimed the doctor.

"Sacred from the butler. It is interdicted to Stoneman. Shall I offer myself as guide to you? My cellars are worth a visit."

"Cellars are not catacombs. They are, if rightly constructed, rightly considered, cloisters, where the bottle meditates on joys to bestow, not on dust misused! Have you anything great?"

"A wine aged ninety."

"Is it associated with your pedigree that you pronounce the age with such assurance?"

"My grandfather inherited it."

"Your grandfather, Sir Willoughby, had meritorious offspring, not to speak of generous progenitors. What would have happened had it fallen into the female line! I shall be glad to accompany you. Port? Hermitage?"

"Port."

"Ah! We are in England!"

"There will just be time," said Sir Willoughby, inducing Dr. Middleton to step out.

A chirrup was in the reverend doctor's tone: "Hocks, too, have compassed age. I have tasted senior Hocks. Their flavors are as a brook of many voices; they have depth also. Senatorial Port! we say. We can not say that of any other wine. Port is deep-sea deep. It is in its flavor deep; mark the difference. It is like a classic tragedy, organic in conception. An ancient Hermitage has the light of the antique; the merit that it can grow to an extreme old age; a merit. Neither of Hermitage nor of Hock can you say that it is the blood of those long years, retaining the strength of youth with the wisdom of age. To port for that! Port is our noblest legacy! Observe, I do not compare the wines; I distinguish the qualities. Let them live together for our enrichment; they are not rivals like the Idæan Three. Were they rivals, a fourth would challenge them. Burgundy has great genius. It does wonders within its period; it does all except to keep up in the race; it is short-lived. An aged Burgundy runs with a beardless port. I cherish the fancy that Port speaks the sentences of wisdom, Burgundy sings the inspired Ode. Or put it, that Port is the Homeric hexameter, Burgundy the Pindaric dithyramb. What do you say?"

"The comparison is excellent, sir."

"The distinction, you would remark. Pindar astounds. But his elder brings us the more sustaining cup. One is a fountain of prodigious ascent. One is the unsounded purple sea of marching billows."

"A very fine distinction."

"I conceive you to be now commending the similes. They pertain to the time of the first critics of those poets. Touch the Greeks, and you can nothing new; all has been said: *Graiis ... præter, laudem nullius avaris.* Genius dedicated to Fame is immortal. We, sir, dedicate genius to the cloacaline floods. We do not address the unforgetting gods, but the popular stomach."

Sir Willoughby was patient. He was about as accordantly coupled with Dr. Middleton in discourse as a drum duetting with a bass-viol; and when he struck in he received correction from the pedagogue instrument. If he thumped affirmative or negative, he was wrong. However, he knew scholars to be an unmannered species; and the doctor's learnedness would be a subject to dilate on.

In the cellar, it was the turn for the drum. Dr. Middleton was tongue-tied there. Sir Willoughby gave the history of his wine in heads of chapters; whence it came to the family originally, and how it had come down to him in the quantity to be seen. "Curiously, my grandfather, who inherited it, was a water-drinker. My father died early."

"Indeed! Dear me!" the doctor ejaculated in astonishment and condolence. The former glanced at the contrariety of man, the latter embraced his melancholy destiny.

He was impressed with respect for the family. This cool vaulted cellar, and the central square block, or enceinte, where the thick darkness was not penetrated by the intruding lamp, but rather took it as an eye, bore witness to forethoughtful practical solidity in the man who had built the house on such foundations. A house having a great wine stored below lives in our imaginations as a joyful house, fast and splendidly rooted in the soil. And imagination has a place for the heir of the house. His grandfather a water-drinker, his father dying early, present circumstances to us arguing predestination to an illustrious heirship and career. Dr. Middleton's musings were colored by the friendly vision of glasses of the great wine; his mind was festive; it pleased him and he chose to indulge in his whimsical, robustious, grandiose-airy style of thinking; from which the festive mind will sometimes take a certain print that we can not obliterate immediately. Expectation is grateful, you know; in the mood of gratitude we are waxen. And he was a self-humoring gentleman.

He liked Sir Willoughby's tone in ordering the servant at his heels to take up "those two bottles": it prescribed, without overdoing it, a proper amount of caution, and it named an agreeable number.

Watching the man's hand keenly, he said: "But here is the misfortune of a thing super-excellent: not more than one in twenty will do it justice."

Sir Willoughby replied: "Very true, sir; and I think we may pass over the nineteen."

"Women, for example; and most men."

"This wine would be a sealed book to them."

"I believe it would. It would be a grievous waste."

"Vernon is a claret man; and so is Horace De Craye. They are both below the mark of this wine. They will join the ladies. Perhaps you and I, sir, might remain together."

"With the utmost good-will on my part."

"I am anxious for your verdict, sir."

"You shall have it, sir, and not out of harmony with the chorus preceding me, I can predict. Cool, not frigid." Dr. Middleton summed the attributes of the cellar on quitting it. "North side and south. No musty damp. A pure air. Everything requisite. One might lie down one's self and keep sweet here."

Of all our venerable British of the two Isles professing a suckling attachment to an ancient port wine, lawyer, doctor, squire, rosy admiral, city merchant, the classic scholar is he whose blood is most nuptial to the webbed bottle. The reason must be, that he is full of the old poets. He has their spirit to sing with, and the best that Time has done on earth to feed it. He may also perceive a resemblance in the wine to the studious mind, which is the obverse of our mortality, and throws off acids and crusty particles in the piling of the years, until it is fulgent by clarity. Port hymns to his conservatism. It is magical: at one sip he is off swimming in the purple flood of the ever-youthful antique.

By comparison, then, the enjoyment of others is brutish; they have not the soul for it; but he is worthy of the wine, as are poets of Beauty. In truth, these should be severally apportioned to them, scholar and poet, as his own good thing. Let it be so.

Meanwhile Dr. Middleton sipped.

After the departure of the ladies, Sir Willoughby had practiced a studied curtness upon Vernon and Horace.

"You drink claret," he remarked to them, passing it round. "Port, I think, Doctor Middleton? The wine before you may serve for a preface. We shall have *your* wine in five minutes."

The claret jug empty, Sir Willoughby offered to send for more. De Craye was languid over the question. Vernon rose from the table.

"We have a bottle of Doctor Middleton's port coming in," Willoughby said to him.

"Mine, you call it?" cried the doctor.

"It's a royal wine, that won't suffer sharing," said Vernon.

"We'll be with you, if you go into the billiard-room, Vernon."

"I shall hurry my drinking of good wine for no man," said the doctor.

"Horace?"

"I'm beneath it, ephemeral, Willoughby. I am going to the ladies."

Vernon and De Craye retired upon the arrival of the wine; and Dr. Middleton sipped. He sipped and looked at the owner of it.

"Some thirty dozen?" he said.

"Fifty."

The doctor nodded humbly.

"I shall remember, sir," his host addressed him, "whenever I have the honor of entertaining you, I am cellarer of that wine."

The reverend doctor set down his glass. "You have, sir, in some sense, an enviable post. It is a responsible one, if that be a blessing. On you it devolves to retard the day of the last dozen."

"Your opinion of the wine is favorable, sir?"

"I will say this—shallow souls run to rhapsody—I will say, that I am consoled for not having lived ninety years back, or at any period but the present, by this one glass of your ancestral wine."

"I am careful of it," Sir Willoughby said, modestly; "still its natural destination is to those who can appreciate it. You do, sir."

"Still my good friend, still! It is a charge; it is a possession, but part in trusteeship. Though we can not declare it an entailed estate, our consciences are in some sort pledged that it shall be a succession not too considerably diminished."

"You will not object to drink it, sir, to the health of your grandchildren. And may you live to toast them in it on their marriage-day!"

"You color the idea of a prolonged existence in seductive hues. Ha! It is a wine for Tithonus. This wine would speed him to the rosy morning—aha!"

"I will undertake to sit you through it up to morning," said Sir Willoughby, innocent of the Bacchic nuptiality of the allusion.

Dr. Middleton eyed the decanter. There is a grief in gladness, for a premonition of our mortal state. The amount of wine in the decanter did not promise to sustain the starry roof of night and greet the dawn. "Old wine, my friend, denies us the full bottle!"

"Another bottle is to follow."

"No!"

"It is ordered."

"I protest."

"It is uncorked."

"I entreat."

"It is decanted."

"I submit. But, mark, it must be honest partnership. You are my worthy host, sir, on that stipulation. Note the superiority of wine over Venus! I may say, the magnanimity of wine; our jealousy turns on him that will not share! But the corks, Willoughby. The corks excite my amazement."

"The corking is examined at regular intervals. I remember the occurrence in my father's time. I have seen to it once."

"It must be perilous as an operation for tracheotomy; which I should assume it to resemble in surgical skill and firmness of hand, not to mention the imminent gasp of the patient."

A fresh decanter was placed before the doctor.

He said: "I have but a girl to give!" He was melted.

Heroic Poem in Praise of Wine

HILAIRE BELLOC

Properly speaking, a poem does not belong in the company of a group of stories. But Belloc's magnificent effort is a classical expression of the higher reaches of the oenophilic emotion; and it occurred to me that to some of my readers, to whom it might be unfamiliar, it would come as a blessed discovery. I know of no nobler celebration of its subject in all English verse, or for that matter in any language with which I am acquainted. One line surely deserves immortality:

Dead Lucre: burnt Ambition; Wine is best.

TO exalt, enthrone, establish and defend,
To welcome home mankind's mysterious friend:
Wine, true begetter of all arts that be;
Wine, privilege of the completely free;
Wine the recorder; wine the sagely strong;
Wine, bright avenger of sly-dealing wrong,
Awake, Ausonian Muse, and sing the vineyard song!

Sing how the Charioteer from Asia came,
And on his front the little dancing flame
Which marked the God-head. Sing the Panther-team,
The gilded Thyrsus twirling, and the gleam
Of cymbals through the darkness. Sing the drums.
He comes: the young renewer of Hellas comes!
The Seas await him. Those Aegean Seas
Roll from the dawning, ponderous, ill at ease,
In lifts of lead, whose cresting hardly breaks
To ghostly foam, when suddenly there awakes
A mountain glory inland. All the skies

Are luminous; and amid the sea bird cries
The mariner hears a morning breeze arise.
Then goes the Pageant forward. The sea-way
Silvers the feet of that august array
Trailing above the waters, through the airs;
And as they pass a wind before them bears
The quickening word, the influence magical.
The Islands have received it, marble-tall;
The long shores of the mainland. Something fills
The warm Euboean combes, the sacred hills
Of Aulis and of Argos. Still they move
Touching the City walls, the Temple grove,
Till, far upon the horizon-glint, a gleam
Of light, of trembling light, revealed they seem
Turned to a cloud, but to a cloud that shines,
And everywhere as they pass, the Vines! The Vines!
The Vines, the conquering Vines! And the Vine breathes
Her savour through the upland, empty heaths
Of treeless wastes; the Vines have come to where
The dark Pelasgian steep defends the lair
Of the wolf's hiding; to the empty fields
By Aufidus, the dry campaign that yields
No harvest for the husbandman, but now
Shall bear a nobler foison than the plough;
To where, festooned along the tall elm trees,
Tendrils are mirrored in Tyrrhenian seas;
To where the South awaits them; even to where
Stark, African, informed of burning air,
Upturned to Heaven the broad Hipponian plain
Extends luxurious and invites the main.
Guelma's a mother: barren Thapsa breeds;
And northward in the valleys, next the meads
That sleep by misty river banks, the Vines
Have struck to spread below the solemn pines.
The Vines are on the roof-trees. All the Shrines
And Homes of men are consecrate with Vines.

And now the task of that triumphant day
Has reached to victory. In the reddening ray
With all his train, from hard Iberian lands

Fulfilled, apparent, that Creator stands
Halted on Atlas. Far beneath him, far,
The strength of Ocean darkening and the star
Beyond all shores. There is a silence made.
It glorifies: and the gigantic shade
Of Hercules adores him from the West.
Dead Lucre: burnt Ambition: Wine is best.

But what are these that from the outer murk
Of dense mephitic vapours creeping lurk
To breathe foul airs from that corrupted well
Which oozes slime along the floor of Hell?
These are the stricken palsied brood of sin
In whose vile veins, poor, poisonous and thin,
Decoctions of embittered hatreds crawl:
These are the Water-Drinkers, cursed all!
On what gin-sodden Hags, what flaccid sires
Bred these White Slugs from what exhaust desires?
In what close prison's horror were their wiles
Watched by what tyrant power with evil smiles;
Or in what caverns, blocked from grace and air
Received they, then, the mandates of despair?
What! Must our race, our tragic race, that roam
All exiled from our first, and final, home:
That in one moment of temptation lost
Our heritage, and now wander, hunger-tost
Beyond the Gates (still speaking with our eyes
For ever of remembered Paradise),
Must we with every gift accepted, still,
With every joy, receive attendant ill?
Must some lewd evil follow all our good
And muttering dog our brief beatitude?

A primal doom, inexorable, wise,
Permitted, ordered, even these to rise.
Even in the shadow of so bright a Lord
Must swarm and propagate the filthy horde
Debased, accursed I say, abhorrent and abhorred.
Accursed and curse-bestowing. For whosoe'er
Shall suffer their contagion, everywhere

Falls from the estate of man and finds his end
To the mere beverage of the beast condemned.
For such as these in vain the Rhine has rolled
Imperial centuries by hills of gold;
For such as these the flashing Rhone shall rage
In vain its lightning through the Hermitage
Or level-browed divine Touraine receive
The tribute of her vintages at eve.
For such as these Burgundian heats in vain
Swell the rich slope or load the empurpled plain.
Bootless for such as these the mighty task
Of bottling God the Father in a flask
And leading all Creation down distilled
To one small ardent sphere immensely filled.
With memories empty, with experience null,
With vapid eye-balls meaningless and dull
They pass unblest through the unfruitful light;
And when we open the bronze doors of Night,
When we in high carousal, we, reclined,
Spur up to Heaven the still ascending mind,
Pass with the all inspiring, to and fro,
The torch of genius and the Muse's glow,
They, lifeless, stare at vacancy alone
Or plan mean traffic, or repeat their moan.
We, when repose demands us, welcomed are
In young white arms, like our great Exemplar
Who, wearied with creation, takes his rest
And sinks to sleep on Ariadne's breast.
They through the darkness into darkness press
Despised, abandoned and companionless.
And when the course of either's sleep has run
We leap to life like heralds of the sun;
We from the couch in roseate mornings gay
Salute as equals the exultant day
While they, the unworthy, unrewarded, they
The dank despisers of the Vine, arise
To watch grey dawns and mourn indifferent skies.

Forget them! Form the Dionysian ring
And pulse the ground, and Io, Io, sing.

Father Lenæan, to whom our strength belongs,
Our loves, our wars, our laughter and our songs,
Remember our inheritance, who praise
Your glory in these last unhappy days
When beauty sickens and a muddied robe
Of baseness fouls the universal globe.
Though all the Gods indignant and their train
Abandon ruined man, do thou remain!
By thee the vesture of our life was made,
The Embattled Gate, the lordly Colonnade,
The woven fabric's gracious hues, the sound
Of trumpets, and the quivering fountain-round,
And, indestructible, the Arch, and, high,
The Shaft of Stone that stands against the sky,
And, last, the guardian-genius of them, Rhyme,
Come from beyond the world to conquer time:
All these are thine, Lenæan.
By thee do seers the inward light discern;
By thee the statue lives, the Gods return;
By thee the thunder and the falling foam
Of loud Acquoria's torrent call to Rome;
Alba rejoices in a thousand springs,
Gensano laughs, and Orvieto sings...
But, Ah! With Orvieto, with that name
Of dark, Eturian, subterranean flame
The years dissolve. I am standing in that hour
Of majesty Septembral, and the power
Which swells the clusters when the nights are still
With autumn stars on Orvieto hill.

Had these been mine, Ausonian Muse, to know
The large contented oxen heaving slow;
To count my sheaves at harvest; so to spend
Perfected days in peace until the end;
With every evening's dust of gold to hear
The bells upon the pasture height, the clear
Full horn of herdsmen gathering in the kine
To ancient byres in hamlets Appenine,
And crown abundant age with generous ease:
Had these, Ausonian Muse, had these, had these...

But since I would not, since I could not stay,
Let me remember even in this my day
How, when the ephemeral vision's lure is past
All, all, must face their Passion at the last.

Was there not one that did to Heaven complain
How, driving through the midnight and the rain,
He struck, the Atlantic seethe and surge before,
Wrecked in the North along a lonely shore
To make the lights of home and hear his name no more.
Was there not one that from a desperate field
Rode with no guerdon but a rifted shield;
A name disherited; a broken sword;
Wounds unrenowned; battle beneath no Lord;
Strong blows, but on the void, and toil without reward.

When from the waste of such long labour done
I too must leave the grape-ennobling sun
And like the vineyard worker take my way
Down the long shadows of declining day,
Bend on the sombre plain my clouded sight
And leave the mountain to the advancing night,
Come to the term of all that was mine own
With nothingness before me, and alone;
Then to what hope of answer shall I turn?
Comrade-Commander whom I dared not earn,
What said You then to trembling friends and few?
"A moment, and I drink it with you new:
But in my Father's Kingdom." So, my Friend,
Let not Your cup desert me in the end.
But when the hour of mine adventure's near
Just and benignant, let my youth appear
Bearing a Chalice, open, golden, wide,
With benediction graven on its side.
So touch my dying lip: so bridge that deep:
So pledge my waking from the gift of sleep,
And, sacramental, raise me the Divine:
Strong brother in God and last companion, Wine.

ABOUT THE EDITOR

Among his many talents, Clifton Fadiman is a gifted anthologist whose previous books such as *The Fireside Reader, Fantasia Mathematica, Reading I've Liked,* and *The Mathematical Magpie* have all been widely read and vastly enjoyed. An author, columnist, critic, member of the Book-of-the-Month Club board of judges, and a regular essayist for *Holiday* magazine, Mr. Fadiman is also familiar in the world of entertainment, where he appears frequently on television panel shows, and was for years the master of ceremonies for "Information Please."

ar 12

Wilmington Public Library
Wilmington, N. C.

12/62

RULES

1. Books marked 7 days may be kept one week. Books marked 14 days, two weeks. The latter may be renewed, if more than 6 months old.

2. A fine of two cents a day will be charged on each book which is not returned according to above rule.   No book will be issued to any person having a fine of 25 cents or over.

3. A charge of ten cents will be made for mutilated plastic jackets.   All injuries to books beyond reasonable wear and all losses shall be made good to the satisfaction of the Librarian.

4. Each borrower is held responsible for all books drawn on his card and for all fines accruing on the same.